950×

ALLYN AND BACON, INC.

Boston, 1966

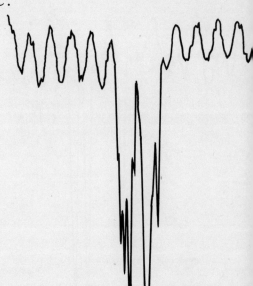

ROBERT T. CONLEY

Professor of Chemistry
Seton Hall University

INFRARED
SPECTROSCOPY

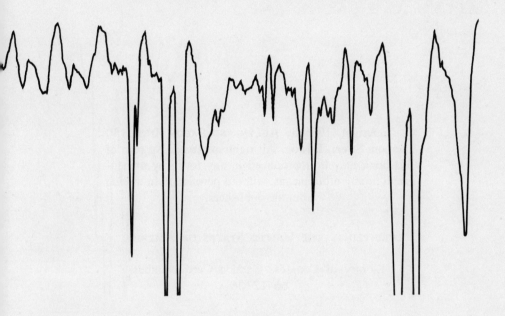

Preface

My intention in this work is to provide the student chemist, equipped with only an elementary background, with a portion of the material with which a practicing chemist using infrared spectroscopy in his daily research work might wish to be familiar. My experience in the undergraduate and graduate classrooms and laboratories in organic chemistry, infrared spectroscopy institutes, and industrial training courses has convinced me that a truly elementary spectroscopy book with a particular emphasis on the practical aspects of the subject was needed. A monograph that would familiarize the reader with the basic theory, instrumentation, qualitative and quantitative analysis methods, and the possible application of infrared spectroscopy to their problems and future work was deemed far more desirable than a highly oriented, mathematical treatment of the subject from either the instrumental or theoretical viewpoints.

Without exception all textual material can be easily assimilated by students at the sophomore college level. With the bibliographic data and suggested reading, the advanced student or professional chemist can channel his reading into the more detailed original literature of each area or according to his specific interests. The material, particularly in the chapters on techniques and qualitative analysis, was selected such that the more commonly used methods or encountered experiences were stressed. In addition, ample tabular material and spectral data were included for both clarity in understanding and for future reference. Since in good portion, the actual application of infrared spectroscopy is subjective by its nature, I feel this is the only possible method for adequately preparing the student or beginning spectroscopist with a suitable background prior to undertaking the more detailed theoretical aspects of the subject.

The content of this text has been based for the most part on the questions I have received over the past five years in the course of preparing students and industrial personnel for practical applications of infrared spectroscopy in their work. These people have been helpful in their critical and constructive comments, which have been in large part the reason for preparing the manuscript. The experienced spectroscopist will find little new in this work. It is hoped, rather, that it will fill an educational gap in the area of instrumental analysis, namely, to equip the organic chemist with the necessary background to read more detailed and advanced works with greater appreciation and understanding.

I take great pleasure in thanking Dr. A. Brent Spooner for his conscientious and critical review of this work while it was in preparation. In addition, I should like to express my appreciation for the effort extended by Peter Balling, William Knopka, and Paul Valint, all graduate assistants in my research group, in reading and commenting on the entire manuscript. As graduate students, they have contributed many hours of valuable time to help other students who may benefit from the contents of this book. As well, the work of Mrs. Marian Zipp in the preparation of the manuscript in its final form was an immeasurable aid in making this work possible.

The unfailing cooperation, assistance, and understanding of my wife, Doris, during the preparation of this book has made it not only possible but a pleasant task as well.

Robert T. Conley
South Orange, New Jersey

Contents

1

Introduction

Infrared spectroscopy has become an indispensable tool for the determination of structural information concerning organic substances. Its application to organic systems has been in the areas of both quantitative and qualitative analysis. Qualitative analysis has been by far the greatest application of this valuable tool in organic chemistry. In general, many organic chemists use this method routinely to examine unknown materials, both in the crude and pure states, for functional group and other structural information.

In recent years, infrared spectrophotometric facilities have become increasingly and more readily accessible to the bench chemist. Low-cost spectrophotometers are now commonplace in most laboratories, and routine analyses are carried out by the organic chemist as part of his daily laboratory investigation. The potential applications of infrared analysis are almost limitless. However, the chemist, in his interest in decreasing the time required to obtain analytical data, should be absolutely sure that the intended application is suitable to infrared techniques. Usually, as routine practice, more than one method should be used to establish the validity of data concerning structural parameters of organic substances. Since the general applications to which the infrared method has been useful are so numerous, it would be well for the reader to acquaint himself with a number of general applications prior to treating the subject in detail.

Most commonly, the organic chemist uses infrared analysis qualitatively for determining the presence or absence of specific functional groups in a reaction mixture. For example, the esterification of phenylacetic acid with ethyl alcohol (by the standard procedure of refluxing the acid in a large excess of

1

alcohol and a trace of mineral acid) yields on removal of the excess alcohol a high-boiling liquid, which, on examination in the crude state, indicates infrared bands not present in the starting acid or alcohol. This information allows the chemist to conclude that the reaction has proceeded to give the ester, and further workup of the reaction is therefore warranted. After purification, the spectrum is characteristic of ethyl phenylacetate and can be used for comparison of subsequent reaction products in a desired synthesis sequence. Alternately, the hydrolysis of a nitrile such as trimethylacetonitrile to trimethylacetic acid by hot mineral acid can be rapidly evaluated by infrared examination of the starting material and the crude reaction product, as shown in Fig. 1.1.

Spectrum A in Fig. 1.1 is that of the trimethylacetonitrile; spectrum B is representative of the hydrolysis product, trimethylacetic acid. These simple applications show how the chemist may shorten substantially the amount of time necessary to confirm the presence or absence of a particular functional

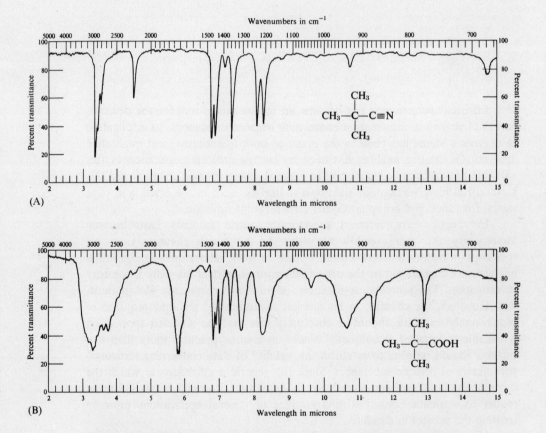

Fig. 1.1 Typical spectral data obtained in the routine examination of the course of an organic reaction. (A) The spectrum of trimethylacetonitrile (pivalonitrile), the starting material before attempted hydrolysis. (B) The spectrum of trimethylacetic acid (pivalic acid), the reaction product obtained after the treatment of trimethylacetonitrile (A) with hot mineral acid.

group. In some instances this technique can detect functional groups whose presence is otherwise impossible to detect by conventional chemical functional group tests.

The infrared spectrum of an organic substance is characteristic of the substance; marked changes are readily noted when the substance is contaminated with appreciable amounts of impurities of other species or isomeric compounds. Consequently, infrared technique is useful for checking raw materials in large-scale organic preparations and for monitoring processes on a continuous basis. Routine product-purification processes can be followed by examining the infrared spectra obtained for the various cuts or fractions from distillations, crystallizations, sublimations, or chromatographic separations. The characteristic spectra of different substances also can be useful in determining such information as reaction rates and equilibrium constants. Applying more detailed refinement in methods, specific band positions allow the determination of intramolecular hydrogen bonding, isomeric structural differences, and conjugation.

In the hands of the physical chemist, more detailed information concerning the molecular structure can be ascertained. For example, bond strengths, bond distances, and thermodynamic properties in many cases can be determined through a detailed mathematical treatment of spectral data.

It should be apparent at this point that the infrared region holds a wealth of knowledge concerning the structure of organic molecules. An experienced chemist interested in the further study of molecular structure will find the infrared spectrum, in combination with other chemical and physical data, a most valuable tool for gaining structural information.

1.1   THE INFRARED REGION

The electromagnetic spectrum is familiar to every chemist. The region of primary concern to us in this text is that region consisting of radiant energies of slightly greater wavelengths than those associated with visible light. Figure 1.2 summarizes the more pertinent features of the electromagnetic spectrum, including the X-ray region, ultraviolet and visible regions, and the infrared region. The study of infrared energy and its interaction with matter comprises a very broad field. Since much of the electromagnetic spectrum falls in the infrared region, the breadth of wavelengths included in this region requires a variety of experimental techniques for its application and measurement.

The units of wavelengths (λ) indicated in Fig. 1.2 are shown in angstroms (A), microns (μ), and centimeters (cm). The definition of the wavelength, as expressed in microns, can be given in terms of other distance units, such as centimeters or angstroms, where one wavelength is the distance between the successive nodes of the wave. One micron (μ) is equal to 10^{-4} cm or equal to 10,000 angstroms (A). For all wavelengths, a frequency unit (ν, the wave cycles per second) may also be used to characterize the radiation.

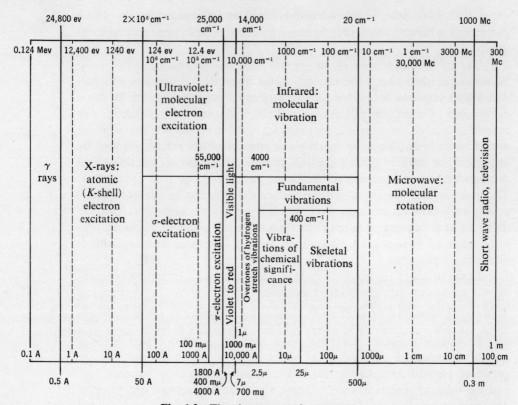

Fig. 1.2 The electromagnetic spectrum.

Since the velocity (velocity of light, $c = 3 \times 10^{10}$ cm/sec) is the same for all wavelengths, the frequency varies inversely with the wavelength ($\nu = c/\lambda$). It should be noted, for ease in becoming familiar with these units and their relationship to spectral presentation, that long wavelengths have low frequencies. In practice, the wavenumber (number of waves per centimeter) is used more extensively than the actual frequency, since both are dependent upon energy (E) according to the fundamental Planck equation, $E = h\nu = hc/\lambda$, where h is Planck's constant ($h = 6.62391 \times 10^{-27}$ erg-sec). The wavenumber and frequency are related to the wavelength as shown in Fig. 1.3.

The usual unit of the wavenumber is the reciprocal centimeter, cm^{-1}. In terms of this unit, the wavenumber is the reciprocal of the wavelength λ when λ is expressed in centimeters. Appendix I lists the wavenumber-wavelength conversions from 2 to 20μ (5000 to 500 cm^{-1}). We can also take the wavenumber as being a unit of energy; thus, 1 cm^{-1} corresponds to 1.9855 $\times$ 10^{-16} erg/molecule, or 11.959 $\times$ 10^7 ergs per mole, or (converting to calories) 2.8584 cal/mole.

On the basis of experimental techniques and applications, the overall infrared region may be subdivided as shown in Table 1.1.

In these three regions we shall treat the 2 to 25μ region in greatest

Table 1.1.   Common Subdivisions of the Infrared Region

Region	Frequency Range (cm⁻¹)	Wavelength Range (μ)
Near-infrared (overtone)	13,300–4000	0.75–2.5
Fundamental rotation-vibration	4,000–400	2.5–25
Far-infrared (skeletal vibration)	400–20	25–500

detail, since it has been by far the best studied. Figure 1.4 indicates the two possible modes of spectral presentation in terms of wavelength or frequency scales being used as the linear abscissa.

1.2   THE SPECTRUM

Before proceeding into the theoretical considerations of infrared spectra, it is best to describe generally, in as simple terms as possible, how a spectrum arises and what basic general factors of infrared spectrophotometry lead to structural information. As the temperature of a substance is raised, it begins to emit radiant energy. The amount of emitted radiation forms a curve as a function of wavelength, depending upon the temperature of the substance and its emissivity. If the emitted radiation is plotted versus wavelength, the curve shown in Fig. 1.5 as dashed lines is obtained. On introduction of a substance such as acetone vapor into the radiation path, the curve, represented as a solid line, shows marked changes in characteristics. Noticeable bands of radiation have been removed from the emission spectrum of the heated substance. The inference is that the acetone has absorbed certain rather specific wavelengths of energy from the beam of radiation.

By substituting a wide variety of materials of organic origin in the beam of the radiating material, it is readily observed that certain wavelengths are

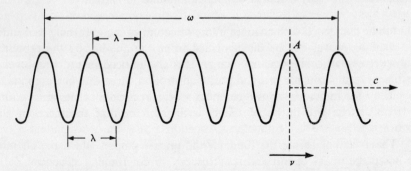

Fig. 1.3   The relationship of wavenumber and frequency to wavelength where: λ = wavelength; ν = number of waves passing point A per second; ω = number of waves per centimeter (wavenumber); c = velocity of light.

$$\lambda = \frac{c}{\nu}; \qquad \omega = \frac{\nu}{c} = \frac{1}{\lambda}$$

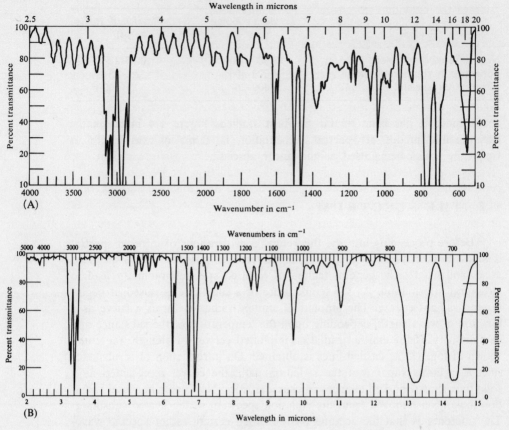

Fig. 1.4 Typical presentation of spectral data in terms of linear wavenumber scale and linear wavelength scale. (The spectrum is of polystyrene, and the reader should note the differences in appearance of the bands caused by each form of presentation.) (A) Linear in wavenumber measured in cm^{-1}. (B) Linear in wavelength measured in microns.

found to be associated with changes in the structure of the absorbing molecule. The resulting curves can be distinguished from one another by the presence or absence of particular bands of energy. It is also noticed that mixing several substances results roughly in a composite absorption curve that corresponds to the sum of the individual constituents; to a degree, certain of the absorptions are found to be a measure of the concentration of that substance in the mixture.

These facts illustrate the fundamental premises upon which the chemist has based the utility of infrared spectroscopy in determining structural data. In summary, these postulates can be stated as follows:

1. Organic substances exhibit characteristic group frequencies in the infrared region.

2. The absorption spectrum of a given substance is generally specific for that and only that substance.

3. The absorption spectrum of mixtures are generally additive, i.e., the sum of the individual spectrum of the components.

4. The intensity of an absorption band is related to the concentration of the substance that absorbs the incident radiation.

These observations can best be described in terms of molecular structure. The bonds that hold a molecule together and the masses of the constituents are so related that the molecule extracts radiation of a frequency, corresponding to one of its normal vibrating frequencies, from the incident beam. Therefore the absorption bands in an infrared spectrum are at frequencies corresponding to the frequencies of vibration of the molecule concerned. As might be anticipated at this point, these frequencies are also dependent upon the spacial interrelationships of the atoms contained in the molecular unit.

From the viewpoint of the organic chemist, the structural and functional differences leading to reactivity of molecules lead in turn to differences in the

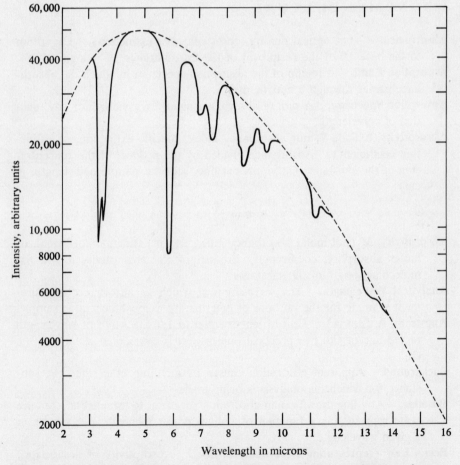

Fig. 1.5 Diagrammatic illustration of emitted infrared radiation as a function of wavelength and sample absorption. Solid line; the absorption of infrared energy by acetone: Dashed line; the infrared energy emitted by the source at elevated temperature.

gross spectral characteristics in all regions of the electromagnetic spectrum. Therefore it is clear that the infrared spectrum, as a major portion of the electromagnetic spectrum of a given substance, constitutes a direct measure of the differences in molecular structure that distinguish it from all other substances.

In order that a general background of the nature of molecular vibrations may be acquired by the reader prior to continuing a detailed discussion of the applications of infrared spectroscopy, a brief discussion of theory concerning this type of molecular spectra should be considered (Chap. 2). For clarity in presentation, a glossary of terms related to infrared spectroscopy is inserted here so that the reader may readily familiarize himself with the terminology used routinely in this field. Since this terminology will be followed throughout this presentation, it would be of value to become thoroughly acquainted with it.

1.3 NOMENCLATURE

Absorbance, A (not optical density, absorbancy, or extinction).   Logarithm to the base 10 of the reciprocal of the transmittance, $A = \log_{10} (1/T)$.

Absorption Band.   A region of the absorption spectrum in which the absorbance passes through a maximum.

Absorption Spectrum.   A plot of absorbance against wavelength or any function of wavelength.

Absorptivity, a (not K, nor absorbancy index, specific extinction, or extinction coefficient).   Absorbance divided by the product of the concentration of the substance (in grams per liter, and the sample path length, in cm):

$$a = \frac{A}{bc}$$

Absorptivity, M (not molar absorbancy index, molar extinction coefficient, or molar absorption coefficient).   Product of the absorptivity a and the molecular weight of the substance.

Analytical Wavelength.   Any wavelength at which an absorbance measurement is made for the purpose of determining a constituent of a sample.

Angstrom, A (not Å).   Unit of length equal to 1/6438.4696 of wavelength or red line of Cd. For practical purposes, it is considered equal to 10^{-8} cm.

Background.   Apparent absorption caused by anything other than the substance for which the analysis is being made.

Baseline.   Any line drawn on an absorption spectrum to establish a reference point representing a function of radiant power incident on a sample at a given wavelength.

Beer's Law (representing Beer-Lambert law).   Absorptivity of a substance is a constant with respect to changes in concentration.

Concentration, c. Quantity of the substance contained in a unit quantity of sample. (In absorption spectrometry it is usually expressed in grams or moles per liter.)

Frequency. Number of cycles per unit time.

Infrared. The region of the electromagnetic spectrum extending from approximately 0.75 to 300μ.

Micron, μ. Unit of length equal to 10^{-6} meter.

Millimicron, $m\mu$. Unit of length equal to one-thousandth of a micron. Almost, but not exactly, equal to 10 angstroms.

Radiant Energy. Energy transmitted as electromagnetic waves.

Sample Path Length, b (not l or d). Internal cell or sample length, usually given in centimeters.

Spectral Position. The effective wavelength or wavenumber of an essentially monochromatic beam of radiant energy.

Spectrograph. Instrument with an entrance slit and dispersing device that uses photography to obtain a record of spectral range. The radiant power passing through the optical system is integrated over time, and the quantity recorded is a function of radiant energy.

Spectrometer, Optical. Instrument with an entrance slit, a dispersing device, and with one or more exit slits, with which measurements are made at selected wavelengths within the spectral range, or by scanning over the range. The quantity detected is a function of radiant power.

Spectrometry. Branch of physical science treating the measurement of spectra.

Spectrophotometer. Spectrometer with associated equipment, so that it furnishes the ratio, or a function of the ratio, of the radiant power of two beams as a function of spectral wavelength. These two beams may be separated in time, space, or both.

Standard Sample. A material of definite composition that closely resembles in chemical and physical nature the materials with which the analyst expects to deal, and which is employed for calibration.

Transmittance, T (not transmittancy or transmission). The ratio of the radiant power transmitted by a sample to the radiant power incident on the sample.

Ultraviolet. The region of the electromagnetic spectrum from approximately 10 to 380 $m\mu$. The term without further qualification usually refers to the region from 200 to 380 $m\mu$.

Visible. Pertaining to radiant energy in the electromagnetic spectral range visible to the human eye (approximately 380 to 780 $m\mu$).

Wavelength. The distance, measured along the line of propagation, between two points that are in phase on adjacent waves; units: A, $m\mu$, and μ.

Wavenumber. Number of waves per unit length. The usual unit of wavenumber is the reciprocal centimeter, cm^{-1}. In terms of this unit, the wavenumber is the reciprocal of the wavelength when the latter is in centimeters in vacuo.

SUGGESTED READING

1. R. P. Bauman, *Absorption Spectroscopy.* Wiley, New York, 1962.
2. W. J. Potts, Jr., *Chemical Infrared Spectroscopy, Vol. 1, Techniques.* Wiley, New York, 1963.
3. R. N. Jones and C. Sandorfy in *Technique of Organic Chemistry, Vol. IX, Chemical Applications of Spectroscopy.* ed. W. West. Interscience, New York, 1956.
4. R. C. Gore and E. S. Waight in *Determination of Organic Structures by Physical Methods,* eds. E. A. Braude and F. C. Nachod, Academic, New York, 1955.

2

Theoretical Considerations

2.1 MOLECULAR VIBRATIONS

Molecular spectra may be divided into three categories: rotational, vibrational, and electronic. Rotational spectra result from the absorption of photons by molecules, with the complete conversion of the energy of the photons into energy of molecular rotation. Vibrational spectra occur when the absorption of radiant energy produces changes in the energy of molecular vibration. Only certain discrete energies are permitted the molecule, and the absorption of light corresponds to a transition between two of these energy levels. Thus vibrational spectra are discrete rather than continuous. The energy differences found in vibrational spectra are approximately a hundred times greater than those in rotational spectra. Since the rotational spectral changes are relatively small, they have the effect of widening the vibration-rotation band.

Molecules can absorb photons whose energies are exactly equal to the difference between two vibrational energy levels, and hence a vibrational absorption spectrum results. To a rather good approximation, a molecule can be regarded as an assembly of balls and springs, the balls representing the nuclei and the springs representing the chemical bonds. Such a system can vibrate according to a vast number of complex patterns. A fairly complex absorption spectrum is to be expected for most compounds because a molecule containing n atoms has $3n - 6$ normal vibrations ($3n - 5$ for a linear molecule). A characteristic fundamental frequency will be associated with each of these normal vibrations.

The quantity $3n - 6$ is obtained in the following manner: In order to describe completely the motion of the nuclei of a molecule, three coordinates must be specified for each nucleus; e.g., the x, y, and z Cartesian coordinates. Thus, for a molecule with n atoms, $3n$ coordinates are required in all, and the molecule is said to have $3n$ degrees of freedom. Not all these are vibrational degrees, however. Three of them describe the translation of the molecule as a rigid unit. This may be characterized completely by using the three coordinates of the center of mass.

Similarly the rotation of a nonlinear molecule is given completely by three coordinates; for example, two angles describing the orientation of a line fixed in the molecule with regard to a coordinate system fixed in space, and a third angle describing rotation about this line. The remaining $3n - 6$ degrees of freedom must then describe motions of the nuclei relative to each other, with the system as a whole fixed in space, i.e., they describe vibrational motions. Hence, there is a total of $3n - 6$ fundamental vibrations. For a linear molecule (one for which the equilibrium positions of all the nuclei are on the same straight line), there are $3n - 5$ fundamental vibrations. This is due to the fact that only two angles are needed to describe rotation because rotation about the molecular axis has no component.

One must not expect to observe exactly this number of bands in the spectrum. The number may be increased by bands that are not fundamentals, namely, combination tones, overtones, and difference tones. A combination tone is the sum of two or more different frequencies such as ν_1 and ν_2 (i.e., the absorbed photon excites vibrations 1 and 2 simultaneously). An overtone is a multiple of a given frequency, as 2ν (first overtone), 3ν (second overtone), etc. A difference tone is the difference between two frequencies, such as $\nu_1 - \nu_2$. The molecule is already in one excited vibrational state (ν_2) and absorbs enough additional radiant energy to raise it to another excited vibrational state (ν_1).

Some vibrational frequencies are forbidden to appear in the infrared spectrum by the action of selection rules. These selection rules are most restrictive for highly symmetrical molecules. The general requirement for infrared activity of a vibration is that the vibration must produce a periodic change in the dipole moment. If no such change occurs, the vibration is forbidden in the infrared. Of course the molecule can still carry out the vibration, but it will not be activated by the absorption of infrared radiation, and therefore will not be detected in the infrared spectrophotometer.

As an illustration of the operation of selection rules, let us consider a molecule that has a center of symmetry. This is a point such that a straight line drawn from the equilibrium position of any atom of the molecule to this point, and then extended an equal distance beyond, encounters the equilibrium position of an identical atom. Ethylene, carbon dioxide, benzene, and *trans*-1,2-dibromoethylene all have centers of symmetry. As shown in Fig. 2.1, for example, two of the normal vibrations of 1,2-dibromoethylene can be illustrated in the following manner: The circles indicate the equilibrium positions

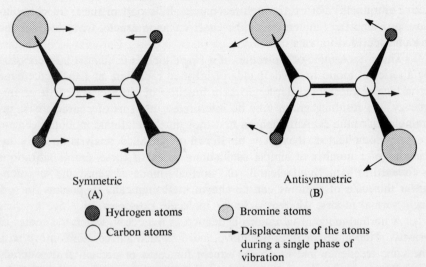

Symmetric
(A)

Antisymmetric
(B)

⬤ Hydrogen atoms   ◯ Bromine atoms

◯ Carbon atoms   ⟶ Displacements of the atoms
during a single phase of
vibration

Fig. 2.1 Symmetric and antisymmetric vibrations of *trans*-1,2-dibromoethylene.

of the atoms; the arrows indicate the displacements of the atoms during one phase of each vibration. During the other phase the displacements are exactly opposite in direction.

Fundamental vibrations are always either symmetric or antisymmetric to a center of symmetry. A vibration that is symmetric to a center of symmetry is one for which the displacement vector for every other atom will, when reflected at the center of symmetry, coincide with the vector of the corresponding mirror atom (Fig. 2.1A). For an antisymmetric vibration, each displacement vector will, when reflected at the center of symmetry, be the negative of the actual displacement vector for the mirror atom. Vibrations that are symmetric to the center of symmetry cannot produce a change in the dipole moment. The dipole moment is zero for the equilibrium configuration, and it remains zero throughout the entire vibration, since a displacement by any one atom is counterbalanced by the displacement of its opposite (Fig. 2.1A). Such vibrations are "forbidden" in the infrared. Conversely, the vibration shown in Fig. 2.1B does produce a change in the dipole moment. The moment is zero in the equilibrium position, but it certainly is not zero at either extreme of the vibration. Therefore this vibration is allowed in the infrared.

The atoms of any molecule are constantly oscillating about their positions of equilibrium. The amplitudes of these vibrations are extremely minute (10^{-9} to 10^{-10} cm) and their frequencies are high (10^{13} to 10^{14} cps). Since these frequencies are of the same order of magnitude as those of infrared radiations, some direct relationship might be expected to exist between the motions of the atoms within molecules and their effects on infrared radiation incident upon them. Actually, those molecular vibrations that are accompanied by a change of dipole moment (the so-called infrared active vibrations) absorb through resonance all or part of the incident radiation, provided the frequencies of the latter coincide exactly with those of the intramolecular vibrations.

Thus, if a sample of molecules of a single kind is irradiated in succession by a series of monochromatic bands of infrared radiation, and the percentage of radiation transmitted is plotted as a function of either wavelength or frequency, the resulting graph may be interpreted in terms of characteristic intramolecular motion. Although on first thought these atomic motions seem to be very complicated, they may be shown by detailed analysis to be summations of a number of simple oscillations. Each of these simple vibrations is referred to as a "fundamental" of "normal" mode of vibration. Any nonlinear molecule of n atoms can be shown mathematically to possess $3n - 6$ such normal modes, whereas a linear molecule possesses $3n - 5$.

A normal mode of vibrations is defined as a mode in which the center of gravity of the molecule does not move, and in which all the atoms move with the same frequency and in phase. Except for cases of accidental degeneracy (two or more vibrational states having the same energy are said to be degenerate), each normal mode is independent of the others in that any one can occur without affecting the others. Hence it is possible for all these vibrations to occur simultaneously while each retains its characteristic frequency. Thus an analysis of an infrared spectrum constitutes an analysis of the mechanics of the molecule in question.

The concept of a normal vibration may be clarified by an analogy with a mechanical mode. Suppose that a model of the benzene molecule, C_6H_6, is constructed by using weights in the ratio of $12:1$, respectively, for the carbon and hydrogen atoms, these weights being held in proper orientation by suitable springs. Suppose further that the carbon-hydrogen springs are now stretched slightly by moving each of the six pairs of weights so that the hydrogens are moved twelve times as far from the equilibrium position as are the carbons. If the weights are now released simultaneously, a vibration will occur in which the weights will move back and forth along the connecting bonds. The center of gravity of the whole model remains at rest, and the weights move only along the line of the connecting springs, since no original impetus was given to the weights in any other direction. This is a characteristic vibration of the model in that it has a definite frequency and it does not excite any other vibration in the model. This stretch motion is exactly analogous to one of the $3n - 6$, or 30, normal modes of the benzene molecule.

By measuring the frequencies of the infrared radiation absorbed by a substance, the infrared spectrometer determines the characteristic mechanical frequencies of its molecules.

2.2 MOLECULE AS RIGID ROTATOR

The simplest possible model of a rotating molecule can be visualized by considering the two atoms of masses m_1 and m_2 to be pointlike and fastened at a distance r from the ends of a weightless rigid rod. In so doing, one neglects the finite extent of the atoms and the fact that in reality the atoms are not rigidly bound to each other but rather may have their distance altered under the influence of their rotation.

In classical mechanics the energy of rotation E of a rigid body is given by

$$E = \tfrac{1}{2}I\omega^2 \qquad (2.1)$$

Here ω is the angular velocity of rotation and I is the moment of inertia of the system about the axis of rotation. The angular velocity is related to the number of rotations per second, ν_{rot} (rotational frequency) by

$$\omega = 2\pi\nu_{rot} \qquad (2.2)$$

The moment of inertia is defined by $I = \Sigma m_i r_i^2$ and the angular momentum of the system is given by $P = I\omega$.

The rotational energy depends essentially on the moment of inertia. For the rigid rotator model, this is

$$I = m_1 r_1^2 + m_2 r_2^2 \qquad (2.3)$$

where

$$r_1 = \frac{m_2}{m_1 + m_2} r \qquad \text{and} \qquad r_2 = \frac{m_1}{m_1 + m_2} r$$

and r_1 and r_2 are the distances of the masses m_1 and m_2 from the center of gravity, and r is the distance of the two mass points from each other. On substitution

$$I = \frac{m_1 m_2}{m_1 + m_2} r^2 \qquad (2.4)$$

i.e., the moment of inertia is the same as that of a mass

$$\mu = \frac{m_1 m_2}{m_1 + m_2} \qquad (2.5)$$

at a distance r from the axis; μ is called the *reduced mass*. Hence, one may consider the rotation of a single mass about a point at a fixed distance r from the axis of rotation. Such a system is called a *simple rigid rotator*.

According to classical electrodynamics, an intramolecular motion leads to radiation of light only if a changing dipole moment is associated with it. For a rigid rotator, this can be caused by the rotating mass point's possessing a charge or being associated with a permanent dipole moment that lies in the direction of the perpendicular from the mass point of rotation. The latter applies to all diatomic molecules that consist of unlike atoms, since for these the centers of the positive and negative charges do not coincide, i.e., such molecules have a permanent dipole moment, which lies in the internuclear axis. During the rotation, the component of the dipole in a fixed direction changes periodically, i.e. (classically), light of frequency ν_{rot} should be emitted. For molecules consisting of two like atoms, no dipole moment arises, and therefore no light is emitted. Only if a permanent dipole moment is present can an infrared frequency be absorbed and thereby a rotation of the system be produced or a rotation already present be increased. According to classical theory, the absorbed or emitted spectrum of the rotator is continuous, since ν_{rot} may take any value.

According to quantum theory, the emission of a light quantum takes place as a result of a transition of the rotator from a higher to lower level, while the absorption of a quantum of the proper frequency produces a transition from a lower to a higher level. The wavenumber of the emitted or absorbed quantum is

$$\nu = \frac{E'}{hc} - \frac{E''}{hc} \tag{2.6}*$$

where E' and E'' are the rotational energies in the upper and lower state, respectively.

2.3 HARMONIC OSCILLATOR

The simplest possible assumption about the form of vibration in a diatomic molecule is that each atom moves toward or away from the other in simple harmonic motion, i.e., the displacement from the equilibrium position is a sine function of the time. Such a motion of the two atoms can be easily reduced to the harmonic vibration of a single mass point about an equilibrium position, i.e., to the model of the harmonic oscillator.

In classical mechanics, a harmonic oscillator may be defined as a point mass of mass m, which is acted upon by a force F, proportional to the distance x from the equilibrium position, and directed toward the equilibrium position. Since force = mass × acceleration,

$$F = kx = m \frac{d^2x}{dt^2} \tag{2.7}$$

The proportionality factor k is called the *force constant*. The solution of the differential equation is

$$x = x_0 \sin (2\pi\nu_{osc}t + \phi) \tag{2.8}$$

Here the vibrational frequency ν_{osc} is given by

$$\nu_{osc} = \frac{1}{2\pi} \sqrt{\frac{k}{m}} \tag{2.9}$$

The amplitude of the vibration is x_0 and ϕ is a phase constant dependent on the initial conditions.

Since the force is a negative derivative of the potential energy V, it follows from $F = kx$ that, for the harmonic oscillator,

$$V = \tfrac{1}{2}kx^2 = 2\pi^2m\nu_{osc}^2x^2 \tag{2.10}$$

---

* In this discussion, the symbol ν is used interchangeably for frequency and wavenumber, for simplicity, since the frequency ν is directly proportional to the wavenumber ($\tilde{\nu}$).

We can also define a harmonic oscillator as a system whose potential energy is proportional to the square of the distance from its equilibrium position.

The restoring force exerted by two atoms of a molecule on each other when they are displaced from their equilibrium position is at least approximately proportional to the change of internuclear distance. If we assume that this relation holds exactly, it follows that the atoms in the molecule will execute harmonic vibrations when they are left to themselves after being displaced from their equilibrium positions.

For the first atom of mass m_1,

$$m_1 \frac{d^2 r_1}{dt^2} = -k(r - r_e) \tag{2.11}$$

and for the second atom of mass m_2,

$$m_2 \frac{d^2 r_2}{dt^2} = -k(r - r_e) \tag{2.12}$$

where r_1 and r_2 are the distances of the two atoms from the center of gravity, r is the distance of the two atoms from each other, and r_e is the equilibrium distance. By substitution of Eq. 2.3, we obtain from both equations

$$\left(\frac{m_2 m_1}{m_1 + m_2} \right) \frac{d^2 r}{dt^2} = -k(r - r_e) \tag{2.13}$$

On introducing the reduced mass μ and replacing r under the differential sign by $(r - r_e)$ ($r_e = $ constant), then

$$\mu \frac{d^2(r - r_e)}{dt^2} = -k(r - r_e) \tag{2.14}$$

Hence the vibrations of the two atoms of a molecule have been reduced to the vibration of a single point mass of mass μ, whose amplitude equals the change of internuclear distance in the molecule. From Eq. 2.9 combined with Eq. 2.14, it follows that the classical vibrational frequency of the molecule is

$$\nu_{\text{osc}} = \frac{1}{2\pi} \sqrt{\frac{k}{\mu}} \tag{2.15}$$

If the molecule in its equilibrium position has a dipole moment, as is always the case for molecules consisting of unlike atoms, this dipole moment will, in general, change if the internuclear distance is linear. Therefore the dipole moment changes with a frequency of the mechanical vibration. On the basis of classical electrodynamics, this would lead to the emission of light of frequency, ν_{osc}. Conversely, the oscillator would be set in vibration by absorption of light of frequency, ν_{osc}.

Quantum-theoretically, emission of radiation takes place as a result of a transition of the oscillator from a higher to lower state, and absorption takes place by the converse process. The wavenumber of the emitted or absorbed light is given by

$$\nu = \frac{E(\nu')}{hc} - \frac{E(\nu'')}{hc} = G(\nu') - G(\nu'') \tag{2.16}$$

where ν' and ν'' are the vibrational quantum numbers of the upper and the lower state, respectively. In order to determine which particular transitions can actually occur, we have to evaluate the matrix elements R_x^{nm}, R_y^{nm}, of the dipole moment (cf. Ref. 3). For the oscillator these matrix elements are zero except when the permanent dipole moment is different from zero and when, in addition, ν' and ν'' differ by unity; that is to say that the selection rule for the vibrational quantum number of the harmonic oscillator is

$$\Delta\nu = \nu' - \nu'' = \pm 1 \tag{2.17}$$

Hence

$$\nu = G(\nu + 1) - G(\nu) = \omega \tag{2.18}$$

i.e., quantum-theoretically (just as classically), the frequency of the radiated light is equal to the frequency $\nu_{osc} = (C\omega)$ of the oscillator. This is true no matter what the ν value of the initial state may be. It must be pointed out that for a system that is not exactly a harmonic oscillator, transitions can also appear with $\Delta\nu > 1$, whereas for the rotator the selection rule holds strictly even if the system deviates from the model of the rigid rotator. For a molecule consisting of two like atoms (H_2, N_2, O_2 . . .), the dipole moment is zero, and therefore no transitions between the different vibrational levels occur: There is no infrared emission or absorption.

If the theoretical results obtained for the spectra of the rigid rotator and harmonic oscillator are compared with the observed absorption spectra, the following interpretation may be made:

1. The spectrum in the far-infrared, since it consists of a series of nearly equidistant lines, is a rotation spectrum. The molecule rotates about an axis perpendicular to a line joining the nuclei and through the center of mass. It behaves like a rigid rotator, and transitions between the rotational levels give rise to the spectrum.

2. The spectrum in the near-infrared, since it consists essentially of a single, very intense line, is a vibration spectrum. The nuclei carry out approximately harmonic vibrations in the internuclear axis.

2.4   NATURE OF NORMAL VIBRATIONS

It is evident that a polyatomic molecule can have many vibrational energy levels, and hence the vibrational modes are spectroscopically active. The frequencies of the fundamental vibration bands would be equal to the $3n - 6$ classical normal vibration frequencies of the molecule. In practice the situation is complicated by the fact that not all the frequencies are active, by the presence of spectral lines due to overtones, and by the formation of combination tones. The nature of the normal vibrations of a polyatomic molecule may be illustrated by reference to the case of the symmetrical triangular molecule YX_2 as shown in Fig. 2.2. The displacements of the three atoms may be represented by means of the coordinates x, y, and q; x is the relative displacement from the symmetry axis of the atom Y in the plane of the mole-

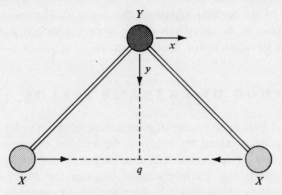

Fig. 2.2 The nature of the normal vibrations of a polyatomic molecule as illustrated by the symmetrical triangular molecule YX_2.

cule; y is the relative displacement of Y with respect to the mass center of the two X atoms; and q is the relative displacement of the X atoms along the line joining them. By carrying out the normal coordinate treatment, the expressions giving the displacement (Q_1, Q_2, and Q_3 in the directions of the three normal coordinates), since $3n - 6$ is now equal to 3, are

$$Q_1 = a_1 y + b_1 q$$
$$Q_2 = a_2 y - b_2 q$$
$$Q_3 = cx$$

This means that in the first two normal vibrations having frequencies ν_1 and ν_2, there is no displacement of the Y atom in the x direction; in both cases, however, there are y and q displacements, but in one normal vibration, the q displacement is in the opposite direction to that of the other. The third normal vibration of frequency, ν_3, is characterized by a displacement of the Y atom in the x direction; there is no resultant displacement in the q direction, so that the X atoms remain at a fixed distance apart in the course of their motion.

These conditions are satisfied by the motions represented in Fig. 2.3. The diagrams may be taken as giving an approximate picture of the nature of the normal vibrations of a symmetrical triangular molecule such as H_2O, H_2S, SO_2, etc. The actual vibration motion of the YX_2 molecule will be complicated, but regardless of the complexity it can be treated as equivalent to the superposition of the three types of oscillation illustrated in Fig. 2.3.

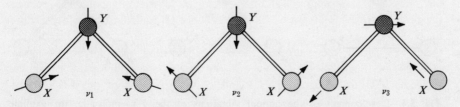

Fig. 2.3 Isolated vibrations of the YX_2 molecule.

In each of the normal vibrations the nuclei of the three atoms will be moving in phase, in the directions of the arrows, although the amplitudes of vibration may be different for the three nuclei.

2.5 METHOD OF EXTREME FIELDS

A general indication concerning the nature of the normal vibrations of a molecule may be obtained by applying the method of extreme fields. The general character of a normal vibration depends essentially on the exact nature of the particular forces operative between the nuclei that determine the potential energy of the molecule. By postulating extreme fields, a relatively complex molecule may be regarded as effectively split up into simple units, for which the normal vibrational modes are known. The actual vibrations may then be taken as being intermediate between those that would result from the application of extreme fields such as those discussed below.

The method may be explained by reference to the symmetrical triangular molecule YX_2. Suppose the forces acting between the two X atoms is very much larger than that operating between the Y atom and the X atoms. The system YX_2 may then be regarded as made up of the atom Y and the diatomic molecule X_2. Keeping in mind that there must be no change in the linear

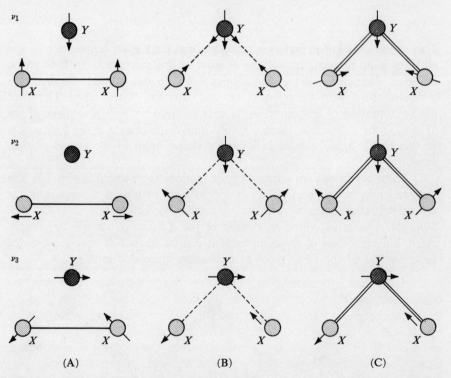

(A)   (B)   (C)

Fig. 2.4 Development of the normal vibrations of the YX_2 molecule; the extreme models.

and angular momenta of the molecule as a whole, i.e., the molecule must not rotate or move bodily through space as a result of the vibrational motion, it is evident that three vibrations of the type illustrated in Fig. 2.4A will be possible.

In the first case, ν_1, the system X_2 acts as a rigid bar, and the atom Y vibrates relative to the two X atoms. In the second type of vibration, ν_2, the atom Y is stationary and the two X atoms vibrate with respect to each other. In the third case, ν_3, the X_2 again acts as a bar, undergoing a rocking or tipping motion about its center of gravity, while the Y atom vibrates at right angles to the axis of symmetry and in the plane of the molecule.

The other type of extreme field would be that in which the Y atom was strongly bound to each of the X atoms, while the X atoms were weakly attracted to each other. The system would then be regarded as one consisting of two XY molecules. The resulting vibrations are illustrated in Fig. 2.4B. In the first case, the X and Y atoms of each XY molecule vibrate toward each other; in the second case, the two XY rock about their centers of gravity; in the third type of vibration, each X atom oscillates relative to the Y atom in such a way that one of the former moves toward the latter while the other is moving away, and vice versa. The actual vibrational modes shown as Fig. 2.4C represent states intermediate between the two extremes. The results are seen to be identical with the normal vibrations shown in Fig. 2.3.

2.6   CLASSIFICATION OF NORMAL VIBRATIONS

Various methods of classifying the normal modes have been proposed. One method of classification for molecules possessing an axis of symmetry depends on the direction of change of the electric dipole moment of the molecule that accompanies the vibration. This classification is important because the results provide information on whether the particular frequency will be active or inactive in the infrared vibration spectrum of the molecule. If there is no change in the dipole moment accompanying the vibration, then that particular vibration will be inactive in the infrared spectrum. If the dipole moment does change, the change may be in directions parallel or perpendicular to the symmetry axis.

In the former case the vibration is said to be a *parallel vibration,* and in the latter case it is referred to as a *perpendicular vibration.* Both perpendicular and parallel vibrations will be active in the infrared. In the case of the symmetrical angular YX_2 molecule, all three vibrations are accompanied by changes in the electric dipole moment of the molecule. The vibrations associated with the frequencies ν_1 and ν_2 change the moment in a direction parallel to the axis of symmetry, which in this case is a line bisecting the XYX angle; these are parallel vibrations, and the corresponding infrared bands will have similar structure. The third vibration frequency, ν_3, results in an alteration of the dipole moment in a direction perpendicular to the symmetry axis, and this is called a perpendicular vibration.

For the purpose of identifying various types of normal vibrations, Mecke has suggested classifying them as valence (stretching) vibrations, for which the symbol ν is used, and deformation (bending) vibrations, indicated by the symbol δ. Of the $3n - 6$ vibrational modes of a molecule containing n atoms, $n - 1$ are valence vibrations and $2n - 5$ are deformation vibrations. The ν vibrations involve motions in the direction of valence bonds, whereas the δ vibrations are accompanied by movements at right angles to these bonds. The parallel or perpendicular nature of the vibrations is indicated by use of the symbols π and σ, respectively. Hence ν (π) would represent a parallel stretching vibration and δ (σ) would be a perpendicular deformation vibration. Referring to the YX_2 molecule, the motion of the X atoms in the vibrations of frequencies ν_1 and ν_3 are in the direction of the X—Y bonds and are regarded as valence vibrations. The former is parallel and the latter perpendicular, so that these are $\nu(\pi)$ and $\nu(\sigma)$, respectively. In the ν_2 vibration the X atoms vibrate at right angles to the X—Y bonds; thus the general form of the vibration is seen to consist of a bending of the molecule as a whole. This is to be regarded as a deformation mode, and since it is parallel, it may be symbolized by $\delta(\pi)$. Notations for angular YX_2 molecules may be summarized as follows:

Conventional Symbol: ν_1 ν_2 ν_3
Mecke Symbol: $\nu(\pi)$ $\delta(\pi)$ $\nu(\sigma)$

A further classification of normal vibrations is sometimes convenient when the molecule possesses a center of symmetry. If the vibration does not alter any of the symmetry properties of the molecule, it is said to be a *symmetric vibration*. If the vibration is such that the reflection of the molecule in any plane of symmetry results in a change of sign of the displacements, the vibration is said to be *antisymmetric*. Sometimes a normal vibration is antisymmetric with respect to one symmetry operation and symmetric with respect to all others; nevertheless, it is still called an antisymmetric vibration. For a completely symmetric vibration there must be no change with respect to all the elements of symmetry of the system. If a molecule possesses a center of symmetry, its dipole moment will be zero, and since a symmetric vibration does not produce any change in the dipole moment, it follows that for such molecules symmetric vibrations will be inactive in the infrared spectrum.

A method for classifying normal vibrations by utilizing the results of group theory is of particular value for relatively complex molecules. The letters A and B are used to represent nondegenerate vibrations; those in class A are symmetric, i.e., their sign is unchanged for rotation by $2\pi/n$ about the principal n-fold axis, while those in class B are antisymmetric for this operation. A numerical subscript gives the value of n in each case; for example, A_1, A_2, B_1, B_2, B_3, etc. Twofold degenerate vibrations are indicated by the letter E, and threefold degeneracy is designated by the letter F. If the molecule has a center of symmetry, the letters g and u are used as subscripts to indicate that the vibrations are symmetric and antisymmetric, respectively, with respect to inversion at the center of symmetry. In some cases a single prime is used to indicate that the vibration is symmetric upon reflection in a plane perpendicular to the principal axis. A double prime indicates a vibration that is antisymmetric for this operation.

The normal modes of vibration of some simple molecules are illustrated in Fig. 2.5. A dashed circle means that the motion is isotropic, i.e., not restricted to one direction, in the plane of the circle. The activity or inactivity of the various characteristics of the vibrations are indicated in each case. The letters p and d indicate polarized and depolarized Raman lines, respectively.

A question arising at this point concerns the possibility of a mathematical calculation of the normal modes of vibration. Such a calculation should make possible a determination of the structure of the molecule in question. The correct structure of the molecule would be that whose calculated frequencies correspond exactly to those observed in the experimental spectrum. Theoretically the expected frequencies can be calculated, provided the strengths of all the interatomic forces are known. The complexity of such calculations depends on the number of atoms in the molecules and the symmetry of their geometrical arrangement. Water, for example, with three atoms involves a third-degree equation. Benzene, although composed of 12 atoms, is so symmetrical that a fourth-degree equation is the most difficult encountered. The frequencies for this molecule have been found to agree with experimental values. However, if this geometrical symmetry is destroyed by substitution, as in *ortho*-chlorophenol, a rigorous treatment would require the solution of a thirty-third degree equation. Since most of the molecules of interest to the chemist are quite complex, some other method is required to correlate the characteristics of an observed spectrum with the structure of the molecule. Success in this direction has been achieved by a purely empirical approach.

In order to understand the basis for such an empirical method, it would be well to refer again to a discussion of mechanical molecular models. Consider a model of a molecule containing only one C—H bond, such as chloroform, Cl_3CH. If the C—H spring is stretched and released, the carbon and hydrogen weights vibrate rapidly with a characteristic frequency. The chlorine weights, on the other hand, are so heavy they are almost totally unable to follow the vibration. It is true, at least to a first approximation, that the observed stretching frequency is a characteristic of the C—H spring and the masses of these two atoms, and is practically independent of the rest of the molecule.

These observations lead to the basic premise that, to the extent that atomic forces between a carbon and hydrogen atom are a function of these atoms alone, the presence of C—H linkages in a molecule will cause at least two infrared absorptions which are practically independent of the atomic constitution of the rest of the molecule. The validity of this premise has been thoroughly established experimentally. A study of hundreds of molecules containing C—H linkages has shown an absorption around 2900 cm^{-1} (C—H

XYZ Linear

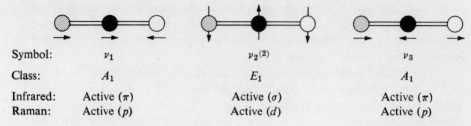

Symbol:	ν_1	$\nu_2^{(2)}$	ν_3
Class:	A_1	E_1	A_1
Infrared:	Active (π)	Active (σ)	Active (π)
Raman:	Active (p)	Active (d)	Active (p)

*YX*₂ Linear

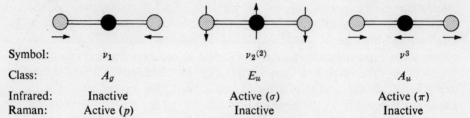

Symbol:	ν_1	$\nu_2^{(2)}$	ν^3
Class:	A_g	E_u	A_u
Infrared:	Inactive	Active (σ)	Active (π)
Raman:	Active (p)	Inactive	Inactive

XYZ Angular

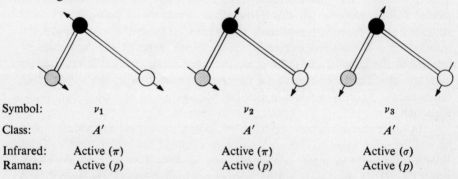

Symbol:	ν_1	ν_2	ν_3
Class:	A'	A'	A'
Infrared:	Active (π)	Active (π)	Active (σ)
Raman:	Active (p)	Active (p)	Active (p)

*YX*₂ Angular

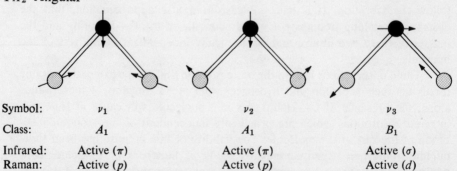

Symbol:	ν_1	ν_2	ν_3
Class:	A_1	A_1	B_1
Infrared:	Active (π)	Active (π)	Active (σ)
Raman:	Active (p)	Active (p)	Active (d)

Fig. 2.5 Normal modes of vibrations

X_2Y_2 Linear

Symbol:	ν_1	ν_2	$\nu_3^{(2)}$	ν_4	$\nu_5^{(2)}$
Class:	A_{1g}	A_{1g}	E_{1u}	A_u	E_{1g}
Infrared:	Inactive	Inactive	Active (σ)	Active (π)	Inactive
Raman:	Active (p)	Active (p)	Inactive	Inactive	Active (d)

XY_3 Pyramidal

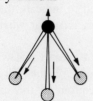 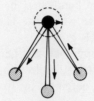 

Symbol:	ν_1	$\nu_{2,4}$	$\nu_{3,5}$	ν_6
Class:	A_1	E	E	A_1
Infrared:	Active (π)	Active (σ)	Active (σ)	Active (π)
Raman:	Active (p)	Active (d)	Active (d)	Active (p)

YX_3 Planar

 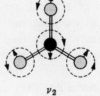 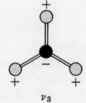 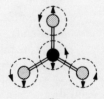

Symbol:	ν_1	ν_2	ν_3	ν_4
Class:	A_1'	E'	A_2''	E'
Infrared:	Inactive	Active (σ)	Active (π)	Active (σ)
Raman:	Active (p)	Active (d)	Inactive	Active (d)

YX_4 Tetrahedral

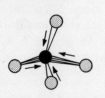 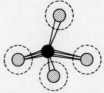 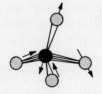

Symbol:	ν_1	$\nu_2^{(2)}$	$\nu_3^{(3)}$	$\nu_4^{(3)}$
Class:	A_1	E	E_1	F_2
Infrared:	Inactive	Inactive	Active	Active
Raman:	Active (p)	Active (d)	Active (d)	Active (d)

of some simple molecules.

stretching) and another around 1450 cm^{-1} (C—H bending). Further veri-
fication may be found by a study of the absorption spectra of molecules in
which the hydrogen atom has been replaced by a deuterium atom of mass 2.
A mathematical treatment shows that the C—D frequency should be given by
the equation $\nu_{C-D}\sqrt{2} = \nu_{C-H}$. In such molecules a frequency in the region of
2100 cm^{-1} (C—D stretching) is observed.

By using a spectrophotometer of high resolving power, it can be shown
that these C—H frequencies are influenced slightly by the relation of the
carbon-hydrogen linkage to the molecule as a whole. For example, the exact
frequency value of these absorption bands may be used to indicate the degree
of saturation of the carbon atom to which the H is attached or whether the
C—H occurs in a CH, CH$_2$, or CH$_3$ group.

Although the mathematical approach has been of great value when applied to simple or highly symmetrical molecules, most of the information
derived from infrared spectra is obtained by application of the empirical
method. This method consists of comparing the spectra of the largest obtainable number of different molecules having a common atomic group. By a
process of elimination it is often possible to find an absorption band whose
frequency remains constant throughout the series. The presence in an unknown of an absorption at this frequency may reasonably form the basis that
the particular atomic group is present.

It must not be assumed that it is, or will be, possible to ascribe every
observed absorption to a specific atomic group. If this were true, it would
make more difficult the possibility of differentiating clearly between isomeric
compounds. Actually only a few of the observed bands can usually be correlated in this manner. The majority of observed bands arise from normal
modes of vibration that are characteristic of the molecule as a whole. These
general absorption bands are very sensitive to structural changes and so fur-
nish us with a fingerprint of the molecule. They also make possible the analysis of isomeric mixtures and provide the basis for quantitative analysis of
other closely related compounds.

The normal vibrations of a molecule do not account for all the absorption bands observed in its infrared spectrum. For example, in the far-infrared
there are absorptions caused by the slower rotations of the molecules or by
the massive lattice vibrations of the crystals. Moreover, throughout the whole
infrared region the absorptions frequently occur at integral multiples (overtone bands) of the fundamentals or at frequencies that are equal to the sum
or difference (combination bands) of fundamentals. In general those bands
absorb very much less strongly than do the fundamentals, and consequently
must be studied with thicker samples.

SUGGESTED READING

1. R. P. BAUMAN, *Absorption Spectroscopy*. Wiley, New York, 1962, Chaps.
   4, 7, and 10.

2. W. J. POTTS, JR., *Chemical Infrared Spectroscopy, Volume 1, Techniques.* Wiley, New York, 1963, Chaps. 2 and 8.
3. G. HERZBERG, *Infrared and Raman Spectra of Polyatomic Molecules.* Van Nostrand, Princeton, New Jersey, 1945.

3

The Infrared
Spectrophotometer

Basically, the instrumentation used in the detection of infrared radiation employs the same optical principles as those embodied in ultraviolet and visible spectrophotometers. Since certain special problems are found in obtaining data in the infrared region, a brief discussion of the infrared spectrophotometer will acquaint the chemist with the basic principles of instrument design as found in most commonly available infrared instruments. As in other forms of spectrophotometry, the instruments used in the infrared region operate according to simple principles. The mechanical and electrical components are designed to transform the very small energy variations due to sample absorptions into an accurate and reproducible spectrum recording.

3.1 OPTICAL CHARACTERISTICS OF THE TYPICAL SPECTROPHOTOMETER

Essentially three basic components typical of all modern spectrophotometers are: a source of infrared radiation, which provides the incident illumination upon the sample to be studied; a monochromator, which disperses the radiant energy into its many frequencies and then, by a series of slits or apertures, selects the narrow band of frequencies to be examined by the detector. This latter component transforms the energy of the band of frequencies into an electric signal, which is amplified sufficiently enough to be recorded. In a diagrammatic form these components can be visualized as shown in Fig. 3.1.

In actual practice, the optical path and principal components of an in-

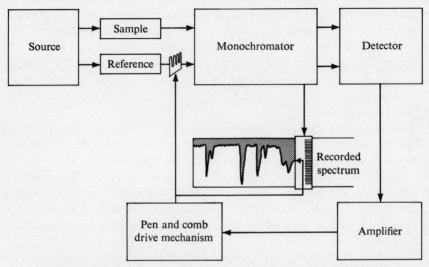

Fig. 3.1 Components of a typical double-beam infrared spectrophotometer.

frared spectrophotometer are much more detailed and can be illustrated as shown in Fig. 3.2 in a simplified manner. Infrared radiation from the source is reflected from mirrors M_s and M_r to give two identical beams focusing on the sample and reference cells, respectively. The radiation transmitted through each cell is directed to the sector mirror S_M. In one instant this rotating mirror is passing radiant energy from the sample into the entrance slit S_E; in the next, it is passing radiant energy from the reference cell focused by mirror M_1 onto the back half of the sector mirror. Essentially, this type of system is focusing the infrared beam from the sample and reference cells on the monochromator entrance slit in a rapid time sequence. The mirror M_2 collimates the beam and reflects it to a prism, or alternately onto a grating. In the case of a prism instrument, the beam passes through the prism P and is reflected off the mirror M_3, and back through the prism a second time for increased dispersion of the radiant beam. The mirror M_3 is mounted on a movable base, which is rotated to allow the various portions of dispersed

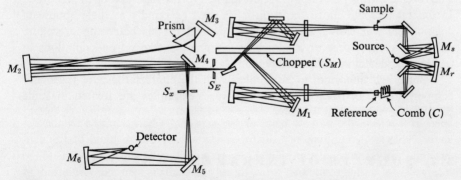

Fig. 3.2 Typical optical path of an optical null, double-beam infrared spectrophotometer. (Courtesy Beckman Instruments, Inc.)

radiation to pass back through the prism. This mirror is generally referred to as the Littrow mirror. In a combination prism-grating instrument, this mirror is replaced by a diffraction grating. At this point, only a narrow band of frequencies are being sent back to the collimating mirror M_2. Another mirror, M_4, focuses this narrow beam on the exit slit S_x and finally from mirror M_5 to a focusing mirror M_6, which bathes the detector with the selected band of infrared frequencies.

Consider now the fact that with no sample or reference absorption the amount of radiation striking the detector is equal from both beams; therefore no signal is produced by the detector. However, with a sample in its respective cell, the two transmitted beams are not equal because of the absorption of radiation by the sample. The rotating sector system then sends a pulsating group of frequencies to the detector. The detector, therefore, transforms this incident radiation into a pulsating electric signal of the same frequency as the rotating sector mirror.

The signal is amplified and used to drive an attenuating comb, C, into the reference beam. Essentially, the comb reduces the amount of energy from the reference beam until the energy balance between the sample and reference is restored. This is known as the optical null method. At this time, the detector ceases to emit a signal. As the reader may already have deduced from the preceding discussion, the extent of reference beam compensation necessary to balance the sample and reference energies is a measure of the absorption by the sample. By placing a recording system in synchronous motion with the attenuator, the extent of sample absorption can be measured.

The entire operation of the optical system, therefore, can be viewed as a function of the amplified detector signal and wavelength drive mechanism. As the Littrow mirror rotates, the frequency of the incident radiation reaching the detector changes. When this frequency equals a vibration-rotation mode of the sample, a change in the amount of energy in the sample beam reaching the detector occurs. A strong absorption of energy causes a proportionally strong detector signal, driving the attenuator into the reference beam to nullify the energy difference and cancel the signal. When this situation occurs, pen motion ceases. This coincides with attainment of the absorption band peak. The reverse of this process will return the pen to the base line of the recorder. In this manner the entire spectrum is scanned as rapidly as the response of components will allow. The principle involved in this balancing procedure ensures a great degree of accuracy by eliminating errors from variations in the source, detector, and atmosphere.

Since it is important to be familiar with the characteristics of the major components of an infrared instrument, these variables are treated in some detail in the subsequent sections.

3.2 SOURCES OF INFRARED RADIATION

Two types of source materials are commonly employed to provide the radiant energy necessary for studies in the infrared region. These materials are either refractory substances, which are heated to a glowing temperature, or a coil of Nichrome wire, which is resistively heated to incandescence. The radiation from such source materials is emitted in a distribution of wavelengths that are characteristic of the temperature of the material. These characteristic emission curves are similar to the curve shown in Fig. 1.5, and also to the curve of an ideal black-body emitter as shown in Fig. 3.3. The position of the greatest amount of emitted radiation can be seen to depend upon the temperature of the glowing or incandescent material. The amount of radiant energy falls off very rapidly as a function of wavelength on each side of this maximum energy position. According to the Stefan-Boltzmann law, the total radiation emitted varies as the fourth power of the temperature. As a consequence, sources of this type create two main problems: First, the variation in intensity with wavelength must be adequately overcome in order to have a linear spectral presentation; second, the highly sensitive thermal response of the source material must be carefully controlled.

Of the refractory source materials, the Nernst glower and the Globar are most commonly employed in commercial instruments. The Nernst glower is usually a hollow tube of zirconium and yttrium oxides which is electrically heated to about 1750° C. On the other hand, the Globar is an electrically heated bar of sintered silicon carbide, operating at temperatures between

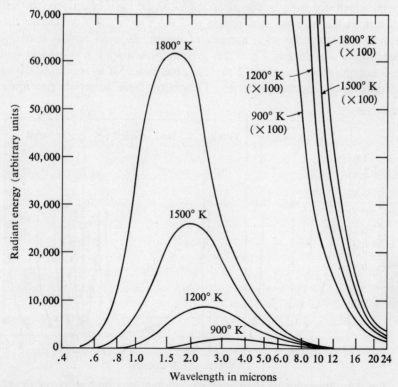

Fig. 3.3 Radiant energy emitted as a function of wavelength for a black-body radiator at several temperatures.

750° C to 1200° C. The Nernst glower is the more intense of the two, but due to its higher operating temperature, it is also slightly more delicate and short-lived. The Globar, because of oxidative susceptibility, cannot be operated at higher temperatures without markedly reducing its life.

In the near-infrared region (0.75μ to 2.5μ), the problem of source materials is considerably simpler. The tungsten lamp ordinarily used in visible spectrophotometry gives continuous radiation up to 3μ. Above this wavelength it is not effective because of the absorption of the emitted radiation by the glass envelope of the lamp. It should be noted an ordinary incandescent lamp can be used to approximately 2μ for near-infrared studies.

3.3 OPTICAL MATERIALS

The monochromator will be treated in Sec. 3.5. Our interest here is in the materials necessary to reflect, transmit, and disperse the infrared radiation as it travels from the source to the detector in order to obtain information about the interaction of the substance being studied with the selected wavelengths of the radiant infrared energy. It is unfortunate that most materials do not have the necessary properties to achieve these tasks over broad ranges in this region. However, such optical materials as natural and synthetic quartz, which are used in the ultraviolet, can be used effectively to transmit radiation in the near-infrared region to 3.0μ. Figure 3.4 summarizes the absorption characteristics of a number of commonly used optical materials as a function of wavelength. From this graphic presentation it is evident that for the common infrared region (2 to 15μ), one is forced to use more expensive and difficult-to-fabricate materials. Generally, these materials are ionic co-

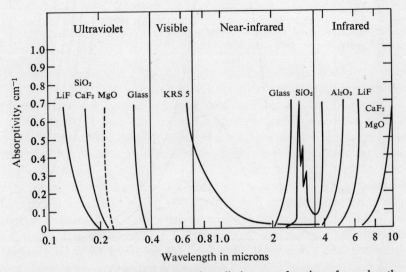

Fig. 3.4 Absorption of electromagnetic radiation as a function of wavelength for a number of optical materials.

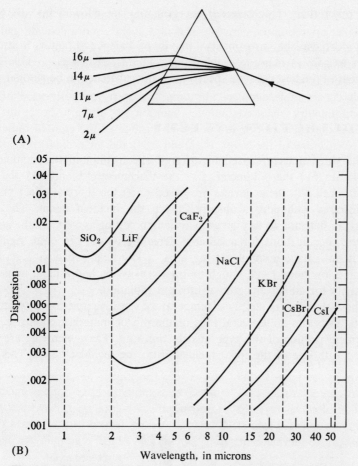

Fig. 3.5 Dispersion of infrared radiation as a function of wavelength for a number of common optical materials used in the various ranges of the infrared region. (A) Dispersion of infrared radiation by a prism. (B) Dispersion of common prism materials.

ordination lattice crystals such as sodium chloride, potassium bromide, silver chloride, and thallium bromoiodide (KRS-5).

Further difficulties are encountered when one examines these substances for their dispersion characteristics, as shown in Fig. 3.5. Those substances having good transmission properties generally have good dispersion only over limited portions of the spectral region. Therefore spectrophotometers having prisms of these materials generally do not achieve high resolution unless the maximum region of dispersion for each material is taken advantage of in a multiple prism instrument. To do this task, many instrument manufacturers have prism interchanges for obtaining high resolution in selected regions of the spectrum. Further, the more recent introduction of diffraction-grating instruments and prism and diffraction-grating combinations has helped in part to resolve some of these difficulties. However, the use of gratings creates diffraction-order separation problems, since unwanted radiation of wavelengths other than those selected energies may be allowed into the optical system.

In most available instruments a maximum balance of factors is attempted in order to gain as many desirable optical characteristics as possible for the attainment of the best possible spectrum of the substance to be studied.

3.4   DETECTION SYSTEMS

The three detectors used in infrared spectrophotometers commercially available are (1) the bolometer, (2) the thermocouple, and (3) the Golay pneumatic cell. All these devices are based upon the thermal effect produced when infrared radiation is absorbed from the incident beam. The energy striking the detector at any given wavelength setting is very small, and as a result the specifications for a suitable detecting device are quite rigid. Generally, it must have a small sensing area, a low heat capacity, a rapid time constant, a low noise level, a high thermal sensitivity, and a high, nonselective absorptivity for all wavelengths of infrared radiation.

The bolometer is simply a temperature-sensitive resistor as pictured in Fig. 3.6. Two thin noble-metal foils or thermistor materials comprise the active element portion of this type of detection unit. These elements are closely mounted with one of the foils shielded from the incident beam. This allows

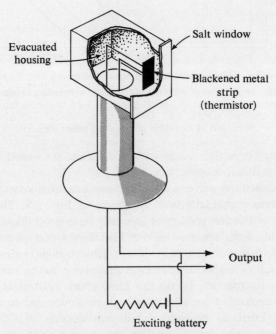

Fig. 3.6   Typical construction features of a bolometer detector.

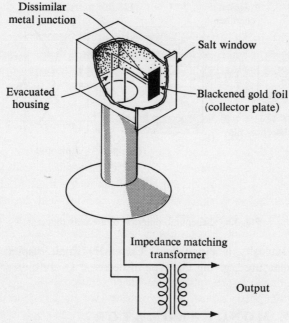

Dissimilar
metal junction

Salt window

Evacuated
housing

Blackened gold foil
(collector plate)

Impedance matching
transformer

Output

Fig. 3.7 Typical construction features of a thermocouple
detector.

one side of this dual element system to be a reference or compensating resistor. These elements, then, constitute the two arms of a balanced Wheatstone bridge circuit. As the sensor absorbs the incident infrared radiation, the bridge circuit becomes unbalanced; this signal is then amplified and measured. The power input to this type of detector can be as low as 10^{-10} watt and yet be detected over the inherent noise in the accompanying electronic circuit system.

Of similar characteristics in the order of signal-response range is the thermocouple detector in Fig. 3.7. A fine, blackened, noble-metal foil is welded to two thermoelectric substances. It is blackened to improve the absorptivity of the infrared radiation focused upon it. The unit is encased in a housing evacuated to minimize heat losses and which has an infrared-transmitting window such as a thin potassium bromide wafer to allow the passage of the radiation to the metal foil.

The most elaborate and most sensitive detector system commercially employed (power inputs as low as 5×10^{-11} watt can be detected) is the Golay cell. This system, as shown in Fig. 3.8, utilizes the expansion of a gas as the sensing device. As radiant energy is absorbed by the gas, it expands in the pneumatic chamber, displacing the flexible, mirrored membrane. A light focused on the mirrored surface of the membrane produces an image of a line grid on the plane of that grid (see Fig. 3.8). When the image and grid are superimposed, the intensity of light transmitted to the photocell is at a maximum. As the membrane expands, the image is displaced and the trans-

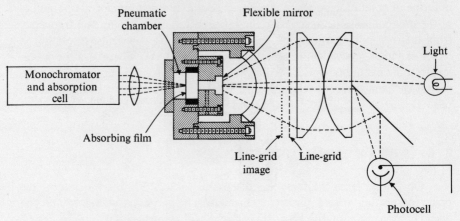

Fig. 3.8   Schematic diagram of a Golay detector.

mitted light intensity is diminished. Extremely small displacements $(10^{-9}$ cm) can be measured, giving this type of detector a very high sensitivity.

3.5   THE MONOCHROMATOR

The source image focused on the monochromator entrance slit (S_E, Fig. 3.2) consists of the total spectral energy emitted by the source (assuming no absorption of that energy prior to entering the monochromator). The collimating mirror reflects as parallel radiation the infrared beam passed by the entrance slit. This radiation is dispersed by the prism into its spectrum. By utilizing the movable mirror (the Littrow mirror), a narrow portion of the dispersed light is passed again through the prism, further dispersed, and focused by the collimating mirror upon the monochromator exit slit (S_x, Fig. 3.2). The exit slit allows the passage of only a narrow frequency range of the dispersed radiation out of the monochromator. This frequency range approximates, for practical purposes of discussion, monochromatic radiation.

In practice, a number of methods are available to increase the dispersion of the infrared radiation by the monochromator. All these methods involve using a prism, a grating, or a combination of both a prism and a grating. The frequency range focused by the collimating mirror on the exit slit depends on the dispersion properties of prism or grating and the width of the entrance slit. The precise portion of the spectrum of radiation being examined at the detector is determined by the Littrow mirror in a prism instrument or by the grating angle in a grating instrument. By rotating either the Littrow mirror or the grating, the frequencies reaching the exit slit are varied until the desired region of the spectrum has been examined. The movement of the Littrow mirror is controlled by a cam, constructed to rotate this mirror at a nonuniform rate to give either a linear frequency change or a linear wavelength change over the entire spectrum. Simultaneously, the movement of the cam also controls the width of the entrance and exit slits. Therefore one can speak in terms of resolution or resolving power of the monochromator as the ability of the monochromator to separate the infrared radiation of any one frequency from that of similar frequencies. In actual practice we can define resolution in terms of either a wavelength scale as the ratio of $\lambda/\Delta\lambda$, where λ is the wavelength to be examined and $\Delta\lambda$ is the wavelength separation between λ and the closest distinguishable wavelengths. In terms of the frequency scale a similar ratio $(\nu/\Delta\nu)$ would also define the resolving power of the monochromator.

3.6   PRISM AND GRATINGS

Obviously, from the foregoing discussion in Sec. 3.5, the function of the prism or grating within the monochromator is particularly important. The dispersion of radiation by the prism is dependent on its refractive index, which in turn changes with changes in the frequency of the radiation. By properly selecting prism materials, improved spectral resolution may be obtained over selected regions of the spectrum. Table 3.1 summarizes the useful wavelength and frequency ranges of some of the more common prism materials. It should be noted that maximum efficiency is obtained in the lower frequency regions of the indicated operating ranges.

Table 3.1.   Optimum Operating Ranges of Prism Materials

Material	Frequency Range (cm⁻¹)	Wavelength Range (μ)
NaCl	5000–650	2–15.4
KBr	1100–385	9–26
LiF	4000–1700	2.5–5.9
CaF₂	4200–1300	2.4–7.7
CsBr	1100–385	9–26
CsI	1000–200	10–50
Glass	Above 3500	Below 2.9
Quartz	Above 2860	Below 3.5

From an examination of Table 3.1, it can be readily noted that for a good portion of the fundamental vibration-rotation region from 2.5 to 15μ, sodium chloride is a prism material of great utility. When using this material, prism interchanges are unnecessary for the region in which most organic compounds have their greatest number of absorption bands. It should be noted that sodium chloride optics have been used to establish almost all the recorded frequency and wavelength values for vibrational modes of most organic functional groups.

Increased resolution can be obtained by using a selected prism for a narrow spectral region. For example, lithium fluoride or calcium fluoride can be used for high resolution of the oxygen-hydrogen (O—H), nitrogen-hydrogen (N—H), and the carbon-hydrogen (C—H) stretching absorptions in the 2.5 to 4.0μ region. Alternatively, to examine most carbon-bromine stretching absorptions, potassium bromide or cesium halide prisms are necessary, since

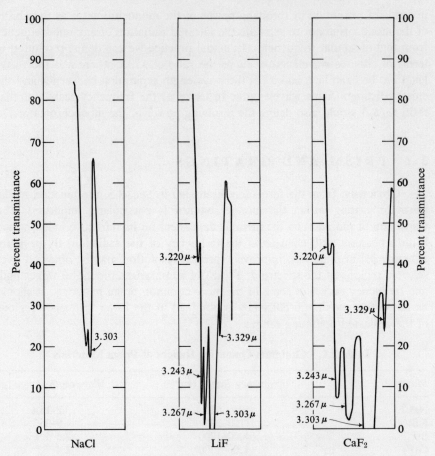

Fig. 3.9 Resolution of the aromatic carbon–hydrogen stretching bands by various prism materials. The sample, polystyrene, was examined as a thin film.

these absorptions fall beyond 15μ. An example of dependency of resolution upon the prism material is shown in Fig. 3.9.

The most commonly employed instruments for qualitative organic work are prism instruments. However, since low-cost grating instruments are gradually becoming available, it would be wise to comment briefly about the use of gratings for infrared studies. Gratings usually give better resolution than that obtained from prisms. A grating (Fig. 3.10) that reflects infrared does so in orders of n cm^{-1} according to the progression n, $2n$, $3n$, $4n$ . . . cm^{-1}, where n is the first-order reflection, $2n$ the second-order reflection, and so forth. In practice, the unwanted orders (since they are multiples of the desired frequency) are rejected by the use of either a foreprism or an optical filter. Therefore, by simply linking the wavelength scan of the prism with that of the grating, a spectrum may be obtained. In Fig. 3.11 the grating can be visualized as replacing the Littrow mirror, M_3 in Fig. 3.2. Figure 3.12 shows the typical optical path of a pure grating instrument.

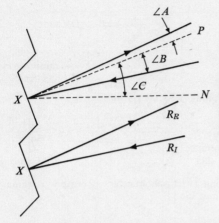

First-order diffraction of infrared radiation by a grating, where: $\angle A$ is the angle
between a perpendicular to the surface
groove and the diffracted ray; $\angle B$ is the
angle between the normal line (perpendicular to the unblazed surface) and the
incident ray; $\angle C$ is the blaze angle.
When $\angle A = \angle B$, the intensity of the
diffracted ray will be at a maximum
(maximum grating efficiency).

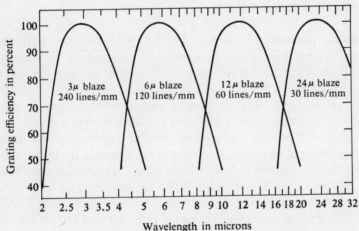

Fig. 3.10 Dispersion of infrared radiation by a diffraction grating.

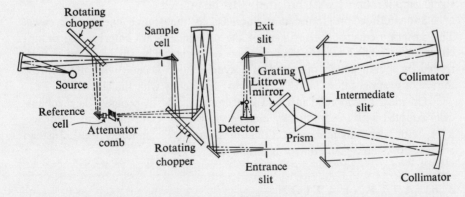

Fig. 3.11 Typical optical path of a prism-grating spectrophotometer. (Courtesy
Beckman Instruments, Inc.)

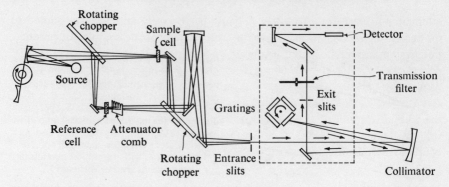

Fig. 3.12 Typical optical path of a grating spectrophotometer. (Courtesy Beckman Instruments, Inc.)

3.7 SLIT FUNCTION

From the previous discussion in Sec. 3.5, the reader may have deduced that optimum operation of the slits could be obtained by very narrow slit widths. This is suggested for the entrance slit, since the narrower the beam, the more efficiently it could be dispersed by the prism. As well, a narrow exit slit would select a very small frequency range from the dispersed spectrum for admission to the detector. Thus, in principle, minimum entrance and exit slit widths should produce the highest possible resolving power from any given prism material or grating. In practice the situation is much more complex, since the characteristics of the source (Sec. 3.2) and detector (Sec. 3.4) actually determine the operating slit width at any specified frequency. The strength of the electronic signal from the detector is dependent upon the absolute difference in radiant energy of the reference and sample beams. It is quite important that the total energy reaching the detector remain constant over the entire frequency range. Since the energy of the source is not linear, but actually changes quite drastically, a slit width or an alternate electronic signal amplification (gain) program must be utilized.

Slit width is programmed to increase as the source energy decreases. This program ensures a constancy of the reference beam entering the monochromator when no sample absorption is occurring. The slit program is controlled by a cam and is operated in a synchronous fashion with the Littrow mirror or grating, interrelating the varying frequency with the slit width.

On most commercial infrared instruments, the slit program is mechanically coupled with the frequency change via a cam. Gain programs (see Sec. 3.9), with their inherent noise difficulties, are not commonly used. Instead a linear adjustable-gain control is employed.

3.8 ATTENUATION

Probably the most intriguing component of the double-beam spectrophotometer is the function of the attenuator, optical comb, or wedge. For the attenuator to perform effectively, it must be precisely and linearly related to the increasing or decreasing percentage absorption of the sample. In practice, this is approximated, since it is almost impossible to design an attenuator that accurately cuts off the reference beam at the 0 and 100% transmittance ranges. This means that at low transmittance due to high absorption by the sample, the weak signal reaching the detector does not accurately represent the true absorption of the sample in the frequency being monitored. Despite this disadvantage, the optical null principle is used almost exclusively because of the many advantages it possesses (see Sec. 3.1).

3.9   SIGNAL AMPLIFICATION

The design of amplifier circuits depends on the optical system and type of detector employed and therefore varies widely with the specific instrument manufacturer. In principle it is possible to examine the function of the amplifier in terms of the signal reaching the detector.

Generally the signal arising at the detector is small (in the range of 0.05 to 1.0 mv). Since this signal level is roughly the same as the stray signals that are picked up by the shielded cables leading from the detector to the amplifier, it is common to find a preamplifier placed as close as possible to the detector, to prevent loss of the signal. The preamplifier raises the signal to a level such that any stray signals beyond this stage will introduce a small, relatively insignificant error. The amplifier receives both the alternating signal from the detector and the stray signals from the cable.

Any random signal arising from the circuitry (from detector to final amplification) is defined as noise. Noise includes thermal electronic motion (Johnson noise), vacuum tube noise, fluctuations in resistors, and fluctuations in the detector due to temperature changes. Since the noise consists of equal amounts of all frequencies, the amount of noise is proportional to the frequency band pass.

On amplification, both the signal and noise will be increased proportionally. By narrowing the band pass with a filter circuit, much of the noise can be removed. However, there is a point beyond which the signal is reduced as much as the noise by the filter. At this point, the signal-to-noise ratio is optimum for the amplification system. The signal-to-noise ratio therefore determines the accuracy with which one can read the signal at the recorder. The extent of attenuation of the signal from the detector (gain) is manually controlled by the operator on most commercial instruments.

3.10   VARIABLES IN SPECTROPHOTOMETER OPERATION

With the components used in available spectrophotometers clearly in mind, it is well to review the interrelationship of the components to the operating efficiency of the instrument. In all spectrophotometers three inter-related variables control this performance, namely: spectral resolution, photo-metric accuracy, and scanning speed. Due to the interplay between these variables, a change in any one will influence the others. For example, if a fast scanning speed is desired, a loss in either photometric accuracy or resolution must be accepted. When higher resolution is necessary, the scanning speed must be reduced.

Resolution. As previously stated in Sec. 3.5, resolution is expressed in terms of the ability of the spectrophotometer to distinguish neighboring spectral wavelengths or frequencies, and is generally associated with the slit width (i.e., high resolution is thought of in terms of narrow spectral slit width). If one considers a particular wavelength or frequency in the spectrum, the spectral slit width increases linearly with any increase in the physical width of the exit slit. However, the radiant energy reaching the detector is proportional to the square of the physical slit width. To improve resolution, the slits must be narrowed. In doing so, the energy to the detector is decreased (as the square of the slit width), lowering the signal-to-noise ratio. In order to compensate for this loss, the gain (the attenuation of the signal from the detector) must be increased. This increase in attenuation raises the noise level proportionally. To maintain a reasonable level of noise on the recorded spectrum, the speed of response of the pen system must be decreased. In order to record a spectrum with suitable photometric accuracy (i.e., the accuracy with which the pen indicates the true transmission of the sample), it is necessary to spend a longer period of time scanning the spectrum. Typical changes in position and intensity of the recorded absorption band as a function of physical slit width are shown in Fig. 3.13.

As described in Sec. 3.6, the ability of the dispersing element (prism, grating, or both) to provide high resolution is dependent upon its ability to disperse the incident radiation over a large angle. Gratings are generally far superior in this respect and consequently make operation possible with enhanced signal-to-noise ratio (higher resolution).

Ultimately, then, the signal-to-noise ratio determines the performance of the infrared spectrophotometer. The noise (Sec. 3.9) depends primarily on the inherent thermal noise in the detector-preamplifier system. The signal is proportional to a number of variables, including:

1. Transmission efficiency of the optical components.
2. Square of the physical slit width.
3. Energy of the source at the wavelengths of interest.
4. Dispersion of the prism or grating.

Other optical system variables are generally fixed by the instrument design. The selection of items 1 and 4 can be determined by the chemist on the basis of the needs of the particular problem. The slit width (2) is generally a variable operating parameter of most instruments and can be fixed by the operator. The radiation (3) from the source can be controlled (in some instruments) over a narrow range by the analyst.

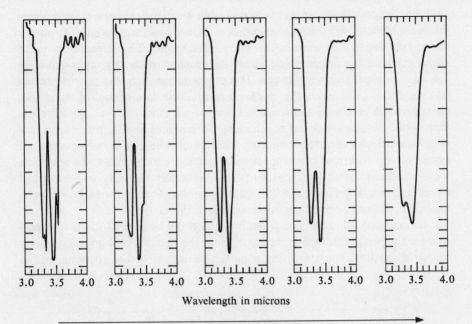

Fig. 3.13 Changes in the positions and intensities of recorded absorption bands as a function of physical slit width. The region shown is the C—H stretching region of polystyrene, examined as a thin film. The spectra were recorded at comparable pen response times and constant scanning speed.

Photometric accuracy. As previously described, photometric accuracy refers to the ability of the pen to record the true transmittance of the sample. In short, therefore, it relates to the accuracy with which quantitative results can be obtained from band-intensity measurements. In addition to those parameters fixed by instrument design, four major factors must be recognized as influencing band intensities:

1. Sampling limitations.
2. Response versus attenuation and scanning speed.
3. Noise.
4. Stray radiation.

Sampling limitations will be discussed in detail in both Chaps. 4 (concerned with techniques) and 6 (pertaining to quantitative analysis). Generally the limitations of sample are those that embody the "common sense" operation of the chemist in his experimental work, together with the inherent problems of chemical interactions and peculiar structural changes of compounds during sample preparations. For example, a few of the "common sense" items include: control of sample and cell purity, choice of proper concentration of samples in solution, complete filling of sample cells, and many others. In the area of chemical interactions, the solvent effects, scattering of energy by the sample, and emission of infrared radiation by hot samples are a few of the factors requiring careful consideration and control by the analyst.

The second factor, response versus gain and scanning speed, is perhaps the least obvious difficulty the chemist must be concerned with. The major factor affecting the response is the attenuation (gain). The attenuation of the signal reaching the detector determines the amount of electric input actuating the servomotor that drives the pen. If the gain is too high, the pen will be set into oscillation; if too low, the spectrum recorded will be devoid of the details normally obtained from the spectral information. Both effects are rather extreme, but are readily detected after the chemist has had a little experience with his particular spectrophotometer. However, if the gain is only moderately excessive, the spectrum may appear to be quite normal. In fact, the spectrum looks excellent for all practical purposes. Generally the only way to detect excessive attenuation is by carefully examining sharp bands for excessive overshoot, i.e., fallacious band depths as shown in Fig. 3.14.

In addition, the response depends both on the balance of the time necessary for the pen to respond to the signal from the detector and on the scanning speed. If the time spent crossing a particular region of the spectrum is too

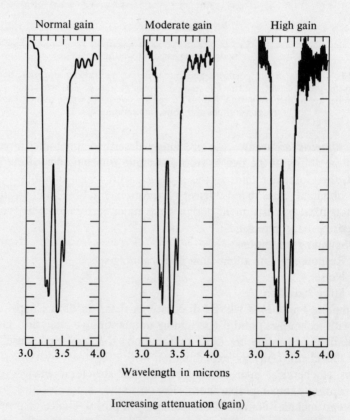

Fig. 3.14 Changes in the recorded spectrum as a function of attenuation. The region shown is the C—H stretching region of polystyrene, examined as a thin film. The spectra were recorded at constant slit width and scanning speed. Note the pen overshoot on the moderate gain curve.

short, the pen will not respond accurately, and some information will be lost (generally the band shapes are distorted). Except for practical limitations of operator time, it is highly unlikely that slower scanning speeds will result in this error.

The third factor is noise. At the absorption maximum (peak height) significant variations can occur. In fact, these variations can be as great as the noise level generally encountered at the background between absorption bands. It is possible to minimize this, again, by slowing down the response of the system, thereby smoothing out the noise fluctuations. In doing this, a longer time interval must be taken in recording the spectral region of interest.

The final factor, stray radiation, is radiation that strikes the detector but which is of different wavelength or frequency from that being isolated by the monochromator. In qualitative analysis, strong bands will appear shifted to shorter wavelengths. In quantitative work, the indicated transmittance will be higher than it should be, and therefore it will affect the accuracy of the determination. The phenomenon of stray radiation will be discussed in greater detail in Chap. 6.

SUGGESTED READING

1. W. J. POTTS, JR., *Chemical Infrared Spectroscopy, Vol. 1, Techniques.* Wiley, New York, 1963.
2. *Synthetic Optical Crystals* (revised). The Harshaw Chemical Company, Cleveland, Ohio, 1955.
3. J. STRONG, "Resolving Power Limitations of Grating and Prism Spectrophotometers," *J. Opt. Soc. Am.,* **39** (1949), 320.
4. V. WILLIAMS, "Infrared Instrumentation and Techniques," *Rev. Sci. Instr.,* **19** (1948), 135.
5. J. STRONG, *Concepts of Classical Optics.* Freeman, San Francisco, Calif., 1958.
6. N. L. ALPERT in *IR, Theory and Practice of Infrared Spectroscopy,* by H. A. Szymanski. Plenum Press, New York, 1964.
7. R. P. BAUMAN, *Absorption Spectroscopy.* Wiley, New York, 1962.
8. W. BRUGEL, *An Introduction to Infrared Spectroscopy.* Wiley, New York, 1962.

ADDITIONAL READING

N. ACQUISTA AND E. K. PLYER, *J. Opt. Soc. Am.,* **43** (1953), 977.
N. H. E. AHLERS AND H. P. FREEDMAN, *J. Sci. Inst.,* **32** (1955), 61.
M. AXELRAD, *Rev. Opt.,* **35** (1956), 437.
L. BECKMAN, E. FUNCK, AND R. MECKE, *Z. Angew Phys.,* **11** (1959), 207.
G. W. BETHKE, *J. Opt. Soc. Am.,* **50** (1960), 1054.
E. L. BLOUNT AND A. R. H. COLE, *J. Sci. Inst.,* **32** (1955), 471.
F. S. BRACKETT, *J. Opt. Soc. Am.,* **47** (1957), 636.
V. J. COATES, *Spectrochim. Acta* (1959), 820.
V. J. COATES AND H. HAUSDORFF, *J. Opt. Soc. Am.,* **45** (1955), 425.
H. M. CROSSWHILE AND W. G. FASTIE, *J. Opt. Soc. Am.,* **46** (1956), 110.
W. E. DEEDS, *Rev. Sci. Insts.,* **27** (1956), 543.

C. Deloupy, A. M. Vergnoux, and F. Rouquayrol, *Rev. Opt.*, **37** (1958), 113.

L. A. Ducanson, J. W. Eddell, M. B. Lloyd, and W. T. Moore, *Spectrochim. Acta*, (1959), 64.

M. A. Ford, W. C. Price and G. Wilkinson, *J. Sci. Inst.*, **35** (1958), 55.

M. J. E. Golay, *J. Opt. Soc. Am.*, **45** (1955), 430.

M. J. E. Golay, *J. Opt. Soc. Am.*, **46** (1956), 422.

J. L. Hales, *J. Sci. Inst.*, **36** (1959), 264.

G. Hass, *J. Opt. Soc. Am.*, **45** (1955), 945.

L. W. Herscher, *Rev. Sci. Inst.*, **20** (1949), 833.

L. W. Herscher, *Spectrochim. Acta*, **14** (1948), 901.

L. W. Herscher, H. E. Ruhl, and N. Wright, *J. Opt. Soc. Am.*, **48** (1958), 36.

V. Von Keussler, *Optik*, **13** (1956), 317.

H. J. Kostowski and A. M. Bass, *J. Opt. Soc. Am.*, **46** (1956), 1060.

K. F. Luft and H. Maillet, *Rev. Opt.*, **33** (1954), 644.

T. P. Merritt and F. F. Hall, Jr., *Proc. IRE.*, **47** (1959), 1435.

I. M. Mills, J. R. Scherer and B. Crawford, Jr., *J. Opt. Soc. Am.*, **45** (1955), 785.

C. A. Mitchell, *J. Opt. Soc. Am.*, **52** (1962), 341.

V. A. Nikitin, *Optics & Spectroscopy*, **4** (1958), 523.

G. G. Petras, *Optics & Spectroscopy*, **9** (1960), 121.

J. R. Platt, *J. Opt. Soc. Am.*, **46** (1956), 609.

J. Pliva, *J. Sci. Inst.*, **31** (1954), 434.

W. S. Rodney, *J. Opt. Soc. Am.*, **45** (1955), 987.

J. E. Stewart, *Appl. Optics*, **1** (1962), 75.

J. E. Stewart and J. C. Richmond, *J. Research, NBS*, **59** (1957), 405.

A. M. Vergnoux, J. Lacourt and F. Rouquayrol, *Rev. Opt.*, **34** (1955), 575.

J. U. White, *Anal. Chem.*, **22** (1950), 768.

J. U. White, N. L. Alpert, A. G. De Bell, and R. M. Chapman, *J. Opt. Soc. Am.*, **47** (1957), 358.

W. L. Wolfe and S. S. Ballard, *Proc. IRE*, **47** (1959), 1540.

4

Infrared Techniques

Almost all compounds, particularly organic substances, absorb in the infrared region. Although this is the chief asset in the utilization of infrared spectrophotometry for gaining structural information, it complicates many of the available sample-preparation procedures. The necessity for a thorough knowledge of the common methods used to obtain information concerning the absorption characteristics of a particular substance prompts a separate discussion relating to laboratory techniques, sample preparation, and the application of these techniques to spectral examination of organic as well as most inorganic substances.

As the reader will recall, many compounds do not absorb at all in the visible and ultraviolet region. Among these are a good number of common solvents. Since this is not the case in the infrared region, methods must be devised to circumvent the loss of information usually encountered in the examination of substances in solution, particularly with solids. Methods used to overcome this deficiency can be summarized as follows: Compounds are examined in more than one solvent to take advantage of the different absorption characteristics of each solvent used: pure materials as liquids, melts, powders, films, or large single crystals are examined without solvent; finely ground powders are dispersed in mineral oil or other heavy liquids, or in inorganic halides such as potassium bromide and pressed into a disc or pellet. Samples can be pressed into or absorbed on films, such as polyethylene; amorphous solids can be microtomed to give thin films for examination; coatings or surface deposits can be examined by reflectance rather than transmittance;

samples can be pyrolyzed and the pyrolysis products examined; and samples can be condensed at low temperatures from the gas phase onto a transparent window (matrix isolation). The list could be extended and again further extended without fully noting all possible preparative procedures that have been used for sample examination. In many cases the criterion to be used for sample preparation rests solely on the chemist's ability to devise a suitable technique to gain the information desired. In practice, several methods are used more frequently than others. Therefore these methods will be described in some detail to acquaint the reader with the basic procedures, their applications, and limitations.

A single infrared spectrum will not provide all the information that can be possibly gained by infrared spectral study of a compound. Changes of phase or diluent frequently yield data not obtainable from the first spectrum taken and either add to or confirm conclusions drawn from the first spectrum. Commonly, one spectral region offers more value than others, since the past history of a given sample usually indicates what information is needed. Therefore some substances are best examined in one particular phase. In the subsequent sections particular note should be taken with regard to the effects of phase changes and diluent changes. The advantages and disadvantages of each technique should be also carefully considered by the reader.

From the foregoing discussion it is apparent that there are no rigid rules concerning the phase to be preferred for any single compound, since it is the nature of the compound rather than the technique that determines the ease or difficulty in gaining spectral information from the infrared region.

4.1   SOLID SAMPLES

In order to examine a solid material in the infrared region it must be filmed, melted, or mulled into a viscous liquid, dispersed in an inorganic halide disc or pellet, finely powdered onto a supporting surface, studied by a reflectance technique or as a solute in several solvents. The examination of powdered materials will often cause scattering of the incident infrared radiation as well as absorption. Amorphous solids that can be deposited as films from solution or melt usually have negligible scattering losses. Scattering results, in most cases, from the reflection of the incident beam at a boundary between the sample and the supporting medium when there are appreciable differences in their respective indices of refraction. By placing the sample in an envelope of material of approximately the same index of refraction, the amount of scattering can be greatly reduced. Therefore the ideal situation would be to have a liquid or solid supporting matrix of approximately the same refractive index as the sample and have either very few or no absorption bands in the region to be examined.

4.1.1 Mulling techniques.   For most organic materials, a refined mineral oil (Nujol) has been found to be a suitable liquid for dispersing powdered samples. Nujol is a mixture of long-chained saturated hydrocarbons. The material has only four regions of absorption from 2 to 15μ, as indicated in its spectrum, Fig. 4.1. The vibrations indicated here are due to the C—H stretching vibration bands at 2850 to 3000 cm^{-1} (3.51 to 3.33μ), the C—H bending modes at 1468 (6.81μ) and 1379 cm^{-1} (7.25μ), and the relatively broad and weak methylene rocking vibration at 720 cm^{-1} (13.88μ). Other vibrations are not observed, since they are relatively weak absorptions, and only a thin Nujol suspension is required to examine the sample. The disadvantage of Nujol is immediately apparent to the reader; it will not be possible to examine aliphatic carbon-hydrogen vibrations in the sample because of the absorption by the suspending medium. Actually, for aromatic compounds and for samples in which only analysis for functional groups are necessary, this medium is very useful.

When the sample requires aliphatic C—H analysis, halogenated hydrocarbons can be substituted for the Nujol as the mulling medium. Usually, hexachlorobutadiene or Fluorolube (perfluorokerosene) are used as alternate materials.

The general procedure most commonly followed is to first grind the dry

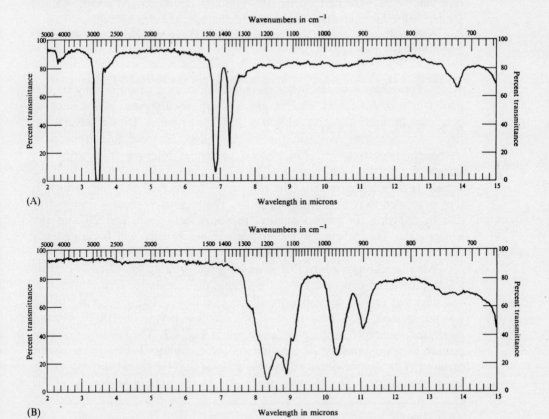

Fig. 4.1 Spectra of (A) Nujol and (B) fluorolube, the common suspending agents used in mull preparation.

sample to a fine powder, either between glass plates, in an agate mortar with pestle, or in an automatic pulverizing instrument. A few drops of the suspending agent is added and the grinding continued until a smooth paste is obtained. A few drops of the paste is sandwiched between polished sodium chloride discs. The discs are pressed together to obtain a thin film, placed in a suitable cell holder and scanned. A number of variations in the grinding procedure should be noted. For example, it is sometimes useful to dissolve the solid in a volatile solvent and grind the precipitated solid sample as the solvent evaporates. This procedure sometimes greatly reduces the effort necessary to pulverize the sample. A second useful technique is to grind relatively amorphous materials, such as polymers, with dry ice so that sufficiently small particle size can be obtained. In most cases these materials are brittle enough to be ground at low temperature. Both procedures have the disadvantage that moisture is readily absorbed during the grinding operation. Since water absorbs strongly in the infrared region and also causes damage to the salt plates, use of these special procedures requires that care be taken to dry the sample before mulling in the Nujol.

In obtaining good spectra from mulled samples, particular attention and care should be exercised during the grinding operation. A poorly ground sample will cause extensive scattering in the low wavelength region. This is due to the failure of the analyst to reduce the size of the particles sufficiently during the grinding operation.

4.1.2 Potassium bromide pellet methods.   Just as a material may be dispersed in a mull, it may also be ground with an inorganic halide such as potassium bromide and pressed into a thin disc or pellet. Dies of several varieties for preparing potassium bromide pellets are available from most instrument manufacturers. The general procedure followed is to grind the sample to a powder, add potassium bromide, and continue grinding until the sample is thoroughly mixed. The mixture is transferred to a die, which is then evacuated to remove the trapped air. The mixture is pressed into a clear disc by applying for several minutes pressures between 8 and 20 tons per square inch. The pellets formed in this manner usually will be completely clear. A typical potassium bromide die for pressing pellets is shown in Fig. 4.2.

An alternate procedure that is rapid, gives good pellets of most organic solids, provides a convenient way for storing the sample for future reference, and does not require an expensive die is as follows: The ground potassium bromide sample is placed in a ½-in. circular cavity in 100-lb blotting paper and assembled in the press as shown in Fig. 4.3. The sandwich is compressed to approximately 20 tons for at least 2 minutes before releasing the pressure. The sample obtained by this process can be placed directly in the spectrophotometer. The blotting paper acts as the sample holder. After the

Fig. 4.2 Typical units for forming potassium bromide pellets. (A) Component parts of a ½-in. circular die. (B) Rectangular pellet die in press being evacuated prior to application of pressure. (Courtesy Beckman Instruments, Inc.)

Rubber plunger
protecting ring

Stainless steel
plunger base

Plunger, stainless
steel

Die body, stainless
steel

O-ring for sealing
the unit for
evacuation

Anvil and Base,
stainless steel

Hose connector
for evacuation

(A)

(B)

51

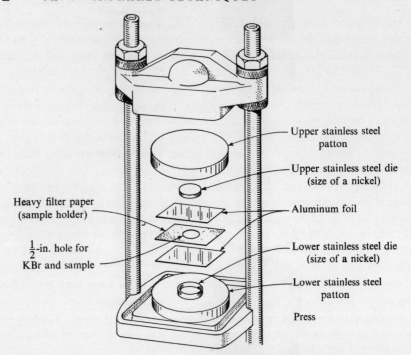

Upper stainless steel patton

Upper stainless steel die (size of a nickel)

Heavy filter paper (sample holder)

Aluminum foil

$\frac{1}{2}$-in. hole for KBr and sample

Lower stainless steel die (size of a nickel)

Lower stainless steel patton

Press

Fig. 4.3   Filter paper "sandwich" technique for forming potassium bromide pellets.

sample has been spectrally examined, the pellet can be desiccated or sealed in a small plastic bag and filed or stored.

The pellet method offers certain advantages over other techniques; it also has some serious disadvantages, which must be considered. The materials used can be varied; however, they should have the following properties: high transmittance throughout the spectral range to be examined (the absence of absorption by potassium bromide to roughly 400 cm^{-1} is a distinct advantage), low sintering pressure, ready availability in a pure nonhydroscopic state, high chemical stability, and a refractive index that closely matches that of most of the samples to be studied. In general, a pellet usually allows the examination of the sample without interfering bands (such as found in the mull technique or in solution methods). However, the percentage of samples having good spectral characteristics in pellet form roughly equals those that give good mull spectra, therefore giving good reason for employing both techniques.

The disadvantages of the pellet method warrant special attention. Since potassium bromide is hydroscopic, it is difficult to prepare a pellet completely free of contaminating moisture. This renders qualitative analysis of the —OH and —NH spectral region difficult, if not impossible, since a positive absorption in this region is almost always present as a result of the absorbed moisture (water).

Perhaps the most adverse effect is the lack of reproducibility of the spectra obtained from pelletized samples. As in mulls, some variations are due to particle size. In other instances, the compound actually reacts with the inorganic halide. The effect of the high temperatures and pressures on forming the pellet can change the physical state of the compound (polymorphic changes) and in some cases the chemical nature of the compound (through partial decomposition). Since the sample is actually not dissolved in the potassium bromide, any partial solution effect can change both the position and intensity of the infrared bands. With these difficulties in mind it is wise to exercise caution in interpreting qualitative or quantitative spectral data obtained when using this technique.

At times, pellets are prepared that contain too much sample. In such instances it is usually necessary to repeat the preparation by either regrinding the pellet with an additional amount of potassium bromide and reforming the pellet or starting with a new sample. As an alternate method, it has been found that the pellet can be thinned by using sandpaper. By using finger cots or a rubber sheet to protect the pellet from moisture, it is possible to reduce its thickness by rubbing on No. 320-A sandpaper. The pellet is then repolished, using a very fine emery paper (No. 4/0). Such a technique is useful when all the sample is in the pellet. Since the pellet is small, the method is quick and easy, and usually excellent spectra can be obtained from the thinned pellets. These spectra are completely comparable with those obtained by regrinding or complete sample repreparation.

Special Pelleting Methods. In addition to utilizing potassium bromide as a solid matrix, fine-particle-size Teflon can be mixed with the powdered sample. A pellet obtained from such a mixture has good spectral qualities. Teflon has at least one advantage over potassium bromide in that it does not have so great a tendency to absorb atmospheric water.

In a similar manner, low-density polystyrene foam can be used as a solid support for spectral purposes. In this procedure the foam can be shaped to the size of the pellet to be formed, and the pulverized solid is simply pressed into the foam matrix. In like fashion, sub-micron polyethylene powder can be used as a solid support yielding a thin film specimen.

4.1.3 Melts and films. If the sample to be examined is a low-melting solid, it is often possible to warm two sodium chloride plates in an oven carefully and prepare a melt of the sample between the salt plates. In practice, it is best to warm the plates on an asbestos mat and to isolate them from the metal holder with thin Teflon or asbestos cushions, to prevent the plates from cracking on cooling. Most low-melting materials will not crystallize readily between the salt plates and can be examined as true melts. Good spectra can often be obtained by allowing the melt to cool and crystallize between the salt plates. The bands are often very sharp and well defined. Since the crystallization may take place with a preferred orientation, the resulting spectrum may be quite different from the spectrum of the same compound obtained by using other techniques such as mulling or solution.

Films of organic polymers can be cast on salt plates from suitable solvents. For most purposes, low-boiling, highly volatile solvents are best, but in some cases high-boiling solvents can be removed by vacuum evaporation at elevated temperatures. For qualitative examination, small quantities of trapped solvent will not interfere with the examination for functional groups. However, for more detailed studies such as quantitative analysis of end groups and kinetic studies of oxidation at elevated temperatures, the solvent must be removed prior to the spectral examination. Films can be prepared in a variety of ways and used directly as thin films in a suitable metal, cardboard, or asbestos holder and examined directly. Films prepared in this manner are very thin and therefore, more often than not, interference fringes are produced as a result of the change in index of refraction at the surfaces of the film. Interestingly, the fringes can be used as a method to calculate the thickness of the film if a suitable number of fringes are observed. This method will be discussed in Sec. 4.2.5 when considering the measurement of the path length of a liquid cell.

4.1.4 Dispersions and powders. If the particle size of a powder can be reduced to less than 2μ, a suitable spectrum can usually be obtained by simply dusting the sample on a sodium chloride plate. Powders may also be suspended in a solvent by an emulsion technique as follows: A finely powdered

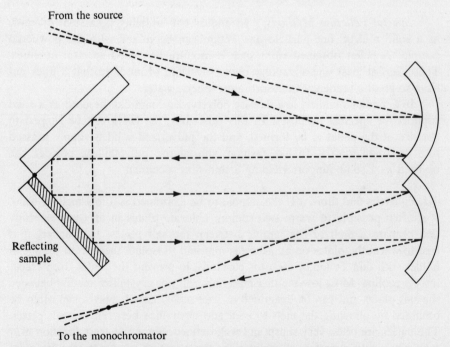

From the source

Reflecting
sample

To the monochromator

Fig. 4.4 Typical system employed in obtaining infrared reflectance data. (Courtesy Beckman Instruments, Inc.)

material is dispersed in a solvent and a small amount of an emulsifying agent (about 1%) is added. For qualitative studies the resulting emulsion can be treated in most respects as if it were a liquid solution. However, both methods are not generally applicable to a large number of substances.

4.1.5 Reflectance techniques.   Attachments for infrared reflectance studies are generally available for most spectrophotometers. A typical reflectance system is diagrammatically shown in Fig. 4.4. The incident beam is reflected off the surface of the sample rather than transmitted through the sample, in order to obtain true reflectance measurements. With the system shown in Fig. 4.5, it is possible to obtain either reflectance or transmittance spectra, depending on the sample. Organic materials approximately 0.1 in. thick are generally opaque and give true reflectance spectra. However, very thin films mounted on a reflecting surface produce a transmittance spectrum (Fig. 4.6).

In many instances, transmittance measurements are extremely difficult to obtain either because the sample absorbs too strongly or because the sample

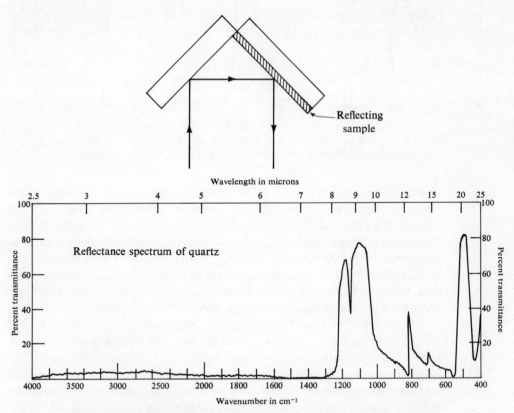

Fig. 4.5 Optical path of the radiant beam in a reflectance unit to produce a reflectance spectrum from the surface of a sample. Note that the spectrum shown is the inverse of the normal transmission curve. (Courtesy Beckman Instruments, Inc.)

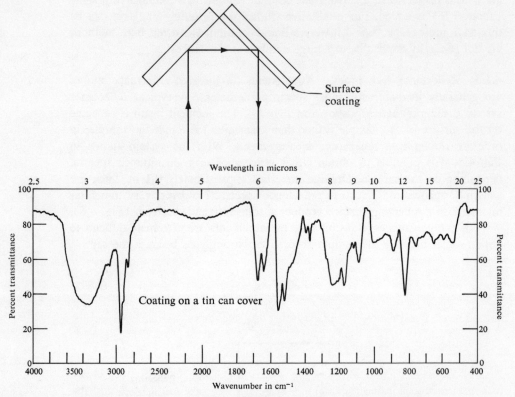

Fig. 4.6 Optical path of the radiant beam in a reflectance unit to produce a transmission spectrum from a thin film sample. (Courtesy Beckman Instruments, Inc.)

of interest may be a coating on a nontransparent surface. In these cases, reflectance spectra may provide the necessary information concerning the sample. The reflectance spectrum usually shows a maximum near the position of maximum absorptivity. Although it is possible to calculate the positions of absorption from reflectance measurements, this usually is very difficult. For many applications the reflectance spectrum itself may provide all the necessary data for identification or characterization by comparison of the reflectance spectrum with similar spectra obtained from known substances.

Some reflectance units have a variable angle such that reflectance studies can be made at angles between 15 and 80 deg. The operation of a variable-angle reflectance attachment is shown in Fig. 4.7. The infrared beam is reflected by a series of mirrors to two perpendicular corner mirrors and then into the instrument's monochromator section. The mounting that holds the mirror can be turned, as shown in the insert in Fig. 4.7, through any angle between 15 and 80 deg without affecting the beam's exit path. When the sample is substituted for corner mirror A, the beam is reflected off the sample at the angle for which the unit has been set. The actual operation of the unit is a simple one. The sample is placed in the holder (replacing mirror A), the

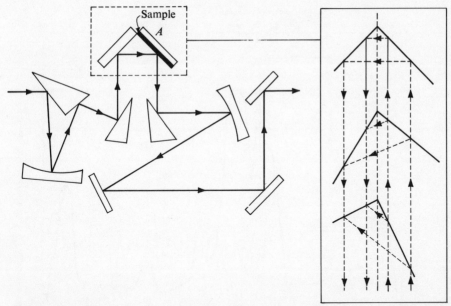

Fig. 4.7 Schematic diagram of a variable-angle reflectance unit. As the reflecting surface is rotated, it can be seen that the incoming and outgoing beams are always parallel to each other and are separated by the same distance no matter what incident angle is chosen. (Courtesy Beckman Instruments, Inc.)

angle of reflectance is chosen, and the spectrum is scanned. Figure 4.8 shows two spectra of a polished rock sample of geode, one taken at 45 deg and the other at 60 deg. In these curves, note that the spectrum is the inverse of the normal transmission spectrum and that the angle at which the spectrum was recorded significantly changes the intensities of the reflectance bands.

4.1.6 Attenuated total reflectance. A method examining samples by a total internal reflection technique, which is far more sensitive than the reflectance technique described in the preceding section, has recently become available for routine sample examination. It has been shown that when a beam of radiation is passed into a prism so that it is totally reflected from the back face, a portion of the energy of the beam escapes from the "totally reflecting" face and then is returned into the prism, as shown in Fig. 4.9. By placing a sample in very close contact with a reflecting surface, the energy escaping temporarily from the prism can be selectively absorbed. This is very much the same as the absorption by the sample in a typical transmittance spectrum. The absorption-like spectra obtained in this manner have some very important features worthy of comment. First, the band intensities are the equivalent of an extremely shallow (approximately 5μ or less) penetration into the sample, and secondly they are completely independent of the sample thickness.

The immediate observation that comes to mind is that this technique completely eliminates precise and extremely short path length cells and film samples as a requirement for infrared sampling. This technique is very useful

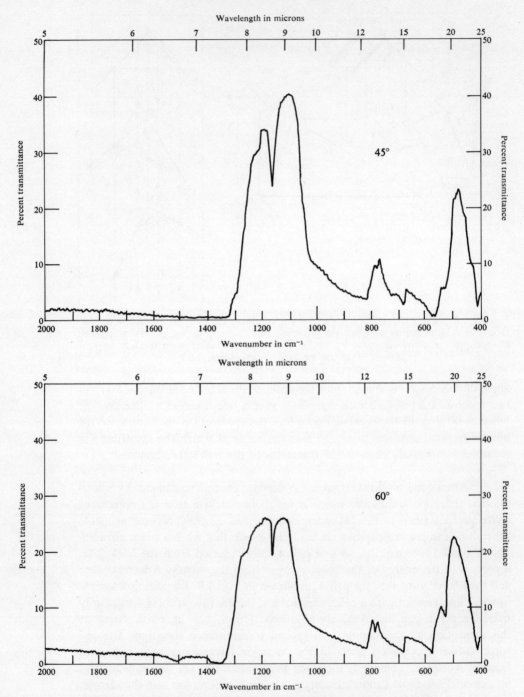

Fig. 4.8 Two reflectance spectra of a geode sample showing typical spectral variations as a function of the angle of reflectance. (Courtesy Beckman Instruments, Inc.)

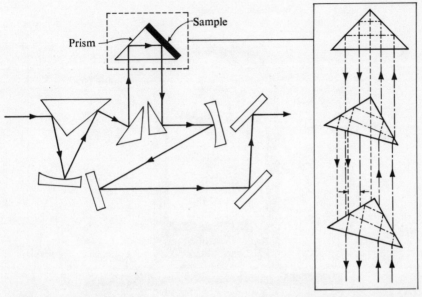

Fig. 4.9 Optical path for a typical attenuated total reflectance unit. Note the similarities between this figure and Fig. 4.7. (Courtesy Beckman Instruments, Inc.)

in the infrared examination of solid materials, but not necessarily restricted to them. Typical of the several possible systems that can be used to obtain attenuated total reflectance (ATR) spectra is the system shown in Fig. 4.10.

The intensity of infrared radiation of a given frequency reflected from the surface of a medium capable of absorption is a complex function beyond the scope of this treatment (cf. "Suggested Reading" at the end of the chapter for the discussion of ATR by J. Fahrenfort). This function is dependent upon the refractive index (n), the angle of incident radiation (θ), and the absorption index k. The absorption index is related to the absorptivity (see Chap. 6) by the following relationship:

$$a = \frac{4\pi nk}{\lambda}$$

At present, the applications of ATR are only partially delineated, and the potential of the method remains to be fully developed.

4.1.7 Pyrolyzate examination. There are serious limitations in the characterization of certain materials, such as organic polymers (see also Chap. 8), by their infrared spectra. The physical state of many polymeric materials prevents the preparation of samples by the conventional techniques described previously. Casting films, melting, mulling, and pelleting methods are impossible, since such materials in many cases are infusible, intractable, and cannot be pulverized. Such materials can be characterized by the examination of their pyrolysis products.

In principle, when a substance is heated to decomposition, a specific

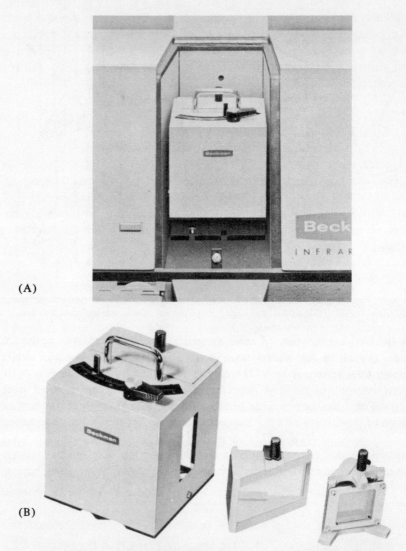

(A)

(B)

Fig. 4.10 Attenuated total reflectance and variable-angle reflectance unit. (A) ATR unit mounted in the sample compartment of the instrument. (B) The dial for determining and setting the reflectance angle can be seen at the top of the assembly at the left. In the middle is the mirror-sample assembly used for variable-angle reflectance studies. At the right is the prism-sample assembly for ATR studies. (Courtesy Beckman Instruments, Inc.)

number of products in a definite ratio will be produced. If these products are collected and the infrared spectrum is determined, the spectrum should be characteristic of the sample. By controlling the pyrolysis conditions precisely, the infrared spectrum should always be the same in both band positions and intensities. Other polymers will differ because of structural changes in the polymer unit, and therefore will differ in the spectrum of the pyrolyzate.

It is interesting that, although one might expect to obtain a poorly defined spectrum, owing to the complexity of the pyrolysis product mixture, a remarkably distinct spectrum is usually obtained. This is probably due to the close similarity of degraded products in structure rather than in molecular weight. By standardizing conditions and compiling a number of spectra of varying materials, this method can be used advantageously to examine samples whose spectra are unobtainable by other methods.

4.2 LIQUID SAMPLES

Liquid substances, such as pure liquids and solutions of solids, liquids, and gases, comprise perhaps the greatest number of individual samples examined qualitatively by infrared spectroscopy. Pure liquids are generally examined initially without a solvent, thus avoiding solvent absorption interferences. In order to examine a liquid free of intermolecular interactions, a solution of the sample in a nonpolar solvent is useful particularly for hydroxylic and polyfunctional substances.

For pure liquids, a thin film between sodium chloride plates, as described for the mull technique, is often sufficient to obtain a suitable spectrum for interpretation for probable functional groups. In many cases where repeated spectra on the same material or closely related materials are needed, spectral comparisons are more easily obtained by using techniques whereby the sample thickness is controllable. To facilitate such comparisons, a cell is used with a fixed path length, as described in Sec. 4.2.3. Optimum cell lengths will vary according to the absorptivity of the samples to be examined (usually from approximately 0.55 to 0.1 mm). The use of a sealed cell of known path length is almost a necessity for volatile liquids or those substances with low viscosities. Generally the spectra obtained using pure liquids reflect a number of molecular parameters of importance such as intermolecular interactions, conformational isomerism, tautomeric isomerism, and intramolecular associations. These interactions are temperature-dependent, and some are dependent as well upon the environment (by the addition of solvent). The accompanying spectral changes can yield a wealth of information concerning the nature of the substance.

4.2.1 Solution spectra. Dilute solution spectra with nonpolar solvents usually eliminate most intermolecular interactions. However, some major interactions may still persist, such as intramolecular hydrogen bonding or, in the case of carboxylic acids, dimerization due to hydrogen bonding. As mentioned previously, new limitations are introduced, owing to solubility of the compound to be examined and solvent absorptions. In the case of compounds that exhibit poor solubility in nonpolar solvents, the use of relatively polar solvents introduces solute-solvent interactions. Since no single solvent is satisfactory for the entire infrared region from 2 to 15μ, a study of the solution spectra from two or more different solvents is usually necessary. Practically speaking, the major advantages gained in solution work are the ease of sample preparation, uniformity of dispersion of the solute, and the ease in fixing both the concentration and path length.

Chloroform, carbon tetrachloride, and carbon disulfide are the three solvents most commonly employed in solution spectral studies. Concentration effects may be studied, using the same thickness of cell, and the intensities of weak and strong absorption bands can be determined at a single concentration by the use of thick and thin cells. Since the frequency ranges that can be used for spectral examination of any solute in a given solvent are limited because of solvent absorptions, even when using compensating matched cells where only major bands interfere, it is well to have available a general summary of solvent absorptions as given in Table 4.1.

Table 4.1.   Common Solvent Absorptions

The listed regions indicate those regions of the spectrum where solvent absorptions are significantly strong, preventing the examination of other absorptions occurring in the same region. Only those solvents of general interest and common usage are recorded here. This table is divided into three sections for convenient examination: 4000- to 2000-cm^{-1} region (2.5 to 5μ); 2000- to 1000-cm^{-1} region (5 to 10μ); 1000- to 650-cm^{-1} region (10 to 15.4μ). The choice of these regions will be clear after the reader becomes familiar with the characteristic bands absorbing in each of the regions (Chap. 5).

		Regions of Absorption	
Solvent	Cell Thickness (mm)	Frequency (cm^{-1})	Wavelength (μ)
4000- to 2000-cm^{-1} region			
Acetone	0.1	3100–2900	3.23–3.45
Acetonitrile	0.1	3700–3500	2.70–2.86
		2350–2250	4.25–4.44
Benzene	0.1	3100–3000	3.23–3.33
Bromoform	1.0	3100–2900	3.23–3.45
	0.2	3100–3000	3.23–3.33
Carbon disulfide	1.0	2340–2100	4.27–4.76
	0.1	2200–2140	4.54–4.67
Carbon tetrachloride	1.0–0.1	none	none
Chloroform	1.0	3090–2980	3.24–3.35
		2440–2380	4.10–4.20
	0.1	3020–3000	3.31–3.33
Cyclohexane	0.1	3000–2850	3.33–3.51
Diethyl ether	0.1	3000–2650	3.33–3.77
Dimethyl formamide	0.1	3000–2700	3.33–3.70
Dioxane	0.1	3700–2600	2.70–3.85
Isopropyl alcohol	0.1	3600–3200	2.78–3.12
Methanol	0.1	4000–2800	2.50–3.57
Methyl acetate	0.1	3000–2800	3.33–3.57
Methyl cyclopentane	0.1	3000–2800	3.33–3.57
Nitromethane	0.1	3100–2800	3.23–3.57
Pyridine	0.1	3500–3000	2.86–3.33
Tetrachloroethylene	1.0–0.1	none	none
Tetrahydrofuran	0.2	3050–2630	3.28–3.80
Water	0.01	3650–2930	2.74–3.41

Table 4.1—Cont.

| Solvent | Cell Thickness (mm) | Regions of Absorption | |
		Frequency (cm^{-1})	Wavelength (μ)
2000- to 1000-cm^{-1} region			
Acetone	0.1	1800–1170	5.55–8.55
		1100–1080	9.09–9.26
Acetonitrile	0.1	1500–1350	6.66–7.41
		1060–1030	9.43–9.71
Benzene	0.1	1820–1800	5.49–5.55
		1490–1450	6.71–6.89
		1050–1020	9.52–9.80
Bromoform	1.0	1350–1280	7.41–7.81
		1220–1070	8.20–9.35
	0.2	1190–1000	8.40–10.00
Carbon disulfide	1.0	1640–1385	6.10–7.22
	0.1	1595–1460	6.27–6.85
Carbon tetrachloride	1.0	1610–1500	6.21–6.66
		1270–1200	7.87–8.33
		1020–1000	9.80–10.00
	0.1	none	none
Chloroform	1.0	1555–1410	6.43–7.09
		1290–1155	7.75–8.66
	0.1	1240–1200	8.06–8.33
Cyclohexane	0.1	1480–1430	6.75–6.99
Diethyl ether	0.1	1500–1010	6.66–9.90
Dimethyl formamide	0.1	1780–1020	5.62–9.80
Dioxane	0.1	1750–1700	5.71–5.88
		1480–1030	6.75–9.71
Isopropyl alcohol	0.1	1540–1090	6.49–9.17
Methanol		1500–1370	6.66–7.30
		1150–1000	8.69–10.00
Methyl acetate	0.1	1800–1700	5.55–5.88
		1480–1360	6.75–7.35
		1300–1200	7.69–8.33
		1080–1000	9.26–10.00
Methyl cyclopentane	0.1	1480–1440	6.75–6.94
		1390–1350	7.19–7.41
Nitromethane	0.1	1770–1070	5.65–9.35
Pyridine	0.1	1620–1420	6.17–7.04
		1230–1000	8.13–10.00
Tetrachloroethylene	1.0	1370–1340	7.30–7.46
		1180–1090	8.47–9.17
		1015–1000	9.85–10.00
Tetrahydrofuran	0.2	1500–1425	6.66–7.02
		1375–1000	7.27–10.00
Water	0.01	1750–1580	5.71–6.33
1000- to 650-cm^{-1} region			
Acetone	0.1	910–830	10.99–12.05
Acetonitrile	0.1	930–910	10.75–10.99
Benzene	0.1	680–650	14.70–15.38
Bromoform	1.0	880–860	11.36–11.63
		760–650	13.16–15.38

Table 4.1—Cont.

Solvent	Cell Thickness (mm)	Regions of Absorption	
		Frequency (cm⁻¹)	Wavelength (μ)
	0.2	710–650	14.08–15.38
Carbon disulfide	1.0	875–845	11.43–11.83
	0.1	none	none
Carbon tetrachloride	1.0	1000–960	10.00–10.42
		860–650	11.63–15.38
	0.1	820–720	12.19–13.89
Chloroform	1.0	940–910	10.64–10.99
		860–650	11.63–15.38
	0.1	805–650	12.42–15.38
Cyclohexane	0.1	910–850	10.99–11.76
Diethyl ether	0.1	850–830	11.76–12.05
Dimethyl formamide	0.1	870–860	11.49–11.63
		680–650	14.70–15.38
Dioxane	0.1	910–830	10.99–12.05
Isopropyl alcohol	0.1	990–960	10.10–10.42
		830–650	12.05–15.38
Methanol	0.1	1000–970	10.00–10.31
		700–650	14.29–15.38
Methyl acetate	0.1	1000–960	10.00–10.42
		840–650	11.90–15.38
Methyl cyclopentane	0.1	980–960	10.20–10.42
Nitromethane	0.1	925–910	10.81–10.99
		690–650	14.49–15.38
Pyridine	0.1	1000–980	10.00–10.20
		780–650	12.82–15.38
Tetrachloroethylene	1.0	1000–650	10.00–15.38
	0.1	935–875	10.69–11.43
		820–745	12.19–13.42
Tetrahydrofuran	0.2	1000–810	10.00–12.34
		775–742	12.90–13.48
Water	0.01	930–650	10.75–15.38

The spectral regions of absorption are indicative of solvent absorption regions that cannot be used. The second column in the table indicates the approximate cell thickness (in mm) for each solvent. For the more common solvents, two cell thicknesses are indicated. Differences should be noted, since a solute of high solubility in a given solvent will allow a thinner cell to be used, thereby eliminating a number of solvent absorption bands.

Figures 4.11, 4.12, and 4.13 show the spectra of chloroform, carbon tetrachloride, and carbon disulfide, in that order. Chloroform, Fig. 4.11, is a rather excellent general solvent. However, commercial chloroform contains small amounts of ethanol (1 to 2%) as a stabilizer. Before using, the ethanol should be removed by passing the solvent through activated alumina. Ethanol-free chloroform may be stored for about a week before phosgene can be detected as an impurity. When using this solvent for measuring band posi-

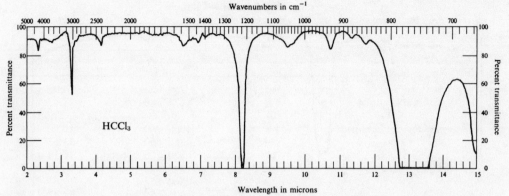

Fig. 4.11 Spectrum of chloroform (as a thin film).

tions, such as carbonyl absorptions or hydroxyl absorptions, it is well to recall that chloroform is a relatively polar solvent that is capable of association with other polar species, and therefore the observed band positions may be shifted to lower frequencies (higher wavelengths) than those observed in less polar solvents, i.e., carbon tetrachloride.

Carbon tetrachloride, Fig. 4.12, shows good spectral characteristics in the 2.5 to 6μ region (high-frequency region from approximately 4000 to 1600 cm^{-1}). In general, polar functional groups, such as carbonyl groups, exhibit their maximum frequencies of absorption in this solvent.

Carbon disulfide, Fig. 4.13, can be seen to be especially well suited for the low-frequency region. Thus information generally not available from the halogenated solvents (chloroform and carbon tetrachloride) can be usually obtained from carbon disulfide solutions. Since this solvent is very toxic and highly flammable, it should be handled cautiously under a hood.

Absorption band shifts occurring through changes in the solvent phase can be useful in qualitative analysis. Therefore, although an apparent disadvantage, the use of a solvent may assist in evaluating the nature of a functional group (see Chap. 5).

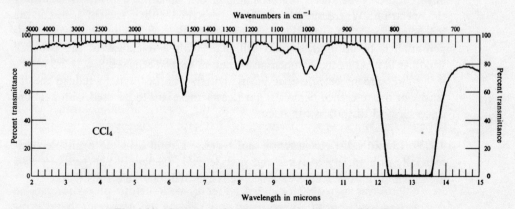

Fig. 4.12 Spectrum of carbon tetrachloride (as a thin film).

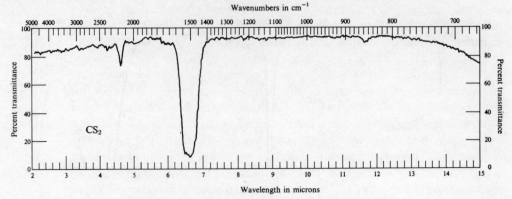

Fig. 4.13   Spectrum of carbon disulfide (as a thin film).

4.2.2   Reference beam compensation.   As discussed in Chap. 3, one of the advantages of the double-beam spectrophotometer is to cancel out atmospheric absorption bands. In a similar fashion, the double-beam principle can be used to cancel out some of the absorption bands due to solvent. For example, the bands occurring in carbon tetrachloride (Fig. 4.12) at approximately 6.40, 7.95, 8.20, 8.95, 9.35, 9.90, and 10.2μ are easily canceled out by placing in the reference beam of the spectrophotometer a matched path-length cell containing pure carbon tetrachloride.

Cancellation of the intense absorption at 12.3 to 13.6μ is not possible. If one examines the spectrum at these wavelengths, no absorption band will be observed. The reason for this is quite obvious if one considers the previous discussion concerning the operation of the spectrophotometers. If no radiation reaches the detector, the pen drive system will be completely inactive. At the end of such a "dead region" the pen becomes activated again, since radiation is reaching the detector and is amplified, and thus actuates the pen drive system.

When using such a compensation device, the sample and reference beams must be balanced for solvent and cell absorption prior to recording the spectrum. Where the two cells are matched and a solvent is used, the balancing operation generally is complete. In the case where no solvent compensation is to be used, a solid salt plate with a thickness of the two cell windows is used as the compensator (not an empty cell; see Sec. 4.2.5).

Wire screens or reference-beam shutters can be used to reduce the intensity of the reference beam. In most cases these are to be used with caution, since spectral distortion can occur.

4.2.3   Liquid cells: construction and types.   Liquid cells are available commercially in a variety of types and path lengths. Generally two types of cells are commonly used, namely, sealed cells and demountable cells.

Sealed cells.   Sealed, fully assembled cells of fixed path lengths ranging from 0.001 to 4 mm are readily available. These cells are usually sealed with an amalgamated lead spacer. Such a cell requires a great amount of care, since when the salt windows deteriorate, dismantling and reassembly is either expensive or time consuming. In the spectroscopy laboratory the sealed cell is useful whenever solution spectra are determined. In this case a matched pair of liquid cells (one containing the sample and solvent, the other containing pure solvent) are used in the sample and reference beams of the spectrophotometer, respectively. The spectrum recorded is then that of the solution minus the solvent, provided the path lengths are almost equal. The only regions of difference between the solution spectrum and the pure solute spectrum will be in those regions where the solvent absorbs strongly. In actual practice, as we shall see later, the sealed cell is important for quantitative analysis, but can be replaced by demountable units for most qualitative infrared applications. Newer sealed units equipped with Teflon spacers are actually demountable in type and therefore will be discussed in the next section. Figure 4.14 indicates the component parts of the typical sealed-cell unit.

The high cost of sealed, matched cells makes it desirable to be able to construct one's own cells. Continuous use will require the frequent dismantling of the sealed cells for repolishing of the windows, and therefore reassembly procedure should be familiar to the practicing spectroscopist. Inexpensive cells can be readily constructed from commonly available materials and polished salt plates (Sec. 4.2.6). For example, end plates of 1/4-in. brass or aluminum, drilled to accept syringe wells made from hypodermic needles, adequately serve as bases for cell construction. Lead spacing materials can be purchased in sheet form and cut to the desired shape easily with a razor blade. The spacers between the salt windows and the top end plate are amalgamated by brushing with mercury until complete coverage is obtained. As indicated in Fig. 4.14, the components are carefully assembled. With the aid of two syringe needles in the liquid port holes to assure good alignment (between the top-plate liquid ports, the holes in the spacers, and the top salt plate), a sealed cell can be assembled rather rapidly.

Demountable cells. For mull work and qualitative solution work, the demountable cell is by far the most useful. Actually, matched pairs of demountable cells can be readily assembled for quantitative work. The demountable cell for solution work is identical in construction to the sealed cell unit except that Teflon spacers are substituted for the amalgamated lead gaskets. Furthermore, for each pair of demountable cells, a whole range of spacers may be used. This gains the advantage of having one cell unit with a variety of sample path lengths. Demountable cells are more easily cleaned and, if necessary, the salt plates can be polished prior to their next use. The major advantage of the sealed cell over the demountable unit is that the spacers are not subject to damage by handling, which does happen when the demountable cells are repeatedly assembled and dismantled. Since one can have a series of simple demountable cells of fixed path lengths, the advantages of the sealed cell can be gained without the necessity of amalgamated seals.

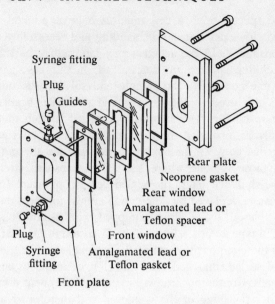

Syringe fitting
Plug
Guides
Rear plate
Neoprene gasket
Rear window
Amalgamated lead or
Teflon spacer
Front window
Plug
Syringe
fitting
Amalgamated lead or
Teflon gasket
Front plate

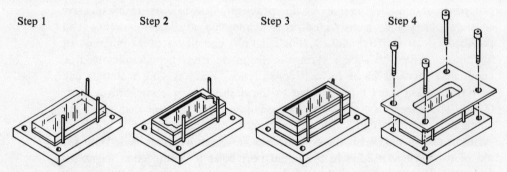

Step 1   Step 2   Step 3   Step 4

Fig. 4.14 Component parts and assembly of a typical sealed cell unit. Step 1: With the front plate inverted, place the gasket and the front window in position. Step 2: Select a spacer of proper thickness and place it on the front window (be sure the filling holes are not obstructed). Step 3: Install the rear window and the gasket as shown. Step 4: Install the rear plate and press it into position. Complete the cell assembly by tightening the retainer screws firmly and evenly. (Courtesy Beckman Instruments, Inc.)

Variable path cells. An alternate to matched solution cells is the utilization of a variable-thickness, compensating, solvent cell that has a micrometer device attached to one moveable plate, allowing the selection of any cell thickness. Cells are available with path lengths up to 6 mm with 0.5μ repeatability of the path-length setting. A typical variable path cell is shown in Fig. 4.15.

Micro and ultramicro cells. Sealed and demountable types of micro and ultramicro sample cells are available. In general these cells have sample volumes ranging from 0.006 to 0.001 ml capacities. By using cell systems of this

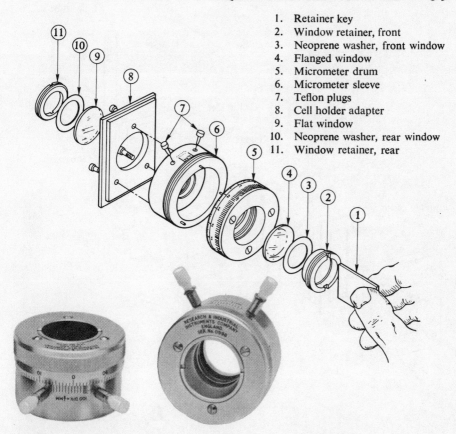

1. Retainer key
2. Window retainer, front
3. Neoprene washer, front window
4. Flanged window
5. Micrometer drum
6. Micrometer sleeve
7. Teflon plugs
8. Cell holder adapter
9. Flat window
10. Neoprene washer, rear window
11. Window retainer, rear

Fig. 4.15 Typical variable path cell. Such units provide a wide range of path lengths in a single cell. (Courtesy Beckman Instruments, Inc.)

type, samples of 20 to 50 μg can be spectrally examined. A typical commercial microcell unit is shown in Fig. 4.16. This cell is designed to be used without a beam condenser in the optical path of the spectrophotometer.

Cavity cells. A convenient cell for microsamples is the cavity cell as shown in Fig. 4.17. These cells are fashioned from a single block of crystal, accurately ground and polished to the proper dimensions. The rectangular cavity is machined out of the crystal block. Such a procedure does not produce a cell of precision optical path length, but this is unimportant for qualitative work using microsamples. At present the smallest path length available is 0.15 ±0.02 mm, the range being indicative of the precision of the machining process. Such a cell requires only 0.5 μl of sample or solution of sample to fill the beam area.

In experimental practice, the use of the cavity cell is quite convenient and rapid. Care of such units and their calibration are described in detail in the last part of Secs. 4.2.4 and 4.2.5, respectively.

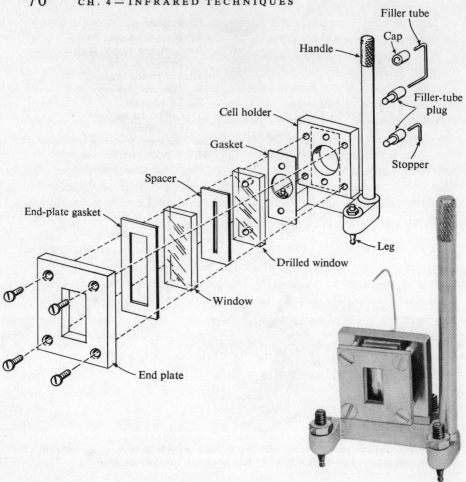

Fig. 4.16 Typical microcell unit for examining small amounts of sample. The liquid cell has a usable area of $1 \times 7\frac{1}{2}$ mm, and it is filled by capillary action. (Courtesy Beckman Instruments, Inc.)

4.2.4 Liquid cells: handling and care. Since materials may precipitate from solution or, in the case of high-boiling solutes, deposit on the cell windows by solvent evaporation, care must be exercised to ensure proper cleaning of the cell. Matched cells, naturally, will require more careful maintenance than will those cells that are readily demountable for complete cleaning and reassembly prior to their next use.

Trace quantities of moisture can never be completely removed from the general solvents employed in infrared analysis. Therefore cells usually show a slightly fogged appearance after several samples have been placed in the cell for scanning. Actually this is not so serious as one might imagine. For quantitative studies this condition can be beneficial rather than detrimental, since once the cells have been slightly clouded, additional clouding takes place much more slowly. This enables the user to eliminate for a period of time, at least, changes in the transmitted beam due to intensity changes in the incident beam from clouding of the window surfaces.

In practice, cells are carefully cleaned after each use by thoroughly flushing them with dry solvent. The solvent is removed by vacuum drying. During this operation a drying tube is attached to one port while aspirator vacuum is applied to the other, as shown in Fig. 4.18.

Demountable cells, such as those used for mulls and liquid film samples, are cleaned carefully with solvent and wiped dry with a soft tissue after each use. It is good practice to determine occasionally the spectra of each cell and sodium chloride single plates in order to check for absorbing deposits that may be in the cells or on the plates. After repeated usage, the cells should be disassembled and the windows polished (see Sec. 4.2.6 for polishing procedures).

Filling and cleaning of cavity cells.   Cavity cells are easily filled by means of a needle and syringe. The tip of the needle may be inserted to the bottom of the cavity so that no air is trapped. When the cell is to be cleaned, solvent may be flushed through the cell in the same manner (see Fig. 4.17).

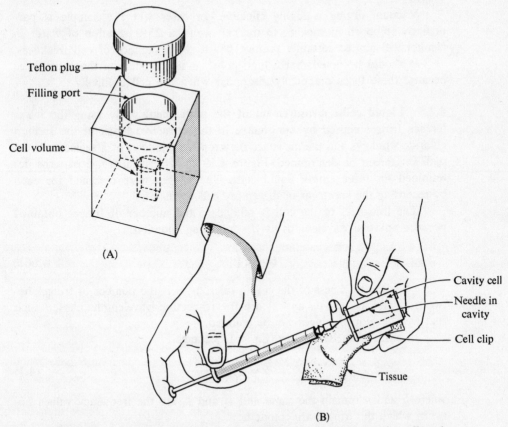

Teflon plug

Filling port

Cell volume

(A)

Cavity cell

Needle in cavity

Cell clip

Tissue

(B)

Fig. 4.17   A cavity cell for microsamples. Part (A) shows the cavity cell, and part (B) illustrates the technique for cleaning it.

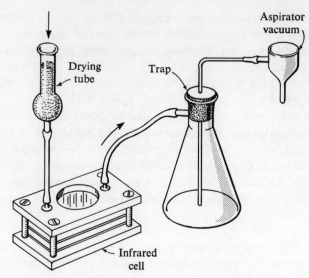

Fig. 4.18 Technique for removing solvent and drying
infrared cells.

Vacuum drying is highly effective. In cases where a sample is particularly stubborn in sticking to the cell walls, a 25% solution of water in
alcohol will almost certainly remove it—at some sacrifice of cell thickness.

It should be noted that a high polish is not needed on the inner faces
because these faces practically disappear when the cell is filled.

4.2.5 Liquid cells: measurement of the path length. By using the interference fringes caused by the change in the refractive index of the sodium
chloride windows and the air space between the windows of a sealed cell, the
path length can be determined. Figure 4.19 shows typical fringe patterns determined for three empty liquid cells. The fringes were obtained for each
by recording the spectrum of the empty cell versus air.

The thickness of the cell is related to the number of fringes obtained
between any two wavelengths by the following equation:

$$b = \frac{n}{2}\left(\frac{\lambda_1 \lambda_2}{\lambda_2 - \lambda_1}\right) \tag{4.1}$$

where b is the thickness of the cell in microns, n is the number of fringes be-
tween λ_1 and λ_2, and λ_1 and λ_2 are the respective wavelengths chosen such
that well-developed fringes can be counted.

In terms of the frequency, Eq. 4.1 becomes

$$b = \frac{n}{2(\nu_1 - \nu_2)} \tag{4.2}$$

where b and n remain the same and ν_1 and ν_2 are the frequency values between which the fringes are counted.

More accurate values for the cell-path length can be determined by the

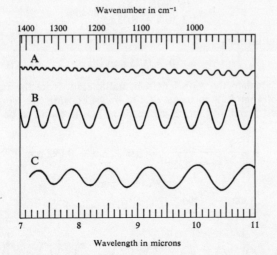

Fig. 4.19 Typical fringe patterns obtained by scanning the spectrum of the empty cell.

number of the peaks and troughs consecutively. A plot of these numbers on the ordinate and the respective wavenumbers on the abscissa will give a straight line whose slope equals 4b. The path length b will be in centimeters.

If a cell gives a poor fringe pattern, it usually indicates poor parallel alignment of the cell windows or the lack of optical flatness of the sodium chloride windows. Poor fringe patterns also result after the cells have been used for a time and the windows' surfaces have been damaged by solvents or moisture. In these cases the cell thickness can be determined by using a standard material, such as a common solvent that has a band of known absorbance. This method will be developed in Chap. 6, since it essentially involves the elements used in quantitative analysis.

Typical calculations. The following examples will assist the reader in path-length determinations for sample liquid cells.

EXAMPLE 1. Calculate the path length in centimeters from the fringes given in spectrum A (Fig. 4.19) in terms of Eq. 4.1. Choosing the fringes between λ_1 and λ_2 (8.05μ and 10.8μ) in Fig. 4.20, it can be seen that $n = 16$ and therefore

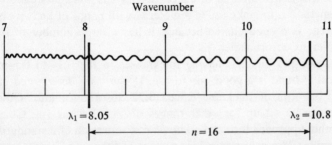

Fig. 4.20 Typical fringes used in the calculation of path length
(from Fig. 4.19, spectrum A).

$$b = \frac{16}{2} \frac{8.05(10.8)}{10.8 - 8.05} = 252.9\mu$$

Converting to millimeters,

$$b = 0.25 \text{ mm}$$

EXAMPLE 2. Calculate the path length in millimeters from the fringes indicated in spectrum B of Fig. 4.19 in terms of Eq. 4.2. Choosing the fringes between v_1 and v_2 (1430 cm^{-1} and 940 cm^{-1}, respectively), n is found to be 9 (Fig. 4.21); therefore

$$b = \frac{9}{2} \frac{1}{(1430 - 940)} = 0.0092 \text{ cm} = 0.092 \text{ mm}$$

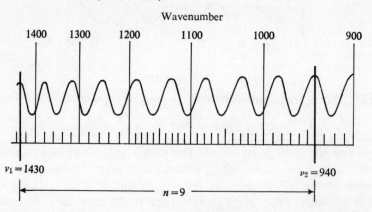

Fig. 4.21. Typical fringes used in the calculation of path length (from Fig. 4.19, spectrum B).

EXAMPLE 3. Using the fringe data C in Fig. 4.19, solve for the cell thickness by numbering the peaks and troughs and plotting these versus the respective frequencies.

As shown in Fig. 4.22, which plots peaks and troughs versus their respective frequencies, a value for the slope $4b$ is obtained ($4b = 0.0217$). Therefore the path length b equals 0.0054 cm, or 0.054 mm.

Calibrating cavity cells. Since the inner surfaces of cavity cells are not highly polished and flat, they do not produce interference fringes. Hence the convenient fringe method of calibration of cell thickness cannot be used. The best method is to make use of a material with bands of known absorbance.

Benzene is a good choice because it has a large number of bands with widely different absorbancies.

For example, for cells having thicknesses in the 0.1- to 0.5-mm range, the 850-cm^{-1} band is a good one to use. It has been determined empirically that each 0.1 mm of thickness equals 0.22 absorbance unit. Other similar equations can be set up for other ranges of path lengths (cf. Chap. 6).

Another approach is to add a known concentration of a standard absorber to the sample. The calibration information is then a permanent part of the spectrum. Calculations can be made from the ratio of sample bands to those

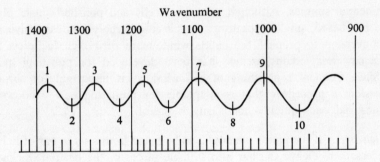

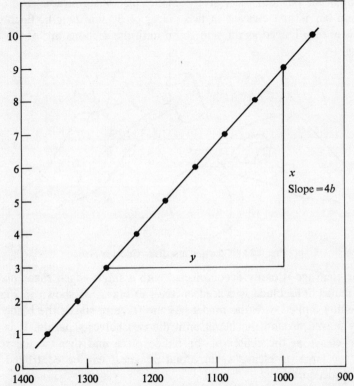

Fig. 4.22 Peak and trough method for determining path length (from Fig. 4.19, spectrum C).

produced by the standard absorber. This method essentially eliminates cell thickness and positioning considerations from the calculations.

4.2.6 Preparation of sodium chloride windows. A variety of halide materials are readily available for cell windows. Sawed blanks and cleaned unpolished plates of sodium chloride, potassium chloride, potassium iodide, potassium bromide, calcium fluoride, lithium fluoride, barium fluoride, calcium iodide, calcium bromide, and KRS-5 may be obtained from a number of commercial sources. Although assembled cells and polished single plates may be purchased, small laboratories find it considerably less expensive and more convenient to prepare the halide windows in their own facilities. Recently a new less tedious method has been developed for polishing halide discs. Since frequent repolishing of cell windows is important for suitable transmission, a procedure that is adaptable for preparing new windows or refinishing old ones quickly and easily is useful.

Cleaving. If the halide window is to be made from a large bar of halide, it is necessary to cleave the bar into suitable pieces of the desired thickness. It is difficult to cleave a thin window from a large bar, and therefore careful sectioning of the bar into successively smaller pieces is desirable. For example a 100-mm bar is first cleaved in two pieces of 50-mm length. Each 50-mm section is in turn halved again, and so on until the sections are of the desired thickness.

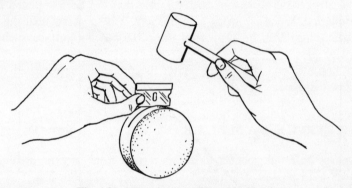

Fig. 4.23   Cleaving a sodium chloride plate.

The cleavage is easily accomplished with a single-edged razor blade and a small mallet. The blade is placed on the salt blank, as shown in Fig. 4.23, and carefully tapped with the mallet. As the fracture starts, the blade is successively moved around the blank until the two halves separate. It is always better to cleave at the center of the halide piece and then, if the resulting piece is too large, to cleave again. Final thickness can be controlled by the grinding procedure.

Grinding. The rough grinding is best carried out with 200-grit paper. By using a wet or dry sanding paper, the salt may be removed from the filled surface of the paper by simply washing it with water, and therefore the paper is reusable. The sanding of the halide disc is carried out with a linear motion; the salt is rubbed on the paper in a back-and-forth motion with no rotation. When the rough cleavage surfaces have been smoothed off, grinding with the 200-grit paper is discontinued.

Further sanding with similar paper of 600 grit will produce a finer finish. Again, this grind should be a linear movement rather than a circular motion.

Rough polishing. When the surface of the plate has the appearance of smooth frosted glass, it is ready for rough polishing. The rough polishing is usually carried out with "silver sheets," which are made for use in polishing silverware and can be purchased at most hardware stores. If sodium chloride plates are being polished, the sheet is sparingly wetted with water. The surface of the plate is then rubbed in a circular motion on the silver sheet. Polishing potassium bromide is usually carried out in a similar fashion except that water is not used to wet the silver sheet. Rather, it is recommended that isopropyl alcohol be used instead. The silver sheet can be used on both sides, and when it no longer gives a satisfactory polish, it should be discarded. If silver sheets are not available, ordinary filter paper with carborundum A, No. 1 fine Aloxite buffing powder or rouge paper can be used as a satisfactory substitute.

Finishing. The salt is removed from the silver sheet and polished, using linear strokes on a piece of folded fabric that has been softened by repeated laundering. When polishing and finishing, it is suggested that the silver sheet and finishing cloth be supported on a smooth flat surface such as a piece of plate glass.

After finishing one side of the plate, the procedure is repeated on the other face of the plate.

4.3 GASEOUS SAMPLES

Gas-phase infrared spectra differ markedly from spectra obtained in the liquid or solid phases. The principal differences are shown in Fig. 4.24. Spectrum A is that of a thin film of propylene oxide liquid, whereas spectrum B is propylene oxide vapor. The differences in the two spectra occur principally because the molecules are essentially free to rotate in the gaseous state and intermolecular interactions are at a minimum. In simple molecules

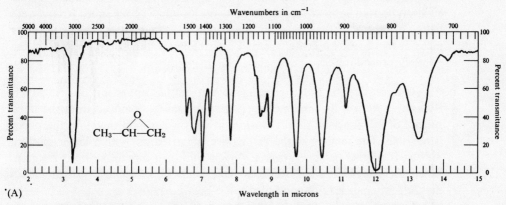

Fig. 4.24 Spectrum obtained from a liquid sample compared with that obtained from a sample in the gaseous state. The spectrum of propylene oxide as a thin liquid film is shown in spectrum A.

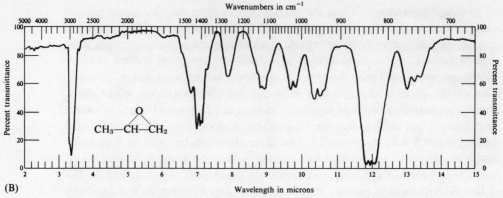

Wavelength in microns

Fig. 4.24—cont. Spectrum obtained from a liquid sample compared with that obtained from a sample in the gaseous state. Spectrum B depicts propylene oxide as a gas.

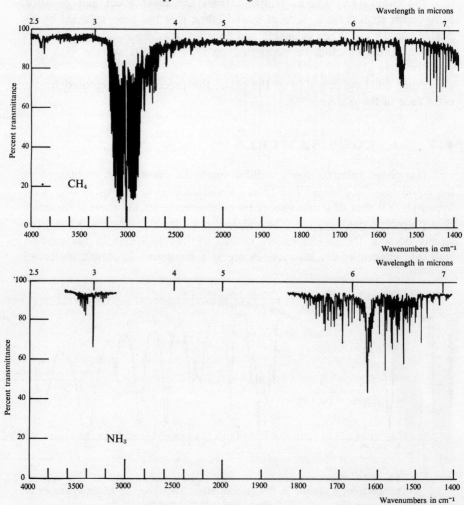

Fig. 4.25 Typical spectra

the gas phase spectra are replete with fine structure, corresponding to transitions in rotational energy levels. Since substances in the gas phase are reduced in concentration, path lengths of several centimeters rather than fractions of millimeters are necessary to obtain gas-phase spectra.

Figure 4.25 exemplifies typical spectra obtained from such simple gases as ammonia and methane. Because of the complex spectra, these gases (particularly ammonia) are frequently used in frequency calibration of a spectrophotometer. For most organic laboratories, gas-phase spectra are not frequently needed, since relatively few organic substances encountered require examination in the gaseous state by the infrared method. Rather, these substances are usually known materials and can be more easily analyzed by vapor-liquid chromatography.

4.3.1 Gas sampling techniques. Numerous special techniques for handling gases have been developed for weighing small quantities of gas and effecting

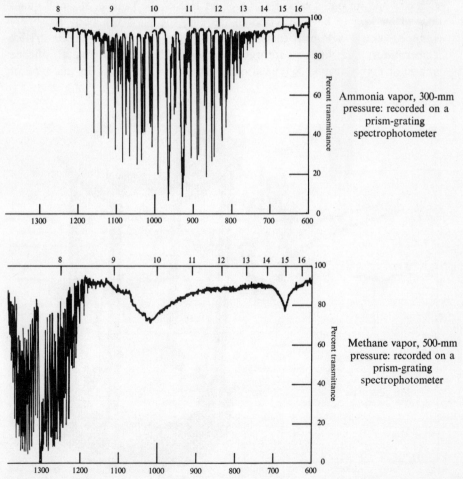

Ammonia vapor, 300-mm pressure: recorded on a prism-grating spectrophotometer

Methane vapor, 500-mm pressure: recorded on a prism-grating spectrophotometer

of gaseous samples.

complete transferral to the gas cell. In the case of liquids that are to be vapor-ized in a heated gas cell, these techniques can be simplified markedly. In common practice, however, the quantity of gas to be admitted to a gas cell is usually introduced from a typical gas accumulation system that is con-trolled by the volume-pressure relationship. The gas cell to be filled is first evacuated and the gas is admitted to the system. In many cases a gas sample direct from a gas bulb can be obtained by prior evacuation of the cell and connecting line system. In general, to obtain spectra of samples at low pres-sures or mixtures of gases in which trace quantities of impurity gases are to be determined, long-path gas cells have been developed.

4.3.2 Gas cells: construction and types. Cells for gaseous samples vary from 5 cm to many meters in length, depending on the gas pressure and in-tensity of the absorption bands of the sample. The simplest type of gas cell consists of a piece of glass or metal tubing with the halide windows sealed on each end and an outlet tube for entry and exit of the sample. If small quan-tities of gas are to be transferred to the cell, the glass cell body is usually equipped with a side arm that can be cooled to liquid nitrogen or dry-ice temperatures. The windows are usually sealed to the cell with glyptal, silicone grease, or epoxy resins. A typical cell is shown in Fig. 4.26. In this type of

Fig. 4.26 Typical cell for examining gaseous samples. (Courtesy Beckman Instruments, Inc.)

cell the limit of length of the cell dimension is the size of the sample port length between the source housing and entrance slit to the monochromator compartment.

In order to increase the effective path length, the gas cell must be modified to reflect the beam 90 deg from the source, through a unit equipped with mirrors that repeatedly reflect the beam between the ends of the long cell before being turned again 90 deg so that it enters the monochromator. A typical multipass gas cell is shown in Fig. 4.27. Cells have been developed for laboratory use up to 40 meters, employing the multireflection technique.

4.4   SUMMARY OF SAMPLING TECHNIQUES: EFFECT ON BAND POSITION

As is realized from the foregoing discussions, the position of bands will change according to the technique used to prepare the sample. These techniques will affect such parameters as the shape of the molecule (conformation, crystal state, orientation, etc.) and the environment in which the molecules are placed (solid matrix, solvation, solvent association, etc.). Generally the largest variation in band position should be associated with the more polar molecules or groups.

In the solid state, identical infrared spectra of solids measured under the same conditions usually indicate that the samples are identical. The solid methods usually reflect the shape of the molecule and crystal lattice. Slight differences in sample preparations, such as time of grinding and mixing with potassium bromide or Nujol, and the time of pressing of pellets, will usually result in identical spectra, provided the concentrations are maintained the same. The infrared spectra measured in Nujol and in potassium bromide pellets are usually quite similar except for the overlapping regions of the sample and Nujol. This may not be the case, however, where crystal-state changes or tautomerism may occur while grinding; or, in the case of potassium bromide, in those cases where the size of the particle, time of mixing the sample with the potassium bromide, and the pressure of pelletizing may vary markedly.

In solutions the solute may exhibit bands from more than one species (conformers or tautomers). In these cases the polarity effects of the solvent will play an important part in band type and position. Due to these factors, small differences in chemical structure may frequently be overlooked, and nonidentical samples may give very similar or even identical spectra. Therefore it follows that for identification purposes, the solid methods are the most reliable indications of structure, despite their many disadvantages.

In the liquid state, molecules that are devoid of polar groups exist in a state in which they are surrounded by other molecular species that do not affect each other electrically. Polar molecules exist in association with each other, and generally the positions of bands are shifted to lower frequencies when compared to the positions of the same bands in nonpolar solvents. In

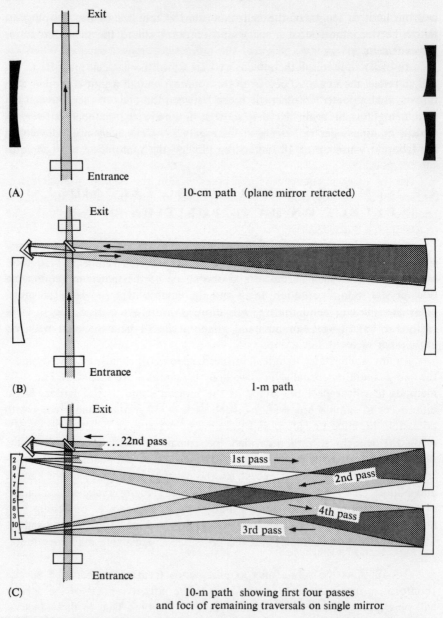

(A)   10-cm path (plane mirror retracted)

(B)   1-m path

(C)   10-m path showing first four passes
                                        and foci of remaining traversals on single mirror

Fig. 4.27 Schematic diagram for a multipass gas cell. Note that the beam is passed either directly through the cell (A) or it is reflected by the mirror system two or more times the length of the cell, which is perpendicular to the normal traverse of the radiant beam. (Courtesy Beckman Instruments, Inc.)

making comparisons in solutions, if intermolecular association is possible, the concentration and temperature will affect the position and intensity of the absorption bands. Intermolecular hydrogen bonding will be affected by the polarity of the solvent, concentration, and temperature. When intramolecular hydrogen bonds are present, absorption due to these bonds also will appear. Although the intermolecular species are concentration-dependent, the intra-molecular forms are not, provided the temperature is unchanged. When the spectrum of a polar solute is measured in solvents of varying polarity, the frequency of absorption generally decreases with increasing polarity. The picture is not quite so simple as it seems, since other factors also must contribute to these solvent effects and there is no simple relationship between frequency and dielectric constant. Generally ketones, acids, esters, amides, nitriles, and similar polar groups show the greatest frequency changes with solvent polarity.

In the gaseous state, most molecules exhibit the highest attainable frequency for a given band at low pressure (presumably, this information is related to the isolated molecule). These data are generally limited in value to qualitative correlations.

In determining structural differences in the examination of unknown materials, it is necessary to minimize the effects of the environment. Therefore, where possible, it is advisable in all possible cases to conduct measurements in nonpolar, dilute solutions. With samples soluble only in polar solvents, polar-solvent data comparisons with knowns are used instead. These data are not so valid as measurements in nonpolar media, and therefore must be interpreted with caution.

SUGGESTED READING

1. W. J. POTTS, JR., *Chemical Infrared Spectroscopy, Vol. I, Techniques.* Wiley, New York, 1963.
2. R. P. BAUMAN, *Absorption Spectroscopy.* Wiley, New York, 1962.
3. W. BRUGEL, *An Introduction to Infrared Spectroscopy.* Wiley, New York, 1962.
4. A. D. CROSS, *Introduction to Practical Infrared Spectroscopy.* Buttersworth, London (1961).
5. J. FAHRENFORT, "Attenuated Total Reflection—A New Principle for the Production of Useful Infrared Reflection Spectra of Organic Compounds." *Spectrochim. Acta,* **17** (1961), 698.

ADDITIONAL READING

D. H. ANDERSON AND O. E. MILLER, *J. Opt. Soc. Am.,* **43** (1953), 777.
D. H. ANDERSON AND N. B. WOODALL, *Anal. Chem.,* **25** (1953), 1906.
D. M. W. ANDERSON, *Analyst,* **84** (1959), 50.
S. ANDERSON, W. J. ANDERSON, AND M. KRAKOWSKI, *Rev. Sci. Inst.,* **21** (1950), 574.
J. S. ARD, *Anal. Chem.,* **25** (1953), 1743.
B. BAK AND D. CHRISTENSEN, *Spectrochim. Acta,* **12** (1958), 355.
A. W. BAKER, *J. Phys. Chem.,* **61** (1957), 450.

E. M. BANAS AND R. R. HOPKINS, *Appl. Spectroscopy,* **15** (1961), 153.

S. A. BARKER, *Chem. and Ind.* (London) (1959), 1418.

E. S. BARR, *Rev. Sci. Inst.,* **12** (1941), 396.

H. E. BENNETT AND W. F. KOEHLER, *J. Opt. Soc. Am.,* **50** (1960), 1.

G. R. BIRD, *J. Opt. Soc. Am.,* **51** (1961), 579.

W. A. BISHOP, *Anal. Chem.,* **33** (1961), 456.

F. BISSETT, A. L. BLUHM, AND L. LONG, JR., *Anal. Chem.,* **31** (1959), 1927.

E. D. BLACK, *Anal. Chem.,* **32** (1960), 735.

K. B. BRADLEY AND W. J. POTTS, JR., *Appl. Spectroscopy,* **12** (1958), 77.

L. F. H. BOVEY, *J. Opt. Soc. Am.,* **41** (1951), 381.

H. R. BROADLEY, *Rev. Sci. Inst.,* **19** (1948), 475.

F. R. BRYAN, *Appl. Spectroscopy,* **17** (1963), 19.

S. BURGESS AND H. SPEDDING, *Chem. and Ind.* (London) (1961), 1166.

S. S. CHANG, K. M. BROBST, C. E. IRELAND, AND H. TAI, *Appl. Spectroscopy,* **16** (1962), 106.

H. T. J. CHILTON, *Spectrochim. Acta,* **16** (1960), 979.

D. A. CLARK AND A. P. BOER, *Spectrochim. Acta,* **12** (1958), 276.

R. E. CLARK, *Appl. Spectroscopy,* **14** (1960), 139.

N. D. COGGESHALL, *Rev. Sci. Inst.,* **17** (1946), 343.

I. COHEN, *J. Chem. Ed.,* **39** (1962), 262.

N. B. COLTHUP, *Rev. Sci. Inst.,* **18** (1947), 64.

R. T. CONLEY AND J. F. BIERON, *Appl. Spectroscopy,* **15** (1961), 81.

M. COUROIS AND S. J. TEICHNER, *Bull. Soc. Chim. Fr.* (1960), 1773.

E. E. CRIDDLE, A. A. GREY, AND C. E. HUBLEY, *Appl. Spectroscopy,* **11** (1957), 137.

H. DANNENBERG, J. W. FORBES, AND A. C. JONES, *Anal. Chem.,* **32** (1961), 365.

W. H. T. DAVISON, *J. Opt. Soc. Am.,* **45** (1955), 227.

R. G. DEVANEY AND A. L. THOMPSON, *Appl. Spectroscopy,* **12** (1958), 154.

W. H. DUERIG AND I. L. MADOR, *Rev. Sci. Inst.,* **23** (1952), 421.

T. H. EDWARDS, *J. Opt. Soc. Am.,* **51** (1961), 98.

R. D. ELSEY AND R. N. HASZELDINE, *Chem. and Ind.* (London) (1954), 1177.

D. S. ERLEY, B. H. BLAKE, AND A. W. LONG, *Appl. Spectroscopy,* **14** (1960), 25.

D. S. ERLEY, B. H. BLAKE, AND W. J. POTTS, JR., *Appl. Spectroscopy,* **14** (1960), 108.

E. F. FERRAND, JR., *Appl. Spectroscopy,* **16** (1962), 22.

E. FISHMAN AND H. G. DRICKAMER, *Anal. Chem.,* **28** (1956), 804.

J. W. FORBES AND A. TELFER, *Anal. Chem.,* **31** (1959), 1904.

M. A. FORD AND G. R. WILKINSON, *J. Sci. Inst.,* **31** (1954), 338.

E. FUNCK, *Optik. Berl.,* **13** (1956), 524.

H. T. GRENDON AND H. L. LOVELL, *Anal. Chem.,* **32** (1960), 300.

M. F. GROSTIC AND G. E. BRONSON, *Appl. Spectroscopy,* **15** (1961), 157.

E. A. HAAHTI AND H. M. FALES, *Chem. and Ind.* (London) (1961), 507.

M. HACSKAYLO, *Anal. Chem.,* **26** (1954), 1410.

R. W. HANNAH, *Appl. Spectroscopy,* **17** (1963), 23.

D. L. HARMS, *Anal. Chem.,* **25** (1953), 1140.

N. J. HARRICK, *J. Phys. Chem.,* **64** (1960), 1110.

H. HAUSDORFF, *Appl. Spectroscopy,* **8** (1954), 131.

B. F. HOCHHEIMER AND G. E. MOORE, *J. Opt. Soc. Am.,* **45** (1955), 891.

R. B. HOLDEN, W. J. TAYLOR, AND H. L. JOHNSTON, *J. Opt. Soc. Am.,* **40** (1950), 757.

J. F. HORWOOD AND D. A. FORSS, *Proc. Roy. Australian Chem. Inst.,* **29** (1962), 285.

M. HYMAN, JR., AND B. H. BILLINGS, *J. Opt. Soc. Am.,* **37** (1947), 113.

D. N. INGERBRIGSTON AND A. L. SMITH, *Anal. Chem.,* **26** (1954), 1765.

J. J. JAFFE AND H. JAFFE, *J. Opt. Soc. Am.,* **40** (1950), 53.

G. J. JANZ AND S. S. DANYLUK, *Appl. Spectroscopy,* **13** (1959), 48.

G. J. JANZ AND W. E. FITZGERALD, *Appl. Spectroscopy,* **9** (1955), 178.

R. N. JONES AND A. NADEAU, *Spectrochim. Acta,* **12** (1958), 183.

J. J. KIRKLAND, *Anal. Chem.,* **29** (1957), 1127.

J. LECOMPTE, *Rev. Opt.,* **34** (1955), 22.

H. P. LEFTIN, *Rev. Sci. Inst.,* **32** (1961), 1418.

F. J. LINNIG AND J. E. STEWART, *Anal. Chem.,* **32** (1960), 891.

E. R. LIPPINCOTT, F. E. WELSH, AND C. W. WEIR, *Anal. Chem.,* **33** (1961), 137.

L. J. LOHR AND R. J. KAIER, *Anal. Chem.,* **32** (1960), 301.

J. P. LUONGO, *Appl. Spectroscopy,* **14** (1960), 24.

N. T. MCDEVITT AND W. L. BAUN, *Appl. Spectroscopy,* **14** (1960), 135.

J. H. VAN DER MAAS AND A. TOLK, *Spectrochim. Acta,* **18** (1962), 235.

H. C. MATTAW, *Appl. Spectroscopy,* **9** (1955), 177.

R. C. MILKEY, *Anal. Chem.,* **30** (1958), 1931.

B. M. MITZNER, *J. Opt. Soc. Am.,* **43** (1953), 806.

B. M. MITZNER AND S. Z. LEVIN, *J. Opt. Soc. Am.,* **44** (1954), 425.

W. S. MOLNAR AND V. A. YARBOROUGH, *Appl. Spectroscopy,* **12** (1958), 143.

W. W. MORRIS, JR., AND W. SALMON, *Anal. Chem.,* **35** (1963), 600.

H. W. MYERS AND W. W. MARTIN, *Anal. Chem.,* **34** (1962), 1038.

G. NENCINI AND E. PAULUZZI, *Appl. Spectroscopy,* **14** (1960), 138.

J. T. NEU, *J. Opt. Soc. Am.,* **43** (1953), 520.

R. A. OETJEN, W. M. WARD, AND J. A. ROBINSON, *J. Am. Chem. Soc.,* **36** (1946), 615.

A. L. OLSEN, *Anal. Chem.,* **30** (1958), 158.

A. L. OLSEN, *Anal. Chem.,* **31** (1959), 321.

F. PALMER, JR., *Phys. Rev.,* **45** (1934), 546.

R. W. PARSONS AND H. G. DRICKAMER, *J. Opt. Soc. Am.,* **46** (1956), 464.

J. B. PERI AND R. B. HANNAN, *Spectrochim. Acta,* **16** (1960), 237.

W. A. PLISKIN AND R. P. EISCHENS, *J. Phys. Chem.,* **59** (1955), 1156.

F. PRISTERA, *Appl. Spectroscopy,* **6** (1952), 29.

G. RAPPAPORT, *Phys. Rev.,* **74** (1943), 115.

G. ROBERTS, *Anal. Chem.,* **29** (1957), 911.

V. ROBERTS, *J. Sci. Inst.,* **32** (1955), 294.

S. W. ROCKWOOD AND H. P. CLARK, *Rev. Sci. Inst.,* **27** (1956), 877.

D. S. RUSSEL, *Can. J. Chem.,* **36** (1958), 1745.

R. RAYSON, *J. Opt. Soc. Am.,* **43** (1953), 928.

W. SCHWEMER, J. E. MURPHY, AND L. WILLIAMSON, *Anal. Chem.,* **29** (1957), 1113.

W. L. SENN, JR., AND H. V. DRUSHEL, *Anal. Chem. Acta,* **25** (1961), 328.

L. H. SHARPE, *Proc. Chem. Soc.* (1961), 461.

G. L. SIMARD AND J. STEGER, *Rev. Sci. Inst.,* **17** (1946), 156.

E. J. SLOWINSKI, JR., *J. Opt. Soc. Am.,* **44** (1954), 342.

E. J. SLOWINSKI, JR., *J. Opt. Soc. Am.,* **47** (1957), 1034.

D. C. SMITH AND E. C. MILLER, *J. Opt. Soc. Am.,* **34** (1944), 130.

F. A. SMITH AND C. CREITZ, *Anal. Chem.,* **21** (1949), 1474.

H. D. SMITH AND J. K. MARSHALL, *J. Opt. Soc. Am.,* **30** (1940), 338.

L. G. SMITH, *Rev. Sci. Inst.,* **13** (1942), 65.

J. E. STEWART, *Anal. Chem.,* **30** (1958), 2073.

J. E. STEWART, *Anal. Chem.,* **31** (1959), 1287.

C. SZONYI AND J. O. CRASKE, *Anal. Chem.,* **24** (1962), 448.

H. A. SZYMANSKI AND R. T. CONLEY, *Anal. Chem.,* **30** (1958), 552.

W. K. THOMPSON, *J. Chem. Soc.* (1963), 998.

A. TOLK, *Spectrochim. Acta,* **17** (1961), 511.

J. U. WHITE, *J. Opt. Soc. Am.*, **32** (1942), 285.

J. U. WHITE AND N. L. ALPERT, *J. Opt. Soc. Am.*, **48** (1958), 460.

J. U. WHITE, N L. ALPERT, W. M. WARD, AND W. S. GALLAWAY, *Anal. Chem.*, **31** (1959), 1267.

S. E. WIBERLEY, J. W. SPRAGUE, AND J. E. CAMPBELL, *Anal. Chem.*, **29** (1957), 210.

D. E. WILLIAMSON AND I. A. NICHOLS, *Rev. Sci. Inst.*, **31** (1960), 528.

5

Qualitative Analysis

5.1 CHARACTERISTIC GROUP FREQUENCIES

The infrared absorption or reflectance spectrum of an organic compound shows a number of absorption bands associated with certain structural units within the molecule. For example, the CH_2 group in an alkane such as CH_3—CH_2—CH_2—CH_2—CH_3 has vibrations similar to those found in a large number of other molecules having the methylene grouping as part of their molecular structure. As pointed out in Chaps. 1 and 2, this constancy in appearance of bands due to particular structural moieties had led to the assignment of the so-called characteristic group frequencies. On the bases of these frequencies, chemists have correlated over the years a large number of vibrating atom pairs to specific, regularly appearing absorption bands. In many cases, new correlations have been developed by applying Eq. 2.15, the simple Hooke's law relationship for the frequency of vibration of a two-atom pair. In such calculations, the force constant must be obtained from other physical information or an empirical relationship derived from this information. Several examples of this approach are developed in Appendix II. With a large number of correlations available for the common organic functional groups, the modern chemist can obtain structural information which a short twenty years ago would have required tedious and time-consuming experimentation.

Figure 5.1 summarizes some of the very simple correlations of functional groups. As seen from this figure, absorption bands at shorter wavelengths, 2 to 10μ (5000 to 1000 cm^{-1}) result from the stretching and bend-

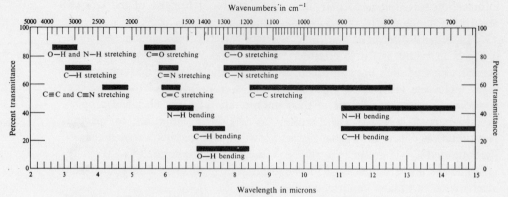

Fig. 5.1 Simple correlations of group vibrations to regions of infrared absorptions.

ing vibrations of groups considered to be diatomic units, i.e., C—H, N—H, O—H, C=O, C=C, etc. Note also that as the masses of the atoms decrease, the frequency increases (compare C—H stretching with C=C stretching in Fig. 5.1). Also, the force-constant change, as reflected in the number of bonds connecting the atom pair, shows a similar effect (compare C≡C, C=C, C—C stretching regions in Fig. 5.1). Since the calculation of the atom pair frequency of vibration reflects only the masses of the atoms and the force constant of the bond between the atoms, a sharp line for all similar absorptions rather than a region in which the absorptions appear might be expected. However, the vibrating unit is affected by external structures attached to both atoms. This structural effect reflects itself in absorption band shifts within relatively narrow regions of the spectrum. For purposes of interpretation, this frequency shift of stretching and bending vibrational modes is extremely valuable information. Bands appearing at longer wavelengths, 7 to 16μ. (1430 to 625 cm^{-1}) are considered to be vibrations of the molecules as a whole, or polyatomic units. Therefore these bands are considered specific for a particular molecule. The region from 7 to 12μ (1430 to 830 cm^{-1}) is frequently referred to as the "fingerprint" region.

The approach to infrared spectral interpretation can be considered parallel to the approach used in examining organic systems. In organic chemistry, particular molecular species are classified by either their ability to undergo a particular mechanistic transformation, i.e., displacements, substitutions, etc., or by the functional groups present, i.e., hydroxylic, ketonic, etc. The use of the "characteristic groups" frequency offers a similar correlative approach for the interpretation of infrared spectra. It is that a particular two-atom unit such as the carbonyl group (C=O) should always appear in roughly the same region of the spectrum. Therefore an infrared spectrum of an organic molecule should be expected to give both positive and negative information regarding molecular structure. The positive information is derived from the characteristic bands appearing in the spectrum. The negative information sorts out molecular units that are absent because of the lack of absorption bands due to that particular functional group.

In order to correlate the large mass of spectral information available, it has been found useful to consider the two-atom vibrating unit or specific combinations of such units in much the same manner as the reactions of organic molecules are treated. That is, certain overall classes of molecules are considered separately because of their unique differences in chemical properties. In part, it is wise for the student to follow this approach to spectral interpretation. Since all organic molecules will contain structural elements of the saturated C—H group (the alkanes) and/or the unsaturated C—H group (the alkenes and aromatics), a thorough knowledge of their absorption characteristics is of utmost importance.

Further, the "characteristic group" frequencies of other functional units, such as oxygen and nitrogen-containing units, should simply be additive to the C—H structural skeleton spectrum. The interpretative process should depend on the position, intensity, and number of new bands appearing in the spectrum in addition to those of the C—H substrate(s) present. In practice, interpretation of an infrared spectrum is not so simple. But certainly the underlying principles that allow the chemist to gain structural information are based on the factors discussed in the foregoing section.

5.2   DISTRIBUTION OF ABSORPTION BANDS IN AN INFRARED SPECTRUM: PRELIMINARY EXAMINATION

The question often asked of the experienced spectroscopist is: How did you reach that conclusion in so short a time? The answer varies widely, but the question seems in part due to the fact that he has examined a large number of spectra of widely divergent types. From the overall shape of the spectrum (i.e., the number, position, and relative intensity of the bands), a quick preliminary assignment of the type of molecule under examination can be made. Figure 5.2 indicates the difference in the overall shape of a molecule whose structural backbone is completely comprised of saturated C—H and a molecule completely made up of unsaturated C—H units (heptane and benzene, respectively).

Of particular importance is the overall gradation of bands due to each molecular unit. In an alkane substrate, as exemplified by the spectrum of heptane, all the high intensity absorptions are located in the low wavelength half of the spectrum (high wavenumber). Conversely, the aromatic substrate, as exemplified by the spectrum of benzene, has its major absorption bands in the long wavelength region of the spectrum. Of course the number and positions of the bands for each substrate type are widely divergent and therefore generally characteristic of each molecular type. Figure 5.3 summarizes this cor-

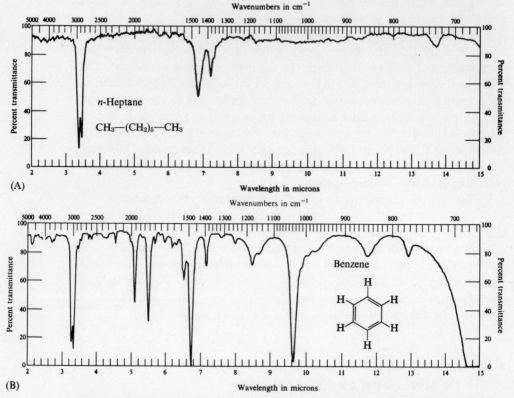

Fig. 5.2   Spectral differences between (A) saturated C—H-containing molecules and (B) unsaturated C—H-containing moieties.

relation diagrammatically and also indicates the type of distribution of band
intensities that would be expected if the two substrates were present in the
same molecule (such as *n*-butylbenzene or a similar substance).

In the previous chapters, a number of factors that determine the number
and intensity of absorption bands have been discussed. Within the molecule,
these include: the masses of the atoms, the force constants of the linkages
between the atoms, the symmetry of the molecule, and the effect of extraneous
structure on the vibration. These factors determine, exclusive of molecular
interactions, the number and relative intensities of the absorption bands that
should be due to a single, isolated molecule. In the practice of infrared spectroscopy, however, such an isolated molecular system is rarely if ever encountered. External interactions affect both the absorption-band position and
intensity. Such factors as the physical state of the substance and intermolecular associations (e.g., hydrogen bonding and solvation) cause band
shifts and changes in band intensities. Therefore the method used to determine
the particular spectrum must be clearly in mind at all times. In the case of
an unknown molecule where the spectrum is to be compared with known substances, it is important that all comparisons are made with spectra obtained
by using the same method of preparation.

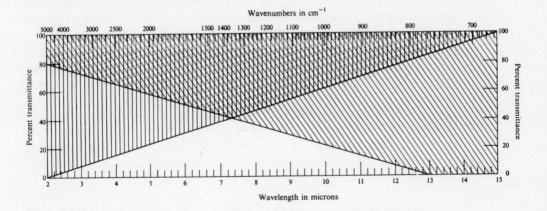

▯ Trend in intensities due to the saturated portion of a molecule

▨ Trend in intensities due to the unsaturated (aromatic) portion of a molecule

Fig. 5.3 Correlations of saturated and unsaturated group absorptions to band intensities in the 2 to 16μ region.

Consider the spectrum of a fairly complex molecule containing a relatively large number of absorption bands. From the present discussion it is evident that this record of vibrational transitions is a more meaningful property than many other physical constants particular to the compound. Certainly the number of absorption bands of varying relative intensities far outweighs such physical measurements as boiling point, melting point, or refractive index. It is possible, therefore, for the chemist to look upon the infrared spectrum as a highly specific physical constant. However, the spectrum is difficult to relate to such a property as the molecular weight of a substance. In terms of the number of bands in the spectrum, such a correlation is completely impossible. In terms of relative intensities of bands, in certain cases where homologous series of substances have been studied, a qualitative correlation relating to molecular weight can be deduced (also, in these cases, a quantitative relationship can also be established).

5.3   INTERPRETATION OF INFRARED SPECTRA, PART 1: SATURATED AND UNSATURATED SUBSTRATES

The subsequent sections will deal with the important infrared absorption characteristics of common functional groups appearing regularly in organic substances. The reader should particularly note the frequently occurring bands due to these groups, and should gain a thorough familiarity with the aliphatic and aromatic substrates. In most cases the more important spectral relationships are exemplified by the inclusion of actual infrared spectra. Band shifts and marked intensity variations between functional groups absorbing in the same general spectral region are pointed out to the reader by suggested comparisons of spectra in the textual portion. At the end of each section the important spectral characteristics are tabulated for easy future reference.

5.3.1   Alkanes and cycloalkanes.   The interpretation of the vibrational spectra of alkanes and cycloalkanes may be divided into two parts: those bands arising from the vibrations of carbon-hydrogen linkages and those involving the movement of the carbon framework, in which case the methyl and methylene groups are considered as mass units.

Carbon-hydrogen stretching vibrations.   All organic compounds have bands between 3100 and 2750 cm^{-1} (approximately 3.30 and 3.65μ) due to carbon-hydrogen stretching vibrations (Fig. 5.4).

When using a spectrophotometer equipped with sodium chloride optics, two or at most three absorption bands are observed in this region for a completely saturated hydrocarbon. At higher resolution, such as that attainable

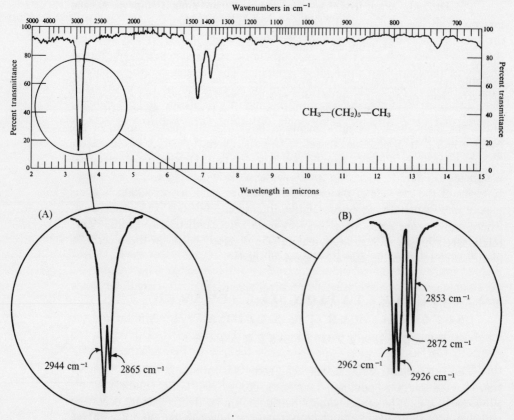

Fig. 5.4   Spectrum of heptane. C—H stretching vibrations as resolved using (A) sodium chloride optics and (B) lithium fluoride optics or a grating.

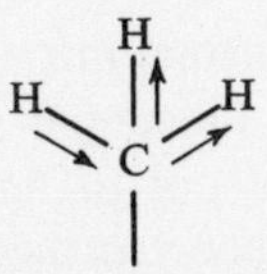

Asymmetric methyl stretching
vibration: 2962 cm⁻¹, 3.38μ

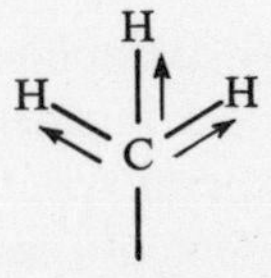

Symmetric methyl stretching
vibration: 2872 cm⁻¹, 3.48μ

Asymmetric methylene stretching
vibration: 2926 cm⁻¹, 3.42μ

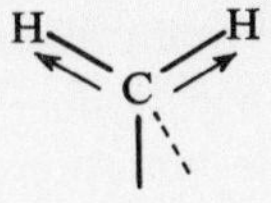

Symmetric methylene stretching
vibration: 2853 cm⁻¹, 3.50μ

Fig. 5.5   Methyl and methylene group stretching vibrations.

with a grating spectrophotometer, at least four bands can be observed in this same region. The circled region and exploded views in Fig. 5.4 exemplify the typical stretching vibrations of the methyl and methylene portion of the molecule under low- and high-resolution conditions.

These bands arise from the vibrations of the methyl and methylene groups. Both the methyl group vibration and the methylene group vibration are split by resonance into two bands, as depicted in Fig. 5.5. It will be noted that each group undergoes both an asymmetric and a symmetric vibrational change of the four- and three-atom grouping. The frequency assignment for each vibration is given below its diagrammatic representation. The positions of these bands are essentially constant in the majority of alkane and cycloalkane systems that have no appreciable angle distortion (i.e., due to ring size or other steric interactions). The asymmetric vibration of the methylene group in cyclopropanes, for example, is shifted to 3050 cm⁻¹ (3.28μ) as a result of angle constriction.

Carbon-hydrogen bending vibrations.   The deformation or bending vibrations of C—H groups can be categorized as shown in Fig. 5.6. The methyl group can undergo two bending vibrations, an asymmetric bend and a symmetric bend. Methylene-group bending vibrations, on the other hand, can be divided into four types of atom movement with respect to adjacent groups. On examination of the spectrum of a typical alkane, Fig. 5.4, only three bands of significant intensity are actually observed.

Due to the close proximity of the methylene scissoring vibration and the asymmetric methyl bending vibration, only a single band is observed in the 1460- to 1467-cm⁻¹ region (approximately 6.82μ). In Fig. 5.7 the shape of this band is exploded for two types of molecules; view A is that of a typical alkane, whereas view B is that of a simple cycloalkane having no methyl substituents. In the latter case, the asymmetric methyl bending vibration is absent, and therefore the band is significantly narrower and sharper than the similar band appearing in the normal alkane spectrum.

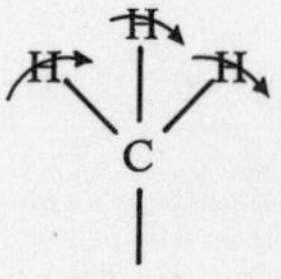

Asymmetric methyl bending
vibration, 1460 cm⁻¹, 6.85μ
(overlapped with methylene
scissoring)

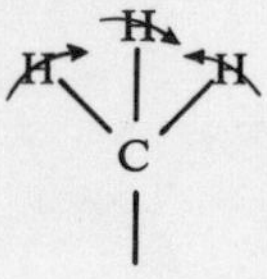

Symmetric methyl bending
vibration, 1379 cm⁻¹, 7.25μ

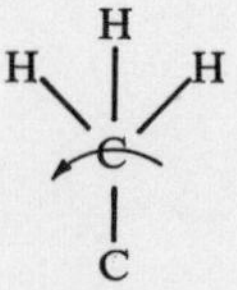

Methyl rocking deformation,
1141–1132 cm⁻¹, 8.76-8.83μ
(overlapped with C—C str.)

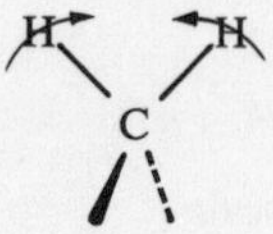

Methylene scissoring deformation
1468 cm⁻¹, 6.81μ
(overlapped with asymmetric
methyl bending)

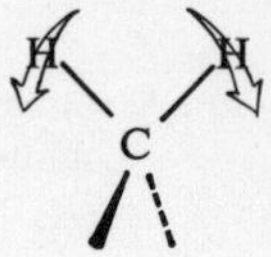

Methylene wagging deformation
1306–1303 cm⁻¹, 7.65-7.67μ
(weak absorption)

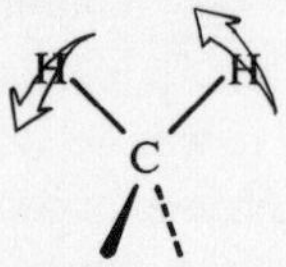

Methylene twisting deformation
(overlapped with methylene
wagging)

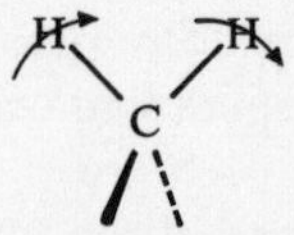

Methylene rocking deformation
720 cm⁻¹, 13.89μ

Fig. 5.6 Methyl and methylene group deformations (bending vibrations).

The small band at 1378 cm⁻¹ (7.25μ) is attributable to the symmetric methyl bending vibration. As noted in Fig. 5.7 and the two exploded views of this region, only the typical alkane systems have this particular band present. It will appear in the cycloalkane spectrum only if the ring bears one or more methyl group substituents. The presence of a methyl group is generally confirmed by examination of the absorptions in this region. When two or three methyl groups are present on a single carbon atom, the 1378-cm⁻¹ band is split into two frequencies by resonance. This phenomenon is generally referred to as the "isopropyl," or "t-butyl," split. In a number of cases, this particular splitting is diagnostic for the geminal dimethyl or related groupings. The specific type of group present in the alkane system is confirmed by the secondary skeletal vibrations. A band at 1170 cm⁻¹ (8.55μ) with a shoulder at 1145 cm⁻¹ (8.73μ) is usually indicative of the isopropyl system. A band at 1255 cm⁻¹ (7.97μ) together with a 1210 cm⁻¹ (8.27μ) vibration is indicative of the tertiary butyl grouping. A quarternary carbon bearing two methyl groups has a characteristic absorption at 1195 cm⁻¹ (8.37μ). The character of these absorptions is changed in compounds bearing a single methyl group adjacent to an oxygen atom or a carbonyl group. This typical

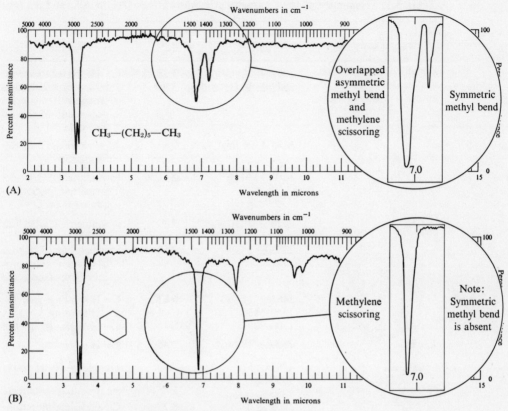

Fig. 5.7 Examples of the spectral changes in the 6.5 to 7.5μ region for alkanes and cycloalkanes (C—H bendings).

splitting is shown in Fig. 5.8, and the correlations for this region are summarized in Table 5.1.

In the spectrum in Fig. 5.4, a fourth, rather weak band appears in the 725- to 720-cm^{-1} (13.8μ) region. This vibration is characteristic of a minimum of four methylene groups, $(CH_2)_4$, in a row and assigned to the methylene rocking vibration. Where three or two methylene groups are in a unit, the vibration is shifted to higher frequencies, 743 to 734 cm^{-1} (13.5μ) and 790 to 770 cm^{-1} (12.8μ), respectively.

Other absorptions are generally much weaker than those discussed in the preceding section and are methylene wagging, twisting, and skeletal vibrations due to carbon-carbon stretching and bending modes. These vibrations generally give rise to weak absorptions of little utility in interpretative work. The only exception to this is in the case of cycloalkanes and those polar molecules where the intensity of the bands is significantly increased.

5.3.2 Alkenes. In nonconjugated compounds containing the C═C group, distinct changes can be observed in the infrared spectrum when compared to the alkane spectrum. In general these changes can be associated with ab-

Table 5.1.   Summary of the Characteristic Absorptions Due to Alkane Linkages

Functional Group	Frequency (cm^{-1})	Wavelength (μ)	Remarks
—CH$_3$	2962 $\pm$ 10 (s)* 2872 $\pm$ 10 (s)	3.38 3.48	C—H stretching-doublet asymmetrical and symmetrical mode, independent of size of molecule
	1450 $\pm$ 20 (m)*	6.89	Asymmetrical C—H deformation
	1380–1370 (s)	7.25–7.30	Symmetrical C—H deformation; higher frequency if on C=C
—CH$_2$—	2926 $\pm$ 5 (s)	3.42	Asymmetrical vibration of H atom
	2853 $\pm$ 5 (s)	3.50	Symmetrical vibration of H atom; independent of size of molecule
	1465 $\pm$ 15 (m) 1350–1150 1100–700	6.83 7.41–8.69 9.09–14.28	C—H bending; sharp C—H twisting C—H rocking; intense
C—H	2890 $\pm$ 10 (w)*	3.46	C—H stretching
—C(CH$_3$)$_3$	1397 (m) 1370 (s) 1250 1208 $\pm$ 6	7.16 7.30 8.00 8.28	Doublet —C—H deformation C—C skeletal vibrations C—C skeletal vibrations
—CH(CH$_3$)$_2$	1385 (s) 1370 (s) 1170 1145	7.22 7.30 8.55 8.73	Doublet —C—H deformation; equal intensity Skeletal vibrations; C—C stretch and C—C—H bending
$\overset{\displaystyle O}{\overset{\displaystyle \|}{—C}}$—O—CH$_3$	1442–1435	6.94–6.97	Similar to the 1380 cm^{-1} for —C—CH$_3$
—CH$_2$—CO (6-ring)	1440–1415	6.95–7.07	
—CH$_2$—CO (5-ring)	1411–1404	7.08–7.12	
—(CH$_2$)$_x$-	740–720	13.51–13.89	$x = 4$; C—C vibration, singlet in liquid; doublet in solid; (may actually be due to CH$_2$ deformation)
C—CH—CH—C with CH$_3$ CH$_3$	1140–1110	8.77–9.01	C—C skeletal vibration

* (s) = strong intensity; (m) = medium intensity; (w) = weak intensity.

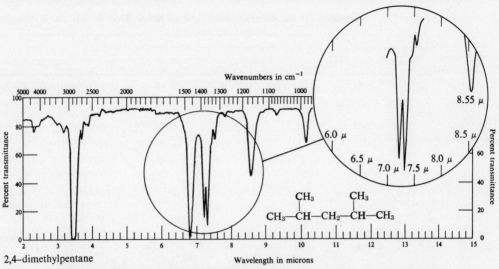

Fig. 5.8 Spectrum of 2,4-dimethylpentane, an example of the spectral changes due to geminal disubstitution. The exploded portion of the spectrum shows the "isopropyl split" of the 7.25μ symmetric methyl bending and the confirming band at 8.55μ (1170 cm^{-1}).

sorptions resulting from vibrations of the $=C\diagup^H$ linkages in the system and those associated with the C$=$C vibrating unit. Figure 5.9 typifies the spectrum of an alkene. In the associated exploded views the reader can visually see the regions of greatest interest for interpretative purposes. In the later discussion of aromatic systems, reference to alkene spectra will be necessary for comparative purposes. It is important, therefore, to be thoroughly familiar with spectral characteristics of this particular unit.

Carbon-carbon double bond stretching vibrations. For an isolated double bond, the absorption peak occurs in the region from 1680 to 1620 cm^{-1} (5.95 to 6.17μ). Compounds possessing a terminal double bond ($R_1R_2C=CH_2$, where R_1 and R_2 are alkyl) have absorptions within the 1658- to 1648-cm^{-1} (6.03 to 6.07μ) region. Table 5.2 summarizes the position of the C$=$C stretching vibrations as a function of the substituents present and the relative geometry of the system. (Note the *cis-* and *trans-*1,2 disubstituted cases.) As pointed out in Chap. 2, a symmetrically substituted C$=$C unit will show no double-bond stretching vibration. It may be extrapolated from this that the intensity of the C$=$C stretching vibration will be most intense in the terminal position (group 5, Table 2). In addition, it could be expected that the intensity of the C$=$C absorption would diminish as the double-bond unit moved from a terminal position toward the center of the molecular chain (i.e., a more symmetrical configuration results). In general, the C$=$C stretching vibration gives rise to a weak band in this region.

In the case of aliphatic conjugation of C$=$C units, there will be a splitting of the olefinic absorption band. In simple conjugated systems, one

Table 5.2. Carbon-Carbon Double-Bond Stretching Bands of Alkenes

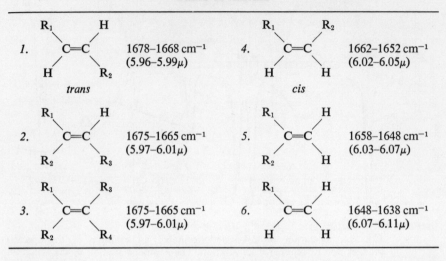

1. R_1⟍   ⟋H
         C=C
     H⟋   ⟍R_2
       trans   1678–1668 cm^{-1} (5.96–5.99μ)

4. R_1⟍   ⟋R_2
         C=C
     H⟋   ⟍H
       cis   1662–1652 cm^{-1} (6.02–6.05μ)

2. R_1⟍   ⟋H
         C=C
   R_2⟋   ⟍R_3 1675–1665 cm^{-1} (5.97–6.01μ)

5. R_1⟍   ⟋H
         C=C
   R_2⟋   ⟍H   1658–1648 cm^{-1} (6.03–6.07μ)

3. R_1⟍   ⟋R_3
         C=C
   R_2⟋   ⟍R_4 1675–1665 cm^{-1} (5.97–6.01μ)

6. R_1⟍   ⟋H
         C=C
     H⟋   ⟍H   1648–1638 cm^{-1} (6.07–6.11μ)

band is stronger than the other and is observed at about 25 cm^{-1} lower frequency (0.09μ longer wavelength in this region) than the corresponding nonconjugated band. When a C=C is conjugated with an aromatic ring, the C=C stretching vibration absorbs in the 1625-cm^{-1} (6.15μ) region (note

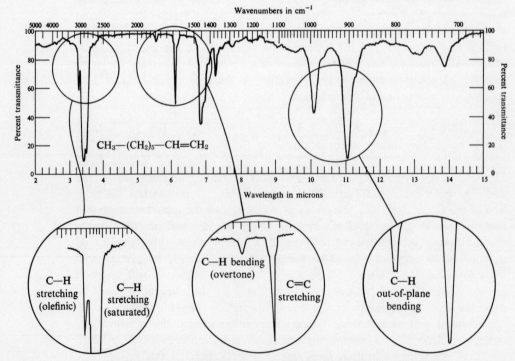

Fig. 5.9 Spectrum of a typical terminal olefin and an enlarged view of the regions of particular importance in interpretation. The spectrum is of octene-1 (thin liquid film).

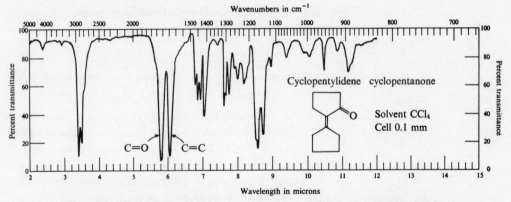

Fig. 5.10   Effect of conjugation on the intensity of the C=C stretching band. Contrast the intensity of the C=C stretching band with that shown in Fig. 5.9, using the saturated C—H band as a reference for the comparison.

that the shift due to conjugation with an aromatic ring is less than that observed with a second double bond). A similar small shift of the double-bond absorption band is also observed when the double bond is conjugated with a carbonyl group or similar multiple-bonded species. In these cases there is a marked increase in the intensity of the olefinic absorption when compared with the intensity of the nonconjugated absorption band, as exemplified in Fig. 5.10 (Compare with Fig. 5.9).

Carbon-hydrogen stretching vibrations.   As in the stretching vibrations of the saturated methylene group, the olefinic methylene group $=C\!\!\!<^H_H$ has a symmetric and an asymmetric vibration, as indicated in Fig. 5.11. The symmetric vibration appears at 2975 cm^{-1} (3.36μ) and is overlapped with alkane carbon-hydrogen stretching absorptions. The asymmetric stretching band of the unsaturated methylene group, however, appears at significantly higher frequencies (3080 cm^{-1}, 3.25μ) than that of the saturated alkane absorptions. The appearance of this band is usually indicative of the olefinic carbon-hydrogen group (or aromatic C—H absorption; see Sec. 5.3.3). Also, the $=C\!\!\!<^H$ stretching frequency at 3020 cm^{-1} (3.31μ) absorbs significantly

Asymmetric methylene stretching vibration; 3090–3070 cm^{-1}, 3.24-3.26μ

Symmetric methylene stretching vibration; 2985-2965 cm^{-1}, 3.35-3.37μ (overlapped with the asymmetric methyl and methylene absorptions of saturated groups)

Fig. 5.11   Olefinic methylene stretching vibrations.

higher than the alkane absorptions and therefore are usually distinguishable for interpretative purposes. These vibrations are shown in Fig. 5.12 and the accompanying enlarged view.

Carbon-hydrogen bending vibrations.   The most significant band in the

spectrum of an unsaturated molecule having a $=C\overset{\displaystyle H}{\diagup}$ group is the out-of-plane bending vibration. These vibrations give rise to intense, characteristic peaks in the 1000- to 800-cm^{-1} (10 to 12.5μ) region, as summarized in Table 5.3. In general the bands in substituted vinyl groups of the type R—CH=CH$_2$ exhibit sharp out-of-plane bending absorptions near 985 (10.15μ) and 910 cm^{-1} (10.99μ). Substitution as in 3,4-dichloro-1-butene tends to shift the bands closer together and to increase slightly the range over which they are observed. If the substituent contains a group that can conjugate with the double bond or if the substituent is an alkoxy group (an enol-ether type) structure (C=C—OR), the band shapes and positions are

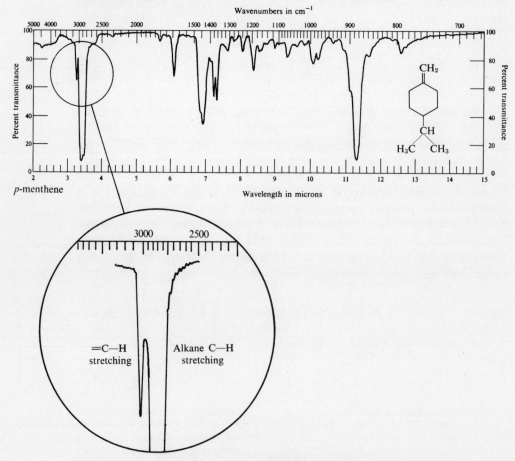

Fig. 5.12   Typical olefinic spectrum indicating the separation of alkane and alkene C—H stretching absorptions.

Table 5.3. Out-of-Plane Carbon-Hydrogen Bending Bands of Alkenes

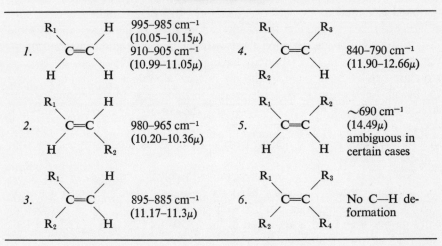

completely changed. In compounds of the type $RR'C{=}CH_2$, a number of structural possibilities exist. Substituents such as halogen or alkyl do not seem to affect the position of the absorption band to a significant extent. However, if the substituent is a nitrile group or a carbonyl group, the out-of-plane bending vibration is shifted from its normal position, in the corresponding hydrocarbons, to the 910- to 880-cm^{-1} region (10.99 to 11.36μ). This shift is not completely restricted to carbonyl compounds, since a number of bridged bicyclic terpenes exhibit similar band shifts for exocyclic methylene groups. A typical example of this shift is shown in the spectrum of methylmethacrylate (Fig. 5.13).

In *trans*-R—CH=CH—R' structures where R or R', or both, is a substituted alkyl group, as in *trans*-1-chloro-2-pentene, the =C—H bending absorption is observed at the same frequency as observed in *trans*-2-pentene

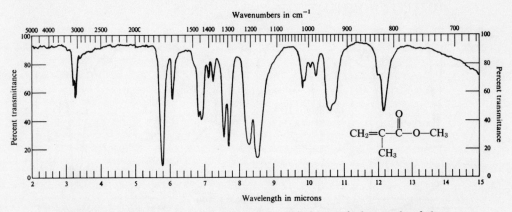

Fig. 5.13 Spectrum of methylmethacrylate. This is a typical example of the effect of conjugation on the position of the out-of-plane C—H bending vibration.

(i.e., 972 cm^{-1}, 10.29μ). However, if the substituent itself is a halogen atom (the halogen is attached directly to the carbon atom of the olefinic linkage) the band is shifted to the 920-cm^{-1} region (10.87μ). Usually, halogen substitution of this type changes the shape and intensity of the band, and in some instances a shoulder appears on the low-frequency side of the major absorption band. In contrast, compounds having the *cis*-R—CH=CH—R′ type of structure exhibit bands due to the *cis* internal double-bond structure; these are broad, weak in intensity, and variable in frequency. In the normal alkane structure containing the *cis* olefinic group, the out-of-plane bending vibration occurs in the 715- to 675-cm^{-1} region (13.99 to 14.82μ). Halogen substitution on one of or both the olefinic carbon atoms shifts the absorption band to 770 cm^{-1} (12.98μ).

Two other bands are characteristic of the olefinic linkage. In the 1400- to 1280-cm^{-1} region (7.25 to 7.81μ) the in-plane carbon-hydrogen deformation or bending vibrations absorb with medium intensity. In a number of cases an overtone band is observed in the 1850- to 1750-cm^{-1} region (5.40 to 5.72μ) as a weak absorption.

Characteristic vibrational frequencies of a number of common alkenes are summarized in Table 5.4. General alkene correlations are given in Table 5.5.

5.3.3 Aromatics. Since the benzene ring is the simplest of the aromatic structures, we should examine it first for correlation with the alkane and alkene systems previously treated in Secs. 5.3.1 and 5.3.2. The spectrum of benzene is characteristic of most aromatic materials. Its modes of vibration give rise to an absorption spectrum quite different from that of an alkane, yet similar (although more complex) to the spectra of the alkenes. As in the alkene spectrum, five regions of absorption can be related to the modes of vibration of the aromatic system. Figure 5.14 typifies a monosubstituted aromatic ring. The characteristic five regions are encircled (compare the typical alkene spectrum, Fig. 5.9). These major regions of absorption will be de-

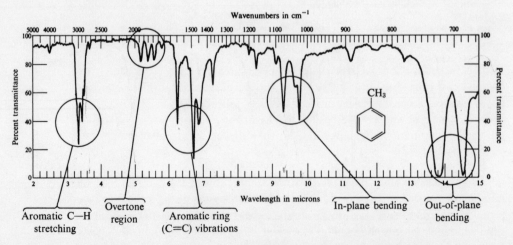

Fig. 5.14 Characteristic regions of absorption of aromatic ring systems.

Table 5.4. Summary of Typical Vibrational Frequencies
of a Number of Common Alkenes

Molecule	ν_{CH}	$\nu_{C=C}$	δ_{CH} (in-plane)	δ'_{CH} (out-of-plane)	Overtone of δ'
A. Monosubstituted Alkenes					
Propylene	3082	1646	1417	996, 919	1831
	3013				
1-Butene	3087	1645	1420	992, 911	1832
1-Pentene	3075	1647	1420	992, 915	1835
1-Hexene	3083	1642	1416	994, 909	1820
1-Heptene	3082	1645	1400	995, 910	1825
3,3-dimethyl-	3094				
butene	3000	1646	1416	1000, 911	1827
B. cis Disubstituted Alkenes					
2-Butene	3029				
	2987	1662	1406	675	
2-Pentene	3018				
	2972	1657	1407	692	
2-Hexene	3012	1654	1407	693	
3-Hexene	3016	1653	1408	715	
C. trans Disubstituted Alkenes					
2-Butene	3021	....	1302	962	
2-Pentene	3029	....	1296	965	
2-Hexene	3027	1668	1300	965	
3-Hexene	3030	....	1289	965	
D. Asymmetrically Substituted Alkenes					
Isobutene	3086				
	2987	1662	1420	887	1790
2-Methyl-					
1-butene	3092	1652	1416	890	1788
2-Methyl-					
1-pentene	3079				
	2969	1652	1414	890	1787
2-Methyl-					
1-heptene	3076	1654	1415	888	1790

scribed in order to point out the unique features of each from which the
chemist can gain structural information. Before proceeding to these generali-
ties, however, a consideration of the modes of vibration of an aromatic ring,
such as benzene, will aid the reader in visualizing the assignments made for
the various aromatic bands appearing in the infrared spectrum of more complex molecules.

Fundamental vibrational modes of benzene.   From the discussion of the
number of possible modes of vibration (Chap. 2), it may be seen that benzene, which contains a total of 12 atoms, should possess $3n - 6$, or 30, possible fundamental vibrations. This does not mean that all fundamental vibrations will have a change in dipole moment associated with it and therefore a

Table 5.5. Summary of the Characteristic Absorptions Due to Alkene (C=C) Linkages

Functional Group	Frequency (cm⁻¹)	Wavelength (μ)	Remarks
C=C (nonconj.)	1670–1615	5.99–6.19	C=C stretching; intensity quite variable
C=C (conj.)	1600–1590	6.25–6.29	C=C stretching; intensity enhanced
—C=CH₂ (vinyl)	3080 ± 10 (m) 2995 ± 10 (m)	3.25 3.35	C—H stretching-doublet asymmetric and symmetric
—CH=CH— (trans)	3040–3010 (m) 965 ± 5 (s) 1300 ± 5	3.29–3.32 10.36 7.69	C—H stretching C—H out-of-plane deformation C—H in-plane deformation; intensity variable
RR'C=CH₂	880–898 (s)	11.36–11.14	C—H rocking; strong characteristic
R—C—H ‖ H—C—R'	965–975 (s) 1325–1275 (m) 1600–1650	10.36–10.26 7.55–7.85 6.25–6.06	C—H rocking; strong characteristic C—H bending, medium C=C stretching, may be absent
R—C—H ‖ R'—C—H	675–729	14.81–13.72	C—H rocking; not too dependable
RCH=CR'R''	840–800 1670	11.90–12.50 5.99	C—H deformation C=C stretching

R   H
 \   /
  C═C
 /   \
H   C═C   H
        /   \
       H   R

(trans-trans)   988   10.12   C—H rocking

R   H
 \   /
  C═C   R
 /   \   /
H   C═C
        /   \
       H   H

(trans-cis)   982   10.18   C—H rocking
               948   10.55
               1020   9.80

Table 5.5—Cont.

Functional Group	Frequency (cm^{-1})	Wavelength (μ)	Remarks
$CH_3(CH{=}CH)_nCH_3$			
$n = 3$	1615	6.19	C=C stretching; strong
$n = 4$	1592	6.28	
$n = 5$	1570	6.37	
$n = 6$	1561	6.41	
Cyclopentene	697	14.35	C—H out-of-plane bending or wagging
Cyclohexene	667–625	14.99–16.00	Same as above

distinctive infrared absorption. Symmetry factors within the molecule markedly reduce the number of infrared active vibrations. Figure 5.15 summarizes the symmetry of the benzene molecule. From these diagrams it can be seen that there are three planes of symmetry through the carbon atoms (diagram A), three planes between the carbon atoms (diagram B), a single plane of symmetry through all atoms of the system (diagram C), and a point of symmetry (diagram D). Because of this high degree of symmetry, a number of fundamental vibrations will have the same energy (cf. Chap. 2 for degeneracy). Therefore the 30 possible modes of vibration are reduced to 20 possible frequencies. Figure 5.16 indicates diagrammatically these frequencies and their assignments. It will be noted from Fig. 5.16 that a number of the vibrations do not have a dipole-moment change involved in the vibration. Therefore the 20 vibrations are still further reduced in number insofar as infrared activity is concerned.

Aromatic carbon-hydrogen stretching vibrations. Aromatic-type structures are best recognized by the presence of the =C—H stretching vibration in the 3030-cm^{-1} region (3.30μ) together with the ring C=C vibrations in the 1650- to 1450-cm^{-1} (6.06 to 6.89μ) region. It has been observed that aromatic C—H vibrations usually produce three bands close to 3.30μ. Monosubstituted aromatics usually show a triplet under high resolution, but as more groups are substituted on the ring, the bands become less distinctive. With sodium chloride prism instruments, the bands frequently appear only as a single band with a shoulder or as a weak shoulder on the saturated C—H band if present. These stretching vibrations show overtones in the 8000- to 5000-cm^{-1} region (1.25 to 2.00μ) (cf. Chap. 7). Figure 5.17 and the exploded view of the 3 to 4μ region shows the typical aromatic C—H absorption bands for toluene.

Aromatic carbon-hydrogen bending vibrations. As noted in Fig. 5.16, there are two types of C—H deformations for aromatic ring systems; namely, out-of-plane bending vibrations appearing below 900 cm^{-1} (11.11μ) and in-plane bending vibrations giving rise to absorptions between 1275 and 960

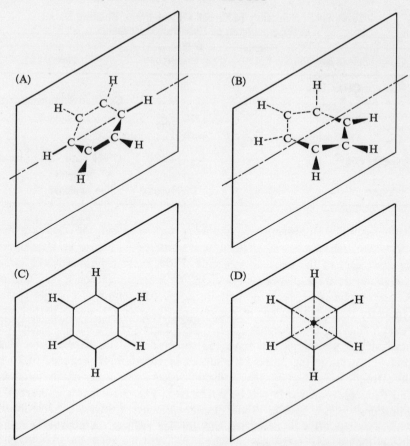

Fig. 5.15 Symmetry of the benzene molecule. (A) One of three planes of symmetry through the carbon atoms of benzene. (B) One of three planes of symmetry through the bonds of benzene (between the carbon atoms). (C) A single plane of symmetry; all 12 atoms lie in the same plane. (D) A point of symmetry; all carbon atoms are equidistant from the point.

cm^{-1} (7.85 and 10.42μ, respectively). Of these types of bending vibrations, the out-of-plane vibrations are the most important for evaluating the number of substituents on the aromatic nucleus (Fig. 5.18). These absorptions are usually the strongest bands in the spectrum attributable to C—H absorptions. In fact these bands are generally more intense than most absorptions, owing to common polar functional groups (exceptions should be noted in later sections). Generally the absorptions due to out-of-plane bending vibrations for benzene derivatives clearly delineate the ring substitution. Electron-attracting groups such as nitro cause an increase in the out-of-plane bending absorption of approximately 30 cm^{-1} (from roughly 0.5 to 0.8μ, depending on the wavelength region). Table 5.6 summarizes the typical C—H out-of-plane bending bands of most benzene derivatives. It is also convenient to describe the position of the C—H out-of-plane bending bands in terms of the number of adjacent hydrogen atoms on the phenyl ring. The band positions

**Table 5.6. Summary of C—H Out-of-Plane Bending Bands
in the Spectrum of Substituted Benzenes**

Phenyl Substitution	Frequency (cm^{-1})	Wavelength (μ)
Benzene	671	14.90
Monosubstitution	770–730	12.99–13.70
	710–690	14.08–14.49
Disubstitution		
1,2	770–735	12.99–13.61
1,3	810–750	12.35–13.33
	710–690	14.08–14.49
1,4	833–810	12.00–12.35
Trisubstitution		
1,2,3	780–760	12.82–13.16
	745–705	13.42–14.18
1,2,4	825–805	12.12–12.42
	885–870	11.30–11.49
1,3,5	865–810	11.56–12.35
	730–675	13.70–14.82
Tetrasubstitution		
1,2,3,4	810–800	12.35–12.50
1,2,3,5	850–840	11.76–11.90
1,2,4,5	870–855	11.49–11.70
Pentasubstituted	870	11.49

presented in this form are summarized in Table 5.7. Presented in this fashion, the correlation holds for condensed aromatics, such as naphthalenes, and for phenanthrenes and aromatic heterocyclic systems such as pyridines and quinolines. In the heterocyclic systems, the heteroatom is treated as a ring substituent.

In-plane bending bands also appear according to the number of hydrogen atoms on the phenyl ring. These absorptions are weak but generally

**Table 5.7. Correlation of C—H Out-of-Plane Bending
to the Number of Adjacent Hydrogens
on the Aromatic Ring**

Number of Adjacent Hydrogen Atoms	Frequency (cm^{-1})	Wavelength (μ)
5*	770–730	12.99–13.70
4	770–735	12.99–13.61
3	810–750	12.35–13.33
2	860–800	11.63–12.50
1	900–860	11.11–11.63

* An additional band also appears between 745 and 690 in monosubstituted cases, 1,3-disubstituted cases, and 1,2,3-trisubstituted cases.

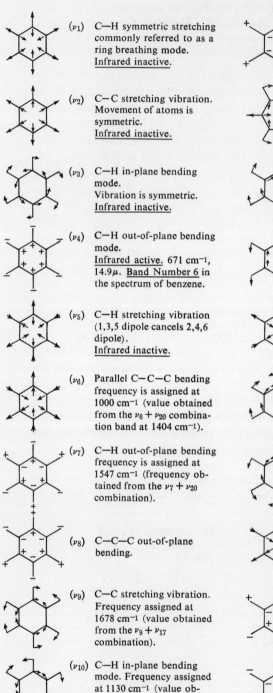

(ν_1) C—H symmetric stretching commonly referred to as a ring breathing mode. <u>Infrared inactive.</u>

(ν_2) C—C stretching vibration. Movement of atoms is symmetric. <u>Infrared inactive.</u>

(ν_3) C—H in-plane bending mode. Vibration is symmetric. <u>Infrared inactive.</u>

(ν_4) C—H out-of-plane bending mode. <u>Infrared active.</u> 671 cm⁻¹, 14.9μ. <u>Band Number 6</u> in the spectrum of benzene.

(ν_5) C—H stretching vibration (1,3,5 dipole cancels 2,4,6 dipole). <u>Infrared inactive.</u>

(ν_6) Parallel C—C—C bending frequency is assigned at 1000 cm⁻¹ (value obtained from the $\nu_6 + \nu_{20}$ combination band at 1404 cm⁻¹).

(ν_7) C—H out-of-plane bending frequency is assigned at 1547 cm⁻¹ (frequency obtained from the $\nu_7 + \nu_{20}$ combination).

(ν_8) C—C—C out-of-plane bending.

(ν_9) C—C stretching vibration. Frequency assigned at 1678 cm⁻¹ (value obtained from the $\nu_9 + \nu_{17}$ combination).

(ν_{10}) C—H in-plane bending mode. Frequency assigned at 1130 cm⁻¹ (value obtained from the $\nu_{10} + \nu_{17}$ combination).

(ν_{11}) C—H out-of-plane bending mode. <u>Infrared inactive.</u>

(ν_{12}) C—H stretching vibration. Infrared active; 3089 cm⁻¹, 3.24μ. <u>Band Number 1</u> in the spectrum of benzene.

(ν_{13}) C=C stretching vibration. Infrared active; 1485 cm⁻¹, 6.73μ. <u>Band Number 4</u> in the spectrum of benzene.

(ν_{14}) C—H in-plane bending mode. Infrared active; 1037 cm⁻¹, 9.64μ. <u>Band Number 5</u> in the spectrum of benzene.

(ν_{15}) C—H stretching vibration. <u>Infrared inactive.</u>

(ν_{16}) C—C stretching vibration. <u>Infrared inactive.</u>

(ν_{17}) C—H in-plane bending mode. <u>Infrared inactive.</u>

(ν_{18}) C—C—C in-plane bending mode. <u>Infrared inactive.</u>

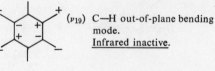

(ν_{19}) C—H out-of-plane bending mode. <u>Infrared inactive.</u>

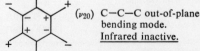

(ν_{20}) C—C—C out-of-plane bending mode. <u>Infrared inactive.</u>

Fig. 5.16   Fundamental

sharp. These vibrations (Fig. 5.18) have only supplementary value, since in the region of their absorption, the C—C, C—O, as well as other singly bonded groups, also show absorption bands.

Aromatic ring vibrations: C=C vibrations.   As already mentioned, the carbon-carbon double-bond absorption bands of the ring together with the carbon-hydrogen stretching and bending bands are the bands most useful in establishing the presence or absence of the aromatic nucleus. The ring vibrations due to the conjugated double-bond system usually appear at 1600 cm^{-1} (6.25μ) and 1500 cm^{-1} (6.67μ). A third band at 1580 cm^{-1} (6.33μ) usually is present when the ring is conjugated with unsaturated groups. When conjugated, the intensity of all three bands is significantly increased. Conjugation also gives rise to a band at 1450 cm^{-1} (6.89μ), which is usually overlapped by the alkane CH$_2$ scissoring and asymmetric methyl band. Some small shifts of the two bands have been recognized as a result of specific substitution types. Unsymmetrical trisubstitution or *para* substitution causes a shift to higher frequencies. Vicinal trisubstitution causes a shift toward lower frequencies.

Overtone and combination bands.   Figure 5.19 and the exploded view therein shows typical weak absorptions in the 5 to 6μ region (2000 to 1667 cm^{-1}). On increasing the thickness of the sample specimen or scale expansion, these weak absorption bands can be utilized for determining and confirming ring substitution (cf., the C—H out-of-plane bending bands). The utility of the region, however, is limited as a result of overlapping absorptions from other functional groups, such as carbonyl groups, and overtones or difference absorptions from other functional groups, such as nitrobenzene. Figure 5.20 exemplifies two such cases in which overlapping vibrations obscure

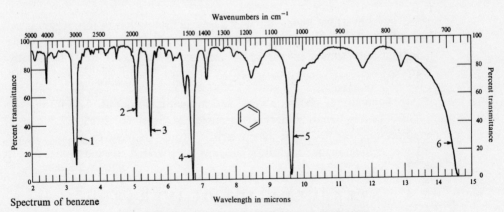

Spectrum of benzene

Bands labeled 2 and 3 are not fundamental vibrations of benzene; rather these bands are combination bands. Band 2 is the combination of $\nu_{11} + \nu_{19}$; both are Raman active vibrations. Band 3 is the combination of $\nu_{18} + \nu_{19}$, also both Raman active vibrations.

vibrations of benzene.

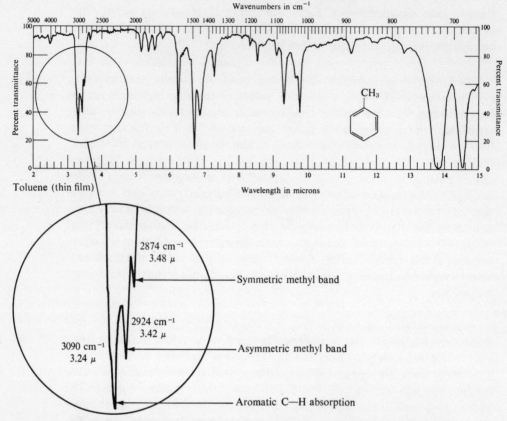

Fig. 5.17 Aromatic C—H absorption contrasted with the aliphatic methyl absorption in the 3 to 4μ region. In this spectrum of toluene (thin film), note the displacement of the aromatic C—H stretching vibration band to higher frequencies (shorter wavelength).

the 5 to 6μ overtone region. In such cases, interpretation in this region is not possible. In those cases where this region is not obscured, the correlations diagrammatically shown in Fig. 5.21 are extremely useful for interpretative purposes.

5.34 Summary of alkane, alkene, and aromatic vibrations.   As in any correlative system the relationships discussed in Secs. 5.3.1 to 5.3.3 can be graphically presented. The characteristic group frequencies of the alkane, alkene, and aromatic ring vibrations are summarized in chart form in Fig. 5.22.

5.4   INTERPRETATION OF INFRARED SPECTRA, PART II: COMMON FUNCTIONAL GROUPS

5.4.1   Triple-bonded and cumulative multiple-bonded groups: the 4 to 5μ region.   Absorptions appearing in the 4 to 5μ region (2500 to 2000 cm⁻¹)

originate from the stretching vibrations of triply bonded groups such as the nitrile group C≡N, the alkyne linkage C≡C, and groups possessing cumulative double bonds, such as the allenes, C=C=C, and the isocyanates, —N=C=O. This region is also the region of major absorption of carbon dioxide. In double-beam instruments, a small band (or trough, i.e., a negative absorption) may appear as a result of carbon dioxide absorption at 2350 cm^{-1} (4.25μ) when the sample and reference paths are not properly compensated. Of the 12 functional classes summarized in Table 5.8, specific attention should be given to the more commonly encountered functional groups.

The alkynes.   The infrared spectrum of alkynes (acetylenes) in the 4.5μ region is worthy of specific comment, since acetylene itself has no infrared-active stretching frequency because of its symmetry. Therefore no band is observed in this region. Similarly, symmetrically disubstituted acetylenes show no absorption band in this region. In most unsymmetrically substituted acetylenes the band is very weak. As the acetylene linkage moves from the terminal position on the carbon chain to an internal position, its intensity is diminished. Since the band is of such low intensity, in complex molecules it may not be detected by examination of the infrared spectrum (i.e., the intensity of other bands being high by comparison, a spectrum normally considered suitable for interpretation will show no absorption band in this region). In monosubstituted acetylenes, the stretching vibration normally gives rise to an absorption band between 2140 and 2100 cm^{-1} (4.67 and 4.76μ). Disubstituted acetylenes (unsymmetric) exhibit a band between 2260 and 2190 cm^{-1} (4.42 and 4.57μ) as well as some weaker secondary absorptions. Considering an alkyl-group substituent as giving rise to a "normal" absorption band for the acetylenic stretching vibration, then conjugation with a vinyl group or a phenyl group shifts the absorption band to lower frequencies. A similar effect has been noted with branching of the alkyl chain.

The ≡C—H stretching vibration for alkynes of the type R—C≡C—H gives rise to an absorption band at the high-frequency end of the carbon-hydrogen stretching region between 3310 and 3200 cm^{-1} (3.02 and 3.12μ). The reader should contrast these values with the values recorded for the =C—H stretching absorption summarized in Fig. 5.22.

The bending vibration of the ≡C—H group gives rise to absorptions in the 700- to 600-cm^{-1} (14.29 to 16.67μ) region. Figure 5.23 indicates the typical absorptions of a terminal alkyne in the liquid state.

The nitrile, isonitrile, and similar groups.   Monomeric aliphatic nitriles exhibit a C≡N stretching vibration near 2245 cm^{-1} (4.45μ). When conjugated with unsaturated linkages including aromatic nuclei, the band is shifted to lower frequencies, 2230 to 2210 cm^{-1} (4.48 to 4.53μ), and the intensity of the absorption band is increased. Generally the conjugated C≡N stretching band is about 30 cm^{-1} lower than its nonconjugated analog. Figure 5.24 shows typical spectra of a conjugated and a nonconjugated nitrile

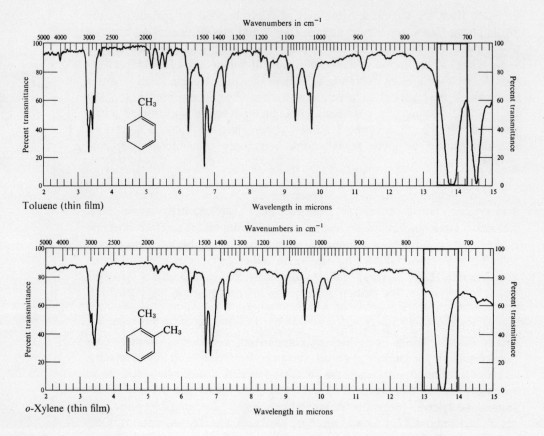

Fig. 5.18 Correlation of the out-of-plane bending bands to the number of

(note the small but definite band shift to lower frequencies in the case of the conjugated system).

In certain cases the intensity of the nitrile stretching band is diminished by neighboring functional groups. This is particularly true if an oxygen-containing group is located near the C≡N linkage. Generally the nitrile absorptions are weak to medium intensity bands.

The isonitrile group R—N≡C (where R is either alkyl or aryl) absorbs in the 2175- to 2120-cm^{-1} region (4.60 to 4.72μ). The alkyl isonitriles exhibit a strong absorption band between 2175 and 2150 cm^{-1} (4.60 and 4.65μ). The aryl derivatives, on the other hand, are shifted to lower frequencies, similar to the conjugated nitrile group. The isonitrile group also exhibits a characteristic C—N absorption band near 1594 cm^{-1} which is not

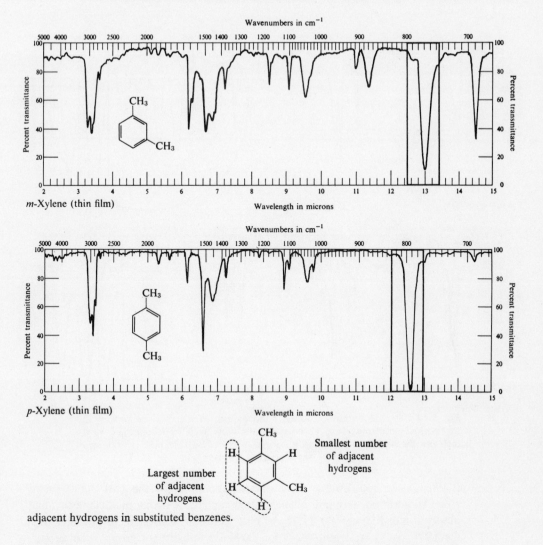

m-Xylene (thin film)

p-Xylene (thin film)

adjacent hydrogens in substituted benzenes.

found in the nitriles. This band is useful in distinguishing between two C≡N types.

Azides exhibit an intense absorption band in the 2160- to 2120-cm⁻¹ (4.63 to 4.72μ) region due to the asymmetric stretching vibration of the N≡N group. A much less intense symmetric band absorbs in the 1340- to 1180-cm⁻¹ region (7.46 to 8.48μ). The frequency of the asymmetric stretching vibration is not markedly affected by changes in environment.

Allenes and other cumulative double-bond systems: Allenes. The stretching vibration of the C=C=C unit appears as a singlet or doublet (depending on the substituent groups at the terminal positions) in the 2200- to 1950-cm⁻¹ region (4.55 to 5.13μ). R—CH=C=CH₂ absorbs at 1970 cm⁻¹

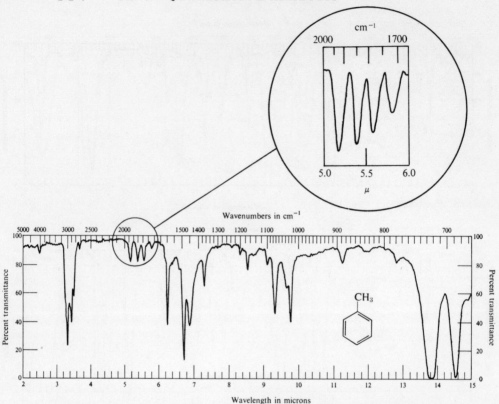

Fig. 5.19 Typical monosubstitution band pattern in the 5 to 6µ region. In the normal spectrum these absorptions are very weak. The enlarged view indicates these absorptions when a sample of increased thickness is examined to develop spectral detail in this region.

(5.08µ) as a doublet due to vibrational coupling of the two double-bond units. In addition, terminal allene systems exhibit a strong methylene bending absorption at 850 cm⁻¹ (11.76µ). This vibration is stronger in intensity than the 1970 cm⁻¹ stretching vibration. When a substituent group such as carboxyl, ester, or amide is conjugated with the allenic system, the double-bond stretching vibration is split into a doublet. For example:

$$\underset{\displaystyle}{CH_2\!\!=\!\!C\!\!=\!\!CH\!\!-\!\!\overset{\displaystyle \overset{O}{\|}}{C}\!\!-\!\!NH_2}$$

has a C=C stretching doublet at 1953 cm⁻¹ and 1931 cm⁻¹ (5.12 and 5.18µ, respectively).

Isocyanates. The isocyanate group has one of the most intense absorptions in the infrared spectrum. The asymmetric —N=C=O ($-\overset{+}{N}\!\!\equiv\!\!C\!\!-\!\!\overset{-}{O}$) stretching vibration gives rise to an extremely high intensity absorption band in the 2275- to 2230-cm⁻¹ region (4.40 to 4.48µ). The position of this

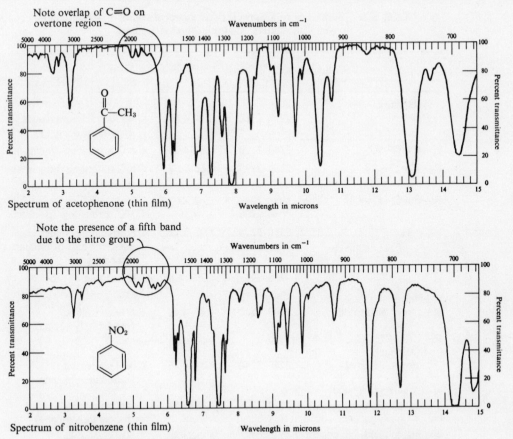

Fig. 5.20 Typical examples of functional group absorptions that interfere with the use of the 5 to 6μ region for interpretive purposes.

absorption is relatively unaffected by conjugation. Most aliphatic and aromatic isocyanates absorb between 2275 and 2263 cm^{-1} (4.40 and 4.42μ). Methyl isocyanate, however, absorbs as 2231 cm^{-1} (4.48μ). The symmetric isocyanate stretching vibration absorbs weakly at 1412 to 1350 cm^{-1} (7.08 to 7.41μ). More often than not, this band is of little practical importance, since it is usually overlapped with aliphatic absorptions in the same region. Figure 5.25 is typical of the isocyanate group absorption. The normal aromatic bands of high intensity should be noted in order to contrast the extremely high intensity of the isocyanate stretching band. Similar strong absorptions for the thiocyanate and isothiocyanate groups are summarized in Table 5.8.

5.4.2   Alcohols and phenols.   The hydroxyl group of alcohols and phenols shows three distinct characteristic absorption regions, as shown in Fig. 5.26. As noted, these vibrations can be ascribed to the O—H stretching vibration, the C—O stretching vibration, and the O—H bending vibration or deformation.

Table 5.8. Summary of Characteristic Absorptions of Triple-bonded and Cumulative Multiple-bonded Groups

Functional Group	Frequency (cm^{-1})	Wavelength (μ)	Remarks
Acetylenes			
—C≡C—	2250–2150	4.44–4.65	C≡C stretching (absent in symmetrical cases)
H—C≡C—R	2140–2100	4.67–4.76	C≡C stretching (medium)
R$_1$—C≡C—R$_2$	2260–2190	4.42–4.57	C≡C stretching (very weak or absent)
R—C≡C—C≡CH	Near 2040	4.90	
	Near 2200	4.55	C≡C stretching (doublet)
≡C—H	3310–3200	3.02–3.12	CH stretching (sharp, characteristic and of medium intensity)
	700–600	14.29–16.67	CH bending
Nitriles			
R—C≡N (saturated)	2260–2240	4.42–4.46	C≡N stretching (moderately strong)
R—CH=CHCH$_2$C≡N (aliphatic, nonconjugated)	2260–2240	4.42–4.46	C≡N stretching (moderately strong)
R—CH=CH—C≡N (aliphatic conjugated)	2230–2220	4.48–4.50	C≡N stretching (moderately strong)
R—C≡N (aromatic)	2240–2200	4.46–4.50	C≡N stretching (moderately strong)
N≡C—CH$_2$CH=CH—C≡N	2260–2240	4.42–4.46	C≡N stretching (moderately strong)
	2230–2220	4.48–4.50	C≡N stretching (moderately strong)
Diazonium Salts			
R—N$_2^+$	2280–2240	4.39–4.46	N≡N stretching (moderately strong)
Isonitriles			
R—N≡C	2200–2100	4.55–4.76	N≡C stretching (moderately strong)
Azides			
CH$_3$—N$_3$	Near 2143	4.67	N$_3$ asymmetric stretching, strong
	Near 1295	7.72	N$_3$ symmetric stretching, weak
R—N$_3$	2169–2080	4.61–4.81	N$_3$ asymmetric stretching, strong
	1343–1177	7.45–8.49	N$_3$ symmetric stretching, strong

Table 5.8—Cont.

Functional Group	Frequency (cm⁻¹)	Wavelength (μ)	Remarks
Allenes $C=C=C$	2200–1950	4.55–5.13	$C=C$ stretching, strong; sometimes observed as doublet
$—CH=C=CH_2$	Near 1970	5.08	Two $C=C$ stretching frequencies due to coupling
	Near 850	11.76	C—H deformation, terminal allene only
$C=C=CHCONH_2$	Near 1950	5.12	$C=C$ stretching; doublet
	Near 1930	5.18	due to coupling
Isocyanates $CH_3—NCO$	2232–2230	4.48	Asymmetric stretching of NCO ($\overset{+}{N}\equiv C—\overset{-}{O}$), strong
	1412–1377	7.08–7.26	Symmetric stretching of NCO, weak
R—NCO (aliphatic or aromatic)	2275–2263	4.39–4.42	Asymmetric stretching of NCO, strong
	1390–1350	7.19–7.41	Symmetric stretching of NCO, strong
Thiocyanate R—S—C≡N (aliphatic)	Near 2140	4.90	C≡N stretching, strong
R—S—C≡N (aromatic)	2175–2160	4.60–4.63	C≡N stretching, strong
Isothiocyanate R—N=C=S (aliphatic)	2140–1990	4.67–5.26	$—\overset{+}{N}\equiv C—\overset{-}{S}$ stretching, strong
R—N=C=S (aromatic)	2130–2040	4.70–4.90	$—\overset{+}{N}\equiv C—\overset{-}{S}$ stretching, strong
Carbodiimide —N=C=N— (aliphatic)	2140–2130	4.67–4.69	N=C=N stretching, strong
—N=C=N— (aromatic)	Near 2145	4.66	Stretching vibration 2145-cm⁻¹ band
	Near 2115	4.73	Stronger than 2115-cm⁻¹ band
Ketene $C=C=O$	Near 2150	4.65	Stretching vibration
	Near 1120	8.93	
Ketenimine $C=C=N$	Near 2000	5.00	Stretching vibration

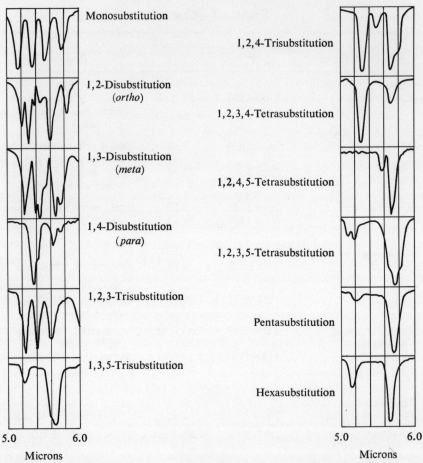

Fig. 5.21 Spectra-structure correlations of benzene ring substitutions in the 5 to 6μ region.

The oxygen-hydrogen stretching vibration. The O—H stretching frequency of a hydroxyl group that is not hydrogen-bonded may be assigned to the 3640- to 3610-cm^{-1} (2.75 to 2.77μ) region of the spectrum. The data obtained for characteristic absorptions in this region are generally derived from band positions measured in dilute solutions of the alcohol or phenol in carbon tetrachloride or chloroform. The presence of the absorption at the lower limit of the frequency range (i.e., 3610 cm^{-1}) are difficult to assign to the truly isolated "free" hydroxyl group, since weakly hydrogen-bonded species absorb between 3600 and 3500 cm^{-1} (2.78 and 2.86μ). Although of little practical value in assignment, primary hydroxyl groups, which are not hydrogen-bonded, absorb at the higher-frequency end of this region (3640 cm^{-1}) followed by secondary (3630 cm^{-1}), tertiary (3620 cm^{-1}), and finally phenolic systems (3610 cm^{-1}).

The position of absorptions in this region are affected by a number of experimental variations, including concentration and temperature. Accurate assignments are usually attempted only when high-resolution equipment can be employed (spectrophotometers equipped with gratings or lithium or calcium fluoride prisms). In an experimental study of hydroxyl absorption the spectrophotometer should be carefully calibrated for wavelength (or wavenumber) accuracy over this spectral region.

Numerous studies of hydroxyl absorption have been carried out. These studies have yielded a wealth of useful information for the chemist with respect to conformations of molecules and steric relationships of neighboring groups within complex organic structures. These studies have been possible because the "free" hydroxyl absorption is sharp and at a position in the spectrum that is not overlapped by other absorptions. The effect of hydrogen bonding can be seen in the pure liquid spectrum shown as typical of an alcohol in Fig. 5.26. The band is shifted to lower wavenumber (longer wavelength) when hydrogen bonding to an electron-rich atom or group occurs. Since two types of hydrogen bonding can occur, it is well to summarize the effect of both types (intermolecular and intramolecular) on the alcohol spectrum. As will be observed in Table 5.10, both types of bonding give rise to absorptions in the same region (3600 to 3200 cm^{-1}, 2.78 to 3.13μ) with a few minor exceptions. As would be expected, the intermolecular hydrogen-bonded species are very much dependent upon concentration. On the other hand, the intramolecular hydrogen-bonded species would not be expected to exhibit such a strong concentration dependency. This difference is manifested spectrally, since the intermolecular hydrogen-bonded band will increase in intensity with increasing concentration, whereas the intramolecular type will not show any change in band intensity (provided the cell path is varied such that the effective number of molecules in the path of the incident radiation is kept the same). For example, in cis-cyclopentane-1,2-diol, the "free" hydroxyl absorption appears at 3633 cm^{-1} (2.75μ) and the intramolecular hydrogen-bonded absorption at 3572 cm^{-1} (2.80μ) in carbon tetrachloride solutions at concentration levels less than 0.005 mole per liter. The intensity ratio of these two absorptions is constant as long as the concentration is not increased to a level where intermolecular bonding can occur. When intermolecular bonding does occur, only the free O—H is weakened, and a new band appears in the 3500-cm^{-1} (2.86μ) region (generally at frequencies lower than the intramolecular hydrogen-bonded band). A similar relationship also exists when bonding occurs with carbonyl groups or nitro groups. In such cases, parallel changes are noted in both the hydroxyl-group stretching region and the C=O or —NO$_2$ group stretching regions. Of particular note is the effect of such bonding with carbonyl groups in carboxylic acids (Sec. 5.4.5), where the hydrogen-bonded hydroxyl absorption is broad and diffuse, stretching the band over the region from 3500 to 2500 cm^{-1} (2.86 to 4.00μ). Occasionally such an absorption has a number of ill-defined smaller bands appearing on the diffuse band envelope.

Phenols, which are hindered by substituent groups in the *ortho* positions,

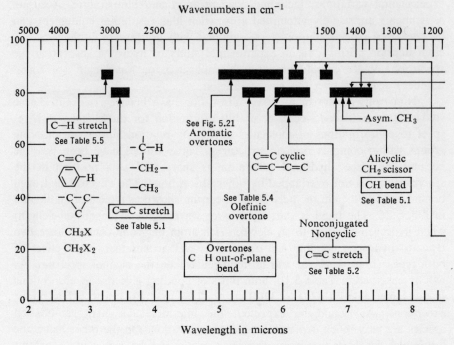

Fig. 5.22   Summary of characteristic alkane,

simply appear as monomeric or dimeric bands. In such cases, bands appear as illustrated in the spectrum in Fig. 5.28.

A number of typical examples of hindered phenolic molecules are shown in Fig. 5.29. The hydroxyl frequencies, measured in Nujol, are summarized below each structure in order to illustrate the effect of the substituent groups on the ability of the hydroxyl group to undergo hydrogen bonding.

Carbon-oxygen stretching vibrations.   The stretching vibration of the carbon-oxygen system in alcohols and phenols gives rise to absorption bands in the 1200- to 1000-cm^{-1} (8.33 to 10.00μ) region of the spectrum. Such absorptions, however, have only limited value for interpretative purposes, since in most polyfunctional organic molecules, other absorptions of similar intensities also appear in this region. However, in compounds where interfering groups are known to be absent, correlations can be quite useful in evaluating substitution on the carbon chain and, in the case of cyclic systems, the configuration of the hydroxyl group.

Table 5.9 summarizes the change in the position of the C—O group absorption band with changes in adjacent structure of the carbon portion of the molecule. Hydroxyl groups in cyclic systems such as the decalols, certain terpenes, steroids, and other natural products can be assigned configurational relationships (or conformations in certain nonrigid systems) based upon the position of the C—O stretching vibration. For example, Fig. 5.30 indicates

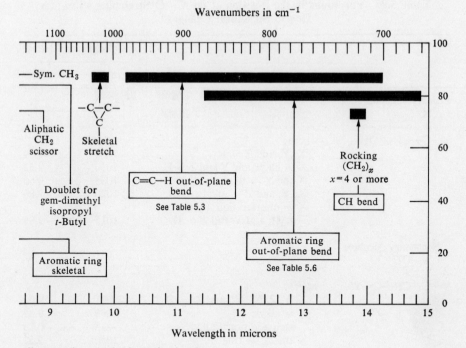

alkene, and aromatic absorption bands.

two different stereochemical orientations for the C-3 hydroxyl group in a steroid having a *trans A/B* ring junction. It is noted that the equatorial C—O stretching vibration absorbs at higher frequency than that for the axial group. This is presumably due to the fact that the vibration in the plane of the ring (equatorial) requires more energy than the vibration perpendicular to the ring (axial). This difference is not restricted simply to the alcohols, and has been observed in ester and ether derivatives of the hydroxyl functional group.

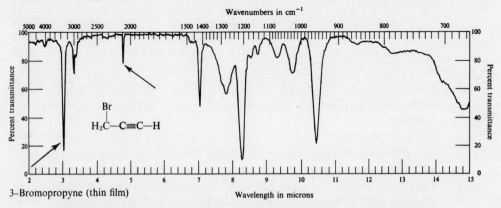

3–Bromopropyne (thin film)

Fig. 5.23 Spectrum of a terminal acetylenic compound. Particular note should be made of the positions of the ≡C—H stretching vibration and the weakly absorbing C≡C stretching vibrations (indicated on the spectrum by the arrows).

Table 5.9. Variations in the Position of the C—O Stretching Vibration Due to Structural Changes*

		Approximate Position	
		(cm⁻¹)	(μ)

Primary Alcohols

```
    X
    |
Y—C—CH₂—OH
    |
    Z
```

		(cm⁻¹)	(μ)
	where:		
	X, Y, and Z = H	~1065	~9.39
	X = alkyl, and Y and Z = H	1050	9.52
	X and Y = alkyl, and Z = H	1035	9.66
	X, Y, and Z = alkyl	1020	9.80
	X = unsaturation (vinyl or aryl), and Y and Z = H	1015	9.85

Secondary Alcohols

```
    X  OH  X′
    |  |   |
Y—C—CH—C—Y′
    |      |
    Z      Z′
```

	where:		
	X, Y, Z, X′, Y′, and Z′ = H	~1100	~9.09
	X = alkyl;	1085	9.22
	each additional alkyl	−15	−0.13
	X and X′ = ring	1050	9.52
	X = unsaturation	1070	9.35
	X and X′ unsaturation	1010	9.90

Tertiary Alcohols

```
    X  OH  X″
    |  |   |
Y—C—C—C—Y″
    |  |   |
    Z  |   Z″
       |
   X′—C—Z′
       |
       Y′
```

	where:		
	X, Y, Z, X′, Y′, Z′, X″, Y″, and Z″ = H	~1150	~8.69
	X = alkyl	1135	8.81
	X and X′ = alkyl;	1120	8.93
	each additional alkyl	−15	−0.13
	X = unsaturation	1120	8.93
	X and X′ = unsaturation	1060	9.43
	X, X′, and X″ = unsaturation	1010	9.90

* Overlap of primary, secondary, and tertiary C—O stretching bands due to varied substitution renders this correlation applicable only to those cases where the system has already been characterized as to the type of hydroxyl-bearing carbon that is present.

Hydroxyl bending vibrations. The deformation vibrations associated with the hydroxyl group should result in two separable absorption bands, namely, an in-plane bending band and an out-of-plane bending band. In all aliphatic alcohols that are hydrogen-bonded, the out-of-plane bending vibration will be observed as a broad band having its band center near 650 cm⁻¹ (15.38μ). The position of this band is variable, depending on the strength of the hydrogen-bonding system. The stronger the hydrogen bond, the higher the

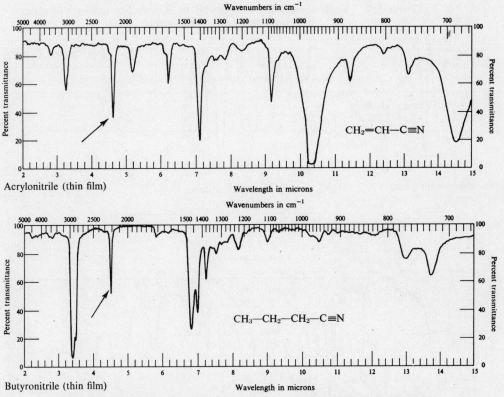

Fig. 5.24 Spectrum of a conjugated and nonconjugated (saturated) nitrile. Contrast the positions of C≡N stretching absorption as indicated by the arrows.

wavenumber of the out-of-plane bending band. In very dilute solutions, where no association of the hydroxyl occurs, no out-of-plane absorption is observed in the 2 to 16μ region.

The in-plane deformation gives rise to a very broad band extending from

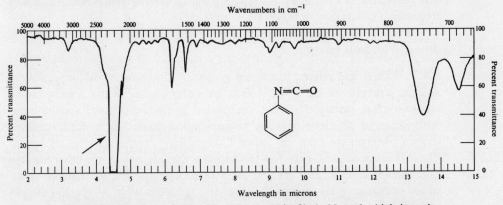

Fig. 5.25 Spectrum of phenyl isocyanate (thin film). Note the high intensity of the N=C=O stretching absorption (arrow) when contrasted with the aromatic C—H out-of-plane bending bands at 13.4μ and 14.6μ.

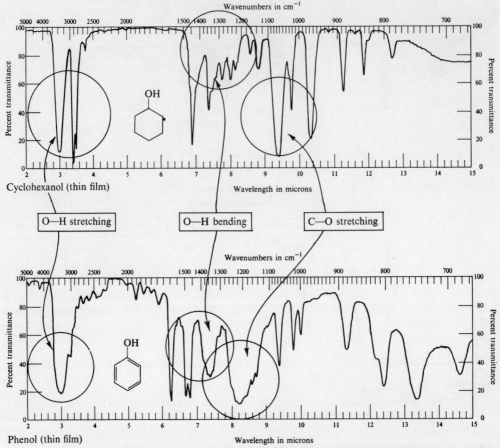

Fig. 5.26 Typical absorptions of the alcohol and phenol functional groups.

approximately 1500 to 1300 cm^{-1} (6.67 to 7.69μ). This band will be broad and diffuse in the pure alcohols and in concentrated solutions. On dilution it will weaken and eventually be replaced by a narrow sharp band at lower frequency (1250 cm^{-1}, 8.00μ).

Table 5.10 summarizes the absorption characteristics of the alcohol and phenol functional groups.

5.4.3 Ethers and related functional groups. The mass of the oxygen atom and the strengths of the C—O bonds are quite similar to the corresponding carbon-carbon system. It is not unexpected to find, therefore, a close similarity in band positions between carbon-carbon stretching and the carbon-oxygen absorptions from the ether linkage. However, since the change in dipole is much larger for the C—O vibration, the intensity of the ether absorption band is considerably greater. As a molecular species, the determination of the presence or absence of the ether linkage from infrared spectral studies is a difficult task. Any molecule containing another C—O linkage, such as an alcohol, an ester, or an acid, together with an ether group tends to make the interpretation for the ether linkage questionable, at best.

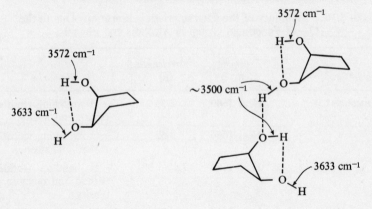

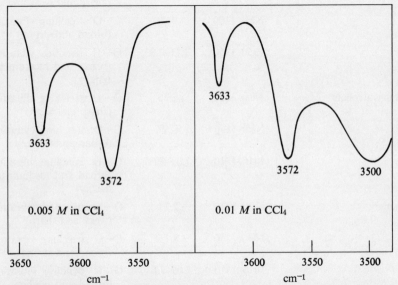

Fig. 5.27 Effect of hydrogen bonding on the O—H stretching vibration in *cis*-cyclopentane-1,2-diol.

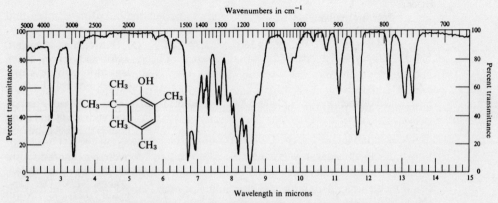

Fig. 5.28 Steric hindrance to hydrogen bonding as exemplified in the spectrum of 6-*t*-butyl-2,4-dimethylphenol (thin film).

Table 5.10.   Summary of the Characteristic Absorptions Due to the C—O—H Functional Group in Alcohols and Phenols

Functional Group	Frequency (cm⁻¹)	Wavelength (μ)	Remarks
Primary alcohols*	Near 3640	2.75	O—H stretching vibration (sharp and weak)
	Near 1050	9.52	C—O stretching vibration (broad and strong)
	1350–1260	7.41–7.93	O—H bending vibration (broad and medium intensity)
Secondary alcohols*	Near 3630	2.75	O—H stretching vibration (sharp and weak)
	Near 1100	9.09	C—O stretching vibration (broad and strong)
	1350–1260	7.41–7.93	O—H bending vibration (broad and medium intensity)
Tertiary alcohols*	Near 3620	2.76	O—H stretching vibration (sharp and weak)
	Near 1150	8.69	C—O stretching vibration (broad and strong)
	1410–1310	7.09–7.63	O—H bending vibration (broad and medium intensity)
Phenols*	Near 3610	2.77	O—H stretching vibration (weak and sharp)
	Near 1230	8.13	C—O stretching vibration (broad and strong)
	1410–1310	7.09–7.63	O—H bending vibration (broad and medium intensity)
Hydrogen-bonded system			
1. Intermolecular hydrogen bonding			
Dimers	3600–3500	2.78–2.86	O—H stretching vibration weak and sharp, overlapped by polymeric hydrogen-bonded O—H
Polymers	3400–3200	2.94–3.13	A strong, broad absorption with solids and pure liquids the only band observed; N—H free and hydrogen-bonded also appear in this region (Table 5.12). The carbonyl overtone (very weak absorption) also absorbs in this region

Table 5.10—Cont.

Functional Group	Frequency (cm⁻¹)	Wavelength (μ)	Remarks
With other functional groups	3600–3500	2.78–2.86	—O—H hydrogen bonding to ethers, ketones, amines, and other polar solvents that absorb in this region
2. Intramolecular hydrogen bonding Polyhydroxylic materials	3600–3500	2.78–2.86	Sharp absorption position, dependent upon the H---O bond distance; critical distance for such bonding appears to be ~3.3A
—OH with other functional groups	3200–2500	2.86–4.00	Broad, diffuse band often not easily distinguished; typical of enol systems such as acetoacetic esters, and amides
π-hydrogen bonding	3600–3500	2.78–2.86	Interaction of π-systems such as olefins with hydroxyl proton; useful for structural information

* Summary is based on typical spectral data obtained from compounds in dilute nonpolar solvent (CCl_4 or $CHCl_3$).

Saturated ethers, such as di-*n*-butyl ether (Fig. 5.31), exhibit a characteristic absorption band of high intensity near 1127 cm⁻¹ (8.87μ). This band is assigned to the symmetric C—O—C stretching vibration. On conjugation with olefinic linkages or aromatic groups, the C—O—C asymmetric stretching absorption is shifted to the 1275- to 1200-cm⁻¹ (7.85 to 8.33μ) region. As might be expected in the case of vinyl ethers, the corresponding stretching frequency of the double bond is increased in intensity. For the symmetric ethers, such as di-*n*-butyl ether, the vibration involving a symmetric stretching vibration of the C—O—C group does not appear in the spectrum because of symmetry factors. In the case of the unsaturated ethers, such as

$$\text{---O---CH}_2\text{---CH}_3 \quad \text{or} \quad \text{CH}_2\text{=CH---O---CH}_2\text{---CH}_3$$

the symmetric stretching vibration absorbs in the 1075- to 1020-cm⁻¹ (9.30 to 9.80μ) region. The intensity of this absorption, however, is considerably weaker than the asymmetric stretching vibration.

For diagnostic purposes, the O—CH₃ group on aliphatic and aromatic

2-*t*-butyl-4-methylphenol

ν_{O-H} 3380 cm^{-1}, 2.96 μ

2,4-di-*t*-butyl-6-methylphenol

ν_{O-H} 3570 cm^{-1}, 2.80 μ
(shoulder at 3462 cm^{-1}, 2.89 μ)

2,6-di-*t*-butyl-4-methylphenol

ν_{O-H} 3510 cm^{-1}, 2.85 μ

2,6-di-*t*-butyl-4-cyclohexylphenol

ν_{O-H} 3530 cm^{-1}, 2.83 μ

Fig. 5.29 Typical O—H stretching absorption bands in hindered phenolics. All values were measured in Nujol.

substrates is of particular importance due to its appearance in numerous naturally occurring substances. The CH$_3$ symmetric stretching vibration can usually be distinguished in the 2850- to 2815-cm^{-1} region (3.51 to 3.55 μ). Although other bands for the ether group are present (see Table 5.11), these are generally noncharacteristic because of absorptions from other aliphatic oxygenated molecules in the same regions.

Acetals and ketals. In acetals and ketals the ether band is split into three branches, which are observed in the following frequency regions:

1. 1190 to 1160 cm^{-1} (8.40 to 8.62 μ).
2. 1195 to 1125 cm^{-1} (8.37 to 8.89 μ).
3. 1098 to 1063 cm^{-1} (9.11 to 9.41 μ).

The normal ether frequency splits into three bands, which can be attributed to modes of vibration similar to the asymmetric C—O stretching vibration:

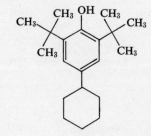

(1)   (2)   (3)

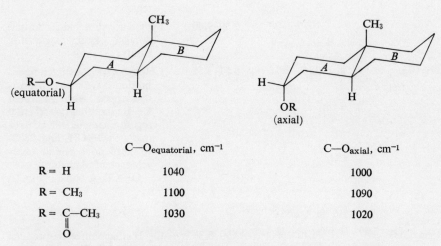

A/B trans

C—O$_{equatorial}$, cm^{-1} C—O$_{axial}$, cm^{-1}

R = H   1040   1000

R = CH$_3$ 1100   1090

R = C—CH$_3$ 1030   1020
    ‖
    O

Fig. 5.30 Example of the change in band position with different configurations.

The vibration 2, in which both oxygen atoms are stretching in phase, results in the most intense absorption band of the three. A fourth band will sometimes be observed in the 1055- to 1035-cm^{-1} region (9.48 to 9.66μ), which

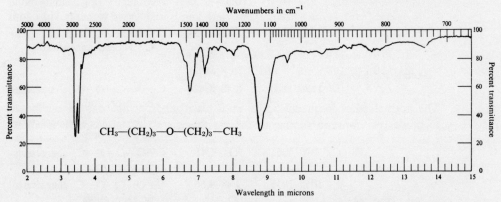

CH$_3$—(CH$_2$)$_3$—O—(CH$_2$)$_3$—CH$_3$

Fig. 5.31 Typical symmetrical aliphatic ether spectrum, di-*n*-butylether (thin film).

Table 5.11. Characteristic Absorptions Due to Ethers and Related Functional Groups

Functional Group	Frequency (cm⁻¹)	Wavelength (μ)	Remarks
Ethers			
Aliphatic	1150–1070	8.69–9.35	C—O—C asymmetric stretching vibration, intense
Aromatic and vinyl	1275–1200	7.85–8.33	C—O—C asymmetric stretching vibration, intense (C=C of vinyl also increased in intensity)
	1075–1020	9.30–9.80	Symmetric stretching vibration (weaker than asymmetric band)
O—CH₃	2850–2815	3.51–3.55	CH₃ symmetrical stretching vibration (asymmetric band is overlapped with saturated C—H vibrations); 2850-cm⁻¹ region characteristic of aromatic —O—CH₃ and 2830- to 2815-cm⁻¹ region characteristic of aliphatic —O—CH₃ group
(epoxides)	3040–3000	3.99–3.33	C—H stretching of the methine group shifted to 3040 cm⁻¹ in strained rings
	3050	3.28	CH₂ stretching vibration of terminal epoxide
	1250	8.00	Symmetrical-ring breathing mode (frequently referred to as the 8μ band)
	950–810	10.53–12.35	Asymmetric ring bending mode (referred to as the 11μ band)
	840–750	11.90–13.33	Called the 12μ band, due to the C—H bending vibration
Acetals and Ketals			
	1190–1160	8.40–8.62	C—O—C—O—C characteristic absorption
	1195–1125	8.37–8.89	C—O—C—O—C characteristic absorption
	1098–1063	9.11–9.41	C—O—C—O—C characteristic absorption
	1055–1035	9.48–9.66	C—O—C—O—C characteristic absorption
	1116–1103	8.96–9.02	Characteristic of acetals *only*

Table 5.11—Cont.

Functional Group	Frequency (cm⁻¹)	Wavelength (μ)	Remarks
Peroxides C—O—O—C			
Aliphatic	890–820	11.24–12.19	Both aliphatic and aromatic absorption are very weak and difficult to assign with certainty
Aromatic	Near 1000		

may be assigned to the symmetric vibration

$$\begin{array}{c} \text{O—C} \\ \diagup \\ \text{C} \\ \diagdown \\ \text{O—C} \end{array}$$

In addition to the bands mentioned above for both acetals and ketals, there is a characteristic band in the spectra of acetals in the 1116- to 1103-cm⁻¹ (8.96 to 9.02μ) region. This band is due to a C—H deformation vibration perturbed by the neighboring C—O group. This band is strong and always present in spectra of acetals, and hence may be used to differentiate between acetals and ketals.

Peroxides.   A characteristic frequency of the O—O peroxide linkage is not very strong and cannot be assigned with any certainty. Tertiary hydroperoxides and tertiary peroxides exhibit strong absorption in the 920- to 830-cm⁻¹ (10.87 to 12.05μ) region. This has been assigned to the O—O stretching vibration, but later studies have indicated that this band should have been assigned to the group skeletal frequency.

$$\begin{array}{c} \text{C} \\ | \\ \text{C—C—O} \\ | \\ \text{C} \end{array}$$

The overall frequency region where one may expect the O—O stretching band to be observed is 1000 to 830cm⁻¹ (10.00 to 12.05μ).

Table 5.11 summarizes the absorption characteristics of the ether functional group and related molecular species. Compare the characteristic frequencies listed with those found in other tables for oxygenated systems (for example, compare Table 5.10 and Table 5.11).

5.4.4 Amines, imines, and ammonium salts.   Amines as a chemical species involving the N—H bond should parallel the previous discussion concerning the hydroxyl group (Sec. 5.4.2). As well, the —NH₂ and —NH₃ groups as vibrating units should be closely related to the —CH₂— and —CH₃ groups, respectively (Sec. 5.3.1). The differences in mass and polarity between nitrogen and both carbon and oxygen should be reflected in the spectral characteristics of the nitrogenous bases, but in principle similar correlations and assignments should be possible.

Nitrogen-hydrogen stretching vibrations.   Primary amines, both aliphatic and aromatic, exhibit stretching vibrations of the —NH_2 similar to those of the methylene group (CH_2). An asymmetric N—H stretching absorption is observed near 3490 cm^{-1} (2.87μ). The symmetric N—H stretching band absorbs near 3400 cm^{-1} (2.94μ). These frequencies are normally related to the nonhydrogen-bonded —NH_2 group and show similarities to the changes observed in hydroxyl absorption accompanying changes in concentration, solvent, and environment. The shift due to these interactions is generally smaller than the corresponding hydroxyl shifts, but is easily observed by using the normal experimental precautions outlined in Sec. 5.4.2. The symmetric band is fairly constant in position when involved in hydrogen bonding with hydroxylic materials. However, when it is not bonded, its position varies with increasing concentration. The shift in the band is toward lower wavenumber, indicating that —N—H----N— association is taking place. The fact that no change is observed when hydrogen bonding is with hydroxylic materials is good evidence for the greater strength of the hydroxyl-nitrogen hydrogen-bonded system (—O—H----N—). The intermolecular hydrogen bonding of amines usually gives rise to a fairly complex, medium-intensity band in the 3300- to 3000-cm^{-1} region (3.03 to 3.33μ). Usually the band position and intensity can be used to distinguish the amino group from the hydroxyl group on preliminary examination of the spectrum (cf. spectra in Fig. 5.32).

Secondary amines exhibit a single band in the 3450- to 3310-cm^{-1} region (2.90 to 3.02μ). In aromatic amines, the N—H stretching band is usually found at the high-frequency end of this range (3450 cm^{-1}), whereas the aliphatic secondary amines absorb at the lower end of this range (3350 to 3310 cm^{-1}). Cyclic structures behave similarly; however, the N—H stretching band in compounds such as piperidine and tetrahydropyrrole is especially weak. Aromatic heterocyclic structures, on the other hand, behave quite differently. The N—H vibration is considerably more intense and is observed at slightly higher frequency (3490 cm^{-1}) than that of the saturated systems. However, in both cases, hydrogen bonding shifts the N—H stretching band to lower frequencies. Imines of the type C=N—H exhibit a similar N—H stretching band in the 3400- to 3300-cm^{-1} region (2.94 to 3.03μ). The imino group is generally confirmed by the weakly absorbing C=N stretching vibration in the 1690- to 1640-cm^{-1} region (5.92 to 6.10μ). It should be noted that this region is also the region for carbonyl (C=O) stretching bands (Sec. 5.4.5). However, the carbonyl absorptions are generally far more intense than the imino C=N stretching absorptions (this is to be expected on the basis of polarity differences between the two groups).

It should have been noted throughout this discussion and will be noted in the discussion to follow that tertiary amines have noticeably few infrared absorptions and therefore are difficult to detect by direct techniques. However, as will be pointed out in further discussion, simple salt-forming reactions

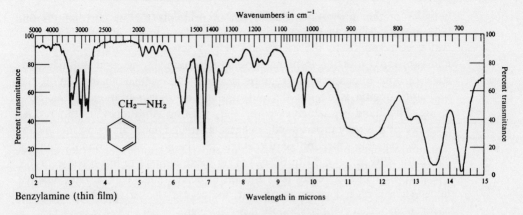

Benzylamine (thin film)

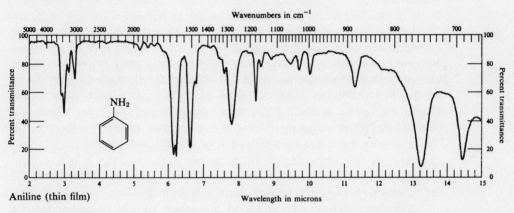

Aniline (thin film)

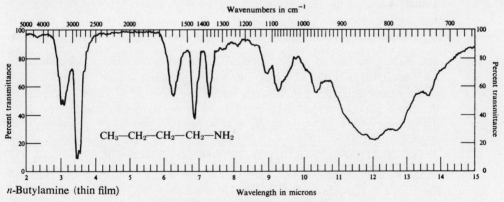

n-Butylamine (thin film)

Fig. 5.32 Spectra typical of amines.

(followed by spectral examination of the salt) can be used to establish the presence of the tertiary nitrogen group.

Nitrogen-hydrogen bending vibrations. As noted in Fig. 5.32, an absorption appears in the 1640- to 1560-cm^{-1} region (6.10 to 6.41μ) and a second broad, diffuse absorption can be seen in the 900- to 650-cm^{-1} region

(11.11 to 15.38μ). Both bands arise from N—H deformation (for this reason, they are not found in tertiary amines). The band found in the 1600-cm^{-1} region corresponds to the methylene (CH$_2$) scissoring vibration (Fig. 5.6) and is referred to as an in-plane bending vibration. Its position is fairly constant in both aliphatic and aromatic amines. The second absorption in the 750-cm^{-1} region is due to the out-of-plane bending vibration of the NH$_2$ group. This band is analogous to the CH$_2$ twisting vibration (Fig. 5.6). The presence of this very broad band is characteristic of the primary amino group.

The bending vibration of the single N—H group of secondary amines (1580 to 1490 cm^{-1}, 6.33 to 6.71μ) is far more difficult to use for interpretative purposes. In most cases it is difficult to detect, since it is a weak absorption. When a phenyl group is present, the region is overlapped by aromatic absorptions, often completely obscuring the band.

Carbon-nitrogen stretching vibrations.   As in alcohols, the carbon-nitrogen stretching vibration is quite similar to the carbon-carbon stretching vibration. However, due to polarity, its intensity is significantly enhanced. In the case of aliphatic substituents, the C—N stretching vibration is observed in the 1230- to 1030-cm^{-1} region (8.13 to 9.71μ). In tertiary amines, this vibration is usually a doublet due to asymmetric and symmetric vibrational possibilities. When an aromatic ring is present, two bands are observed: a high-frequency band due to conjugation of the electron pair of the nitrogen atom with the ring, imparting double-bond character to the C—N bond (1360 to 1250 cm^{-1}, 7.36 to 8.00μ) and a lower-frequency band (1280 to 1180 cm^{-1}, 7.81 to 8.48μ) due to aliphatic C—N stretching.

The characteristic absorptions of the amino group are summarized in Table 5.12.

Ammonium salts.   Salts of the type, R—$\overset{+}{\text{N}}$H$_3$, R$_2$—$\overset{+}{\text{N}}$H$_2$, R$_3$$\overset{+}{\text{N}}$—H, and R$_4$$\overset{+}{\text{N}}$ give rise to useful spectral correlations for amine identification. As is apparent from the foregoing discussion, primary, secondary, and tertiary amine characterization can be difficult on the basis of a single spectrum of the amine because of the weak absorptions of the particular amine type or of the absence of characteristic bands. It is therefore useful in nitrogen-containing systems to resort to simple chemical means to first convert the amino group to an amine salt (usually anhydrous HCl in an inert solvent to form the amine hydrochloride). From Table 5.13, it is readily observed that the salt bands due to the primary amine overlap the carbon-hydrogen stretching band region. However, the tertiary amine gives rise to a characteristic band clearly separated from the C—H absorption. The secondary amine, on the other hand, falls intermediary, and therefore is distinguishable from the primary by the absorption in the 1600- to 1500-cm^{-1} region (Table 5.13). The immonium group, as well, is clearly differentiated by the appearance of the 2000-cm^{-1} (5.00μ) band, which is not present in the tertiary amine salts. This information coupled with information regarding the N—H bands of the free amine provide the chemist with enough information to distinguish the three amine types. A typical ammonium salt spectrum is shown in Fig. 5.33. The ammonium salt bands are summarized in Table 5.13.

Additional discussion of the amino group will be presented in Chap. 7, on the near-infrared region.

Table 5.12.   Characteristic Absorption Bands Found in Amines and Imines

Functional Group	Frequency (cm⁻¹)	Wavelength (μ)	Remarks
Amines			
—NH₂ (nonhydrogen-bonded)	3550–3420	2.82–2.92	N—H asymmetric stretching, weak
	3450–3320	2.90–3.01	N—H symmetric stretching, weak
	1640–1560	6.10–6.41	In-plane bending, strong
	900–650	11.11–15.38	Out-of-plane bending, broad diffuse band
—NH (nonhydrogen-bonded)	3450–3310	2.90–3.02	N—H stretching, weak
	1580–1490	6.33–6.71	N—H bending, weak, sometimes undetected because of overlap with aromatic ring bands
—NH and —NH₂ (hydrogen-bonded)			
Intermolecular	3300–3000	3.03–3.33	N—H stretching, stronger than the nonbonded vibration; sometimes quite complex (appears as more than a single band)
Intramolecular	3500–3200	2.86–3.13	Similar to intermolecular bands; usually quite complex
C—N (saturated carbon)			
C—NH₂	1230–1030	8.13–9.71	C—N stretching (a doublet in tertiary amines)
C—N—C	1150–1100	8.70–9.09	C—N stretching
C—N (unsaturated carbon; vinyl or phenyl)	1360–1250 1280–1180	7.38–8.00 7.81–8.48	A doublet due to double bond character of the C—N bond when conjugated
CH₃—N	1370–1310	7.30–7.64	
Imines			
R—C≡N—H	3400–3300 1590–1500	2.94–3.33 6.29–6.67	N—H stretching, weak N—H bending
R—C≡N— (aliphatic)	Near 1670	5.99	C≡N stretching
R—C≡N— (aromatic)	Near 1640	6.10	C≡N stretching
R—C≡N— (extended conj.)	Near 1618	6.18	C≡N stretching

Table 5.13. Characteristic Absorption Bands Found in Ammonium Compounds

Functional Group	Frequency (cm^{-1})	Wavelength (μ)	Remarks
Ammonium Ion			
$\overset{+}{N}H_4$	3300–3030	3.03–3.30	$\overset{+}{N}H_4$ stretching vibrations
	1430–1390	7.00–7.20	$\overset{+}{N}H_4$ bending vibrations
Amine Salts			
$-\overset{+}{N}H_3$	Near 3000	3.33	$\overset{+}{N}H_3$ asymmetric and $\overset{+}{N}H_3$ symmetric stretching as a broad band overlapping C—H stretching bands
	Near 2500	4.00	Overtones (sometimes absent)
	Near 2000	5.00	Overtones (sometimes absent)
	1600–1575	6.25–6.35	$\overset{+}{N}H_3$ asymmetric bending
	Near 1500	6.67	$\overset{+}{N}H_3$ symmetric bending (analogous to CH$_3$ bendings)
$-\overset{+}{N}H_2$	2700–2250	3.70–4.44	Broad, stretching band (usually a group of bands)
	Near 2000	5.00	Overtone, usually absent
	1600–1575	6.25–6.35	$\overset{+}{N}H_2$ scissoring (analogous to CH$_2$ scissoring)
$-\overset{+}{N}H$	2700–2250	3.70–4.44	N—H stretching plus overtone and combination bands; clearly distinguishable from C—H vibrations
$\overset{+}{N}$	—	—	No characteristic bands
Imine Salts			
$-C{=}\overset{+}{N}{-}H$	2500–2300	4.00–4.34	N—H stretching; overtones and combinations; a group of broad, sharp bands
	2200–1800	4.55–5.56	One or more medium intensity bands; clearly distinguishes imine salts from amine salts
	Near 1680	5.95	C$={=}\overset{+}{N}$ stretching vibration

5.4.5 Carbonyl compounds. An overwhelming amount of investigation has been centered about the infrared spectrum of carbonyl compounds. Undoubtedly, this is because the carbonyl group has wide and varied substituent-group attachments of interest to the organic chemist and because it was

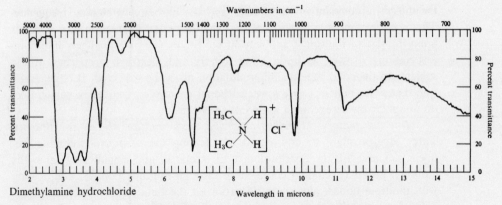

Dimethylamine hydrochloride

Fig. 5.33   Typical ammonium salt spectrum.

recognized in very early correlative work that this particular group acts more like a vibration localized in an individual bond. Aldehydes, ketones, carboxylic acids, esters, amides, lactones, lactams, and anhydrides as well as other carbonyl containing materials all absorb in the 1905- to 1550-cm^{-1} region (5.25 to 6.45μ). Since the various factors affecting the position of the carbonyl-group absorption band have been extensively investigated and numerous studies can be drawn from the literature for exemplification, a brief summary of these factors will assist the reader in understanding the correlation of spectra with structure. Since it is impossible here to develop all the possible details, the reader should consult the references at the end of the chapter for supplementary reading.

Factors that influence band shifts.   As pointed out in Chap. 4, a number of factors must be considered when preparing a compound for spectral study. In previous sections, particular note was made of the effect of saturated versus unsaturated substituents as these groups affected band positions. It has been clearly recognized that the carbonyl group stretching vibration is affected by the following factors:

1. External factors (cf. Chap. 4).
2. Internal factors:
   a. Electronic and steric nature of the substituents.
   b. Hydrogen bonding (cf. Secs. 5.4.2 and 5.4.4).
   c. Vibrational coupling.

External factors.   The carbonyl stretching band is not quite so sensitive to changes in physical state as the hydroxyl group, but is certainly more sensitive than most other groups. Generally the highest recorded frequency is observed in the vapor state. In the liquid state, dilute solutions in nonpolar solvents such as carbon tetrachloride or carbon disulfide give the highest recorded carbonyl stretching-band frequency value (although still lower than that obtained in the vapor state). In more polar solvents, molecules capable of ready distortion of the π electron cloud (i.e., conjugated systems) show appreciable shifts in the carbonyl band. Apparently no good correlation exists between the dielectric constant of the solvent and the carbonyl stretching frequency. This is understandable if one considers that any such interaction also depends upon the size of the solute and solvent molecules (i.e., steric effects inhibiting association) as well as upon other kinetic and electrical properties of the solvent. In the solid state a similar situation might be expected. It is generally true that polar matrices give lower carbonyl absorption frequency values than do nonpolar ones (excluded ionic lattice effects).

   Internal factors: (1) Electronic and steric nature of the substituents. Three factors might be considered as affecting the carbonyl stretching frequency. These are the distribution of electrons in and neighboring upon the carbonyl group (excluding conjugation through multiple bonds), conjugation with multiple bonds, and steric distortion of the bond angles. Actually, such a division is purely arbitrary, since any angle distortion will necessarily change the electron distribution in the region of the carbonyl group (as will, of course, conjugation). Since it is extremely difficult to evaluate the magnitude of such factors, the present discussion must be recognized as a qualitative approach to ascertaining some idea of the expected effect upon the carbonyl stretching frequency.

   In terms of the organic structure involved, the force constant (or electron distribution) of the carbonyl group is a composite of the following simple resonance structures:

$$\begin{array}{cccc}
\overset{R}{\underset{R'}{\diagdown}}C{=}O & \overset{R}{\underset{R}{\diagdown}}\overset{+}{C}{-}\overset{-}{O} & \overset{\overset{+}{R}}{\underset{R'}{\diagdown}}C{-}\overset{-}{O} & \overset{R}{\underset{\overset{R'}{+}}{\diagdown}}C{-}\overset{-}{O} \\
\text{I} & \text{II} & \text{III} & \text{IV}
\end{array}$$

The actual contribution of any particular structure (I through IV) will depend on the ability of groups R and R′ to attract or repel electrons (i.e., the relative electronegativities of R and R′). If the contribution of II is significantly greater than III and IV, the position of the carbonyl frequency should be at higher wavenumber than a carbonyl system in which I is the major contributing structure to the electron distribution in the C=O bond system. On the other hand, if structures III and IV are significant factors in the electron distribution within the carbonyl group, then the band position should shift to lower frequencies as a result of the increased single-bond character of the C=O bond system. As a first approximation this approach (when structures I through IV can be qualitatively evaluated from other data) is useful in roughly correlating a wide variety of carbonyl types.

   For most comparisons, a simple dialkyl ketone is arbitrarily chosen to represent structure I. For example, diethyl ketone

$$CH_3{-}CH_2{-}\overset{\overset{\text{O}}{\|}}{C}{-}CH_2{-}CH_3$$

exhibits an intense carbonyl stretching band at 1715 cm^{-1} (5.83μ) similar to most other dialkyl ketones. Using this frequency as a standard, it is possible to qualitatively deduce other substituted-carbonyl stretching frequencies based on the expected relative contributions of structures II through IV. For example,

$$\begin{array}{ccc} R & R & R \\ \diagdown & \diagdown & \diagdown \\ C{=}O, & C{=}O, & C{=}O \\ \diagup & \diagup & \diagup \\ R''O & Cl & H_2N \end{array}$$

an ester, acid chloride, and amide, respectively, all have the R' group replaced with groups of markedly different electronegativities as compared to the alkyl substituent. In the case of the ester, any increased positive charge on the carbon atom of the carbonyl group would tend to shift the carbonyl stretching frequency to a higher value (structure IIa having a significant contribution to the electron distribution in the carbonyl group). The opposite effect, a major contribution from structure IIb, would be expected to be small in an ester. Similarly, structure IIa' of the acid chloride,

IIa
$$\begin{array}{c} R \\ \diagdown \\ \overset{+}{C}{-}\overset{-}{O} \\ \diagup \overset{\delta+}{} \\ R''O \\ \overset{\delta-}{} \end{array}$$
$\leftrightarrow$
$$\begin{array}{c} R \\ \diagdown \\ C{-}\overset{-}{O} \\ \diagup\diagup \\ R''O \\ + \end{array}$$
IIb

IIa'
$$\begin{array}{c} R \\ \diagdown \\ \overset{+}{C}{-}\overset{-}{O} \\ \diagup \overset{\delta+}{} \\ Cl \\ \overset{\delta-}{} \end{array}$$
$\leftrightarrow$
$$\begin{array}{c} R \\ \diagdown \\ C{-}\overset{-}{O} \\ \diagup\diagup \\ Cl \\ + \end{array}$$
IIb'

IIa''
$$\begin{array}{c} R \\ \diagdown \\ \overset{+}{C}{-}\overset{-}{O} \\ \diagup \overset{\delta+}{} \\ H_2N \\ \overset{\delta-}{} \end{array}$$
$\leftrightarrow$
$$\begin{array}{c} R \\ \diagdown \\ C{-}\overset{-}{O} \\ \diagup\diagup \\ H_2N \\ + \end{array}$$
IIb''

should be a major factor in the electron distribution of the carbonyl group rather than structure IIb'. Indeed, carbonyl groups generally follow this qualitative correlation. Esters are generally found to absorb in the 1736-cm^{-1} (5.76μ) region. Acid chlorides are at even higher observed frequencies (1810 cm^{-1}, 5.53μ). In contrast, the amido group should exhibit an opposite effect due to the increased basicity of the nitrogen atom. Structure IIb'' would be expected to have a pronounced effect on the observed carbonyl frequency. In this case, the shift should be toward lower frequencies than those observed for the dialkyl ketones, since the double-bond character of the carbonyl group is diminished. In simple aliphatic amides the carbonyl absorption is observed near 1680 cm^{-1} (5.95μ), in accord with this qualitative picture.

Although this approach is useful for rough correlations, the reader should be cautioned not to overemphasize such a qualitative approach in the interpretation of infrared spectra. Although useful in many instances, subtle differences in molecular structure of organic compounds, particularly steric phenomena, tend to limit the application of correlations of this type.

In addition to electronic factors previously discussed, conjugation affects the position of carbonyl absorption. As previously noted, the carbonyl stretching vibration of simple aliphatic ketones absorbs near 1715 cm^{-1} (5.83μ). Conjugation of the carbonyl group with a double bond lowers the frequency by about 35 cm^{-1} (about 0.1μ in this region). Aryl group conjugation also lowers the carbonyl frequency, but to a lesser degree than double-bond conjugation. In the case of double-bond conjugation, the intensity of the C=C group is greatly enhanced, giving rise to two strong bands in the 6.0μ region. Generally one band, owing to the carbonyl absorption, is below 6.0μ, and a second slightly less intense absorption appears above 6.0μ as a result of the carbon-carbon double-bond stretching vibration.

Steric hindrance affects the frequency of the carbonyl band in conjugated systems. For example:

Va   CH$_3$—（ring, CH$_3$ ortho top, CH$_3$ ortho bottom）—C（=O, H），   C=O frequency = 1680 cm^{-1} (5.95μ)

Vb   CH$_3$—（ring, CH$_3$ ortho top, CH$_3$ ortho bottom）—C（=O, CH$_3$），   C=O frequency = 1700 cm^{-1} (5.88μ)

The coplanarity of the conjugate system in Va is maintained by the small steric interaction of the aldehydic hydrogen with the *ortho*-methyl groups. In Vb, however, the acetyl group cannot maintain coplanarity, and the effectiveness of the conjugation is severely limited (i.e., the π overlap possible in Va is not possible in Vb, since the carbonyl group does not lie in the plane of the aromatic ring).

The effect of steric strain is most clearly demonstrated in small ring carbonyl compounds. Table 5.14 summarizes the shift of the carbonyl group with ring size for cyclic ketones, lactones (cyclic esters) and lactams (cyclic amides). As seen from Table 5.14, constriction of the bond angle shifts the frequency to a higher value. The utility of this correlation to the chemist is important. The practical problem of establishing ring size of carbonyl compounds in complex molecules can be a long and exhausting task by chemical methods. However, the infrared spectrum clearly distinguishes ring size in those systems possessing a carbonyl group. Unsaturation in conjugation with the carbonyl group, causes shifts to lower frequencies. However, in conju-

Table 5.14.   Effect of Ring Size on the Position of the Carbonyl Stretching Vibration in Ketones, Lactones, and Lactams*

	Carbonyl Stretching Vibration					
	Ketones		Lactones		Amides	
Ring Size	(cm⁻¹)	(μ)	(cm⁻¹)	(μ)	(cm⁻¹)	(μ)
4	1780	5.62	1818	5.50	1745	5.73
5	1745	5.73	1770	5.65	1700	5.88
6	1715	5.83	1735	5.76	1677	5.96
7	1705	5.87	1727	5.79	1675	5.97

* Values given are approximate only; variations due to α-substituents are averaged to obtain a value for the effect of the ring.

gated carbonyl-containing ring systems the correlation of steric strain or ring size with carbonyl position is still possible.

In the case of α-halocycloalkanones, the position of the halogen atom adjacent to the carbonyl group affects the position of carbonyl absorption. It is expected from our foregoing discussion of electrical effects that presence of an α-halogen should shift the carbonyl absorption to higher frequencies; e.g., in acetone, C=O absorption is at 1715 cm⁻¹ (5.83μ), whereas monochloroacetone absorbs at 1724 cm⁻¹ (5.80μ). The general magnitude of the shift increases with the increasing dipole of the carbon-halogen bond (F > Cl > Br > I). However, the magnitude of the effect is also related to the geometry of the halogen with respect to the carbonyl, as illustrated in Fig. 5.34.

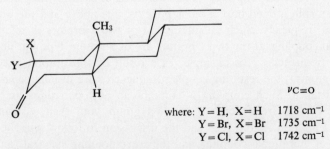

where: Y = H   1718 cm⁻¹
       Y = Br   1733 cm⁻¹
       Y = Cl   1738 cm⁻¹

where: Y = H, X = H   1718 cm⁻¹
       Y = Br, X = Br   1735 cm⁻¹
       Y = Cl, X = Cl   1742 cm⁻¹

Fig. 5.34   Effect of α-halogen substitution on the position of of the carbonyl stretching absorption band.

The halogen atom located axially to the carbonyl group causes only a slight displacement. But equatorially, the carbonyl frequency is increased by about 20 cm^{-1}. Although the interpretation of this phenomenon is still open to some question, the observation is a useful one for establishing the conformation of α-halocycloalkanones.

(2) *Hydrogen bonding.*   When the carbonyl group is hydrogen-bonded with a hydroxylic substance, the carbonyl stretching absorption is displaced to lower frequencies. The association of a hydrogen with the carbonyl group tends to decrease the double-bond character of the carbonyl

$$\overset{\delta^+}{C}-\overset{\delta^-}{O}\cdots\overset{\delta^+}{H}-\overset{\delta^-}{O}$$

thereby shifting the absorption to a lower-frequency value. Perhaps the best example of this phenomenon can be drawn from hydrogen bonding in carboxylic acids. The free carboxylic acid carbonyl stretching frequency appears near 1760 cm^{-1} (5.68μ) for most aliphatic acids. However, in the liquid state or solid state most acids exhibit a strong carbonyl absorption in the 1700-cm^{-1} region (5.88μ), which is due to dimerization of acid molecules (Fig. 5.35).

In addition, a broad absorption band in the 920-cm^{-1} region (10.87μ), characteristic of the hydrogen-bonded dimer, is also observed. This band has been attributed to the out-of-plane bending vibration of the dimeric species.

Enolization of β-diketones, β-ketoacids, and β-ketoamides exhibit similar changes in carbonyl frequencies, owing to internal hydrogen bonding:

The high-intensity broad band attributed to the enol is most easily assigned to the conjugated chelate as a unit, although it may be the result of more than one molecular species. The keto-enol equilibration of these systems can be effectively studied in the infrared region.

(3) *Vibrational coupling.*   The interaction of two vibrating units suitably located can split a band into two components, one above and the other below a common frequency. Such an interaction of two vibrators is referred to as vibrational coupling. If the two vibrators are of a similar type but do not have the same frequencies (for example, as a result of substitution effects at the α-carbon atoms), the resulting coupled frequencies are usually separated by a greater distance. Such coupling is common to acyl peroxides and acid anhydrides. Typical frequencies of coupled groups and their assignments are shown in Fig. 5.36. Table 5.15 and the discussion to follow will show further examples of vibrational coupling and the corresponding spectral ramifications of value in the interpretation of infrared spectra.

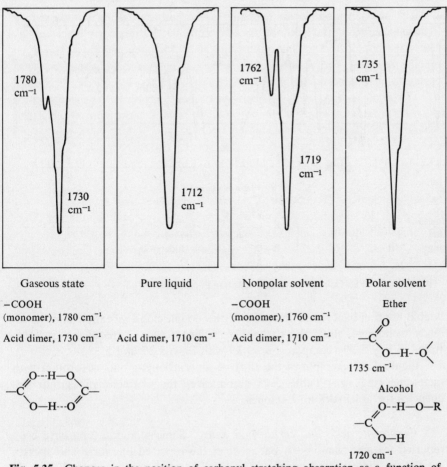

| Gaseous state | Pure liquid | Nonpolar solvent | Polar solvent |

−COOH
(monomer), 1780 cm⁻¹

Acid dimer, 1730 cm⁻¹   Acid dimer, 1710 cm⁻¹   Acid dimer, 1710 cm⁻¹

−COOH
(monomer), 1760 cm⁻¹

Ether

1735 cm⁻¹

Alcohol

1720 cm⁻¹

Fig. 5.35 Changes in the position of carbonyl stretching absorption as a function of the state of the sample exemplified by propionic acid.

Aldehydes and ketones.   Aldehydes and ketones exhibit almost identical carbonyl absorption frequencies. Although the aldehyde group usually absorbs at 10 cm⁻¹ higher frequencies than do the corresponding ketonic absorptions, the carbonyl absorption region cannot be used for simple differentiation of the two types. In order to differentiate the two, the C—H stretching frequency region must be examined. The doublet at the low-frequency end (high wavelength) of the C—H stretching region is generally characteristic of the aldehydic group (the doublet shows near 2820 cm⁻¹ and 2720 cm⁻¹, i.e., 3.55 and 3.67μ, respectively). The band at 3.67μ is usually sharp and clearly separated from other C—H absorptions. This band therefore can be used as a good characteristic group frequency for distinguishing aldehydes from ketones. Figure 5.37 indicates this difference with simple aliphatic aldehyde and ketone spectra.

The effect of conjugation on the carbonyl position is clearly shown in Fig. 5.38. Compare the spectrum of acetophenone, benzophenone, and benzaldehyde with the aliphatic examples in Fig. 5.37. Conjugation with a

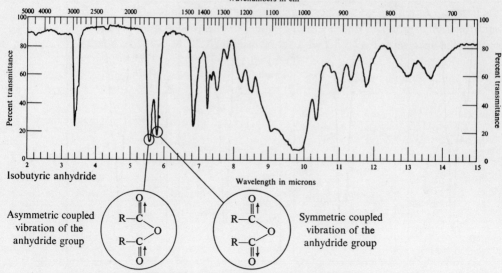

Fig. 5.36   Vibrational coupling in anhydrides.

double bond enhances the intensity of the double-bond vibration and, as already mentioned, shifts the carbonyl vibration to lower frequency, as illustrated in Fig. 5.39 (compare Fig. 5.39 with Figs. 5.37 and 5.38).

Figure 5.40 exemplifies the shift of the carbonyl-group absorption with increasing ring size. Table 5.15 summarizes the characteristic group frequencies for aldehydes and ketones.

Carboxylic acids and carboxylate salts.   Some scattered data have been reported for acid monomers, but most of the reported literature and spectra are for the dimeric acid species. The O—H stretching vibration of the acid monomer absorbs near 3595 cm^{-1} (2.78μ). The dimeric form, however, exhibits a broad O—H stretching band in the 3000- to 2500-cm^{-1} region (3.33 to 4.00μ). This band usually overlaps the C—H stretching region and is typical of carboxylic acids. The carbonyl frequency of the monomer (1760 cm^{-1}, 5.68μ) also is observed at higher frequencies than that of the dimeric form (1710 cm^{-1}, 5.85μ). In addition to these two absorptions, which are easily interpreted as due to the carboxylic acid group, the 920-cm^{-1} (10.87μ) broad band due to O—H out-of-plane bending of the dimer adds confirming interpretative evidence for the acid structure. Figure 5.41 exemplifies typical aliphatic and aromatic acid spectra. Compare these curves with other carbonyl-containing compounds.

As a salt, the carboxyl group changes markedly. As might be expected, the stretching vibrations of the carboxylate ion (—CO$_2^-$) should parallel those found in other three-atom vibrators (cf. the methylene group or amino group). Indeed, this is found to be the case. Figure 5.42 indicates a typical carboxylate spectrum together with the graphic representations of the asymmetric and symmetric vibrations due to the carboxylate group.

Esters. Often the ester spectrum is misinterpreted as that for the ketonic functional group by the beginning student. The reader should carefully contrast the spectra in Fig. 5.43 with those in Figs. 5.37 to 5.39. In general, the ester carbonyl stretching absorption is at higher frequency than the corresponding ketonic species. This absorption is usually found near 1735

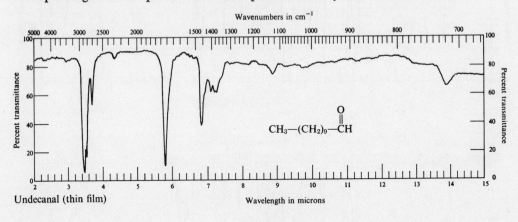

Undecanal (thin film)

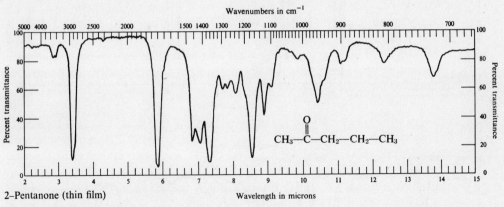

2-Pentanone (thin film)

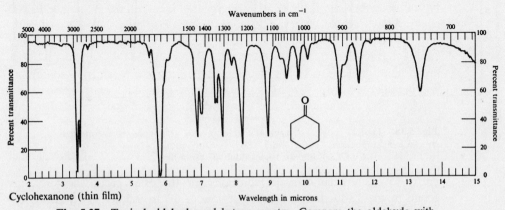

Cyclohexanone (thin film)

Fig. 5.37 Typical aldehyde and ketone spectra. Compare the aldehyde with the ketones and note the difference in the 3 to 4μ region.

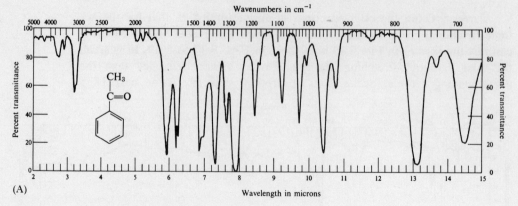

(A)

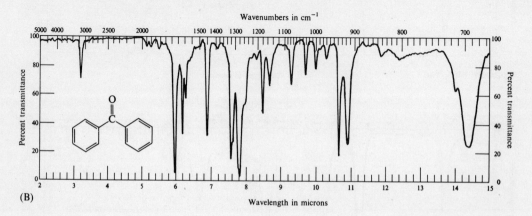

(B)

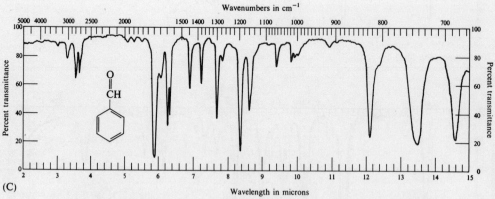

(C)

Fig. 5.38 Typical spectra of aromatic ketones and aldehydes as exemplified by (A) acetophenone (thin film), (B) benzophenone (as a solution in CCl₄), and (C) benzaldehyde (thin film).

cm⁻¹ (5.76μ). Characteristic vibrations for the ester group, however, are found in the 1300- to 1050-cm⁻¹ region (7.69 to 9.52μ). Two strong absorptions appear in this region as a result of the asymmetric and symmetric vibration of the C—O—C group of the ester (see Sec. 5.4.3 for characteristic

C—O—C absorptions of ethers). The asymmetric band (the higher-frequency band of the two) is usually stronger than the carbonyl stretching frequency and is quite broad (compare with ketonic spectra). This band is quite characteristic of the ester functional group (see Table 5.14 for detailed assignments).

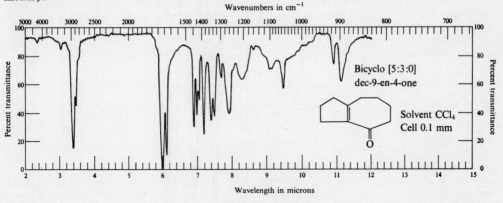

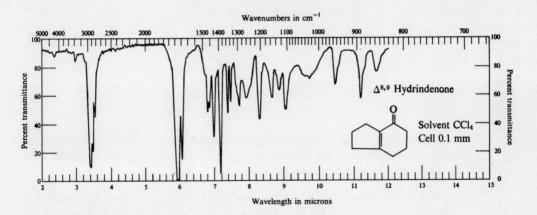

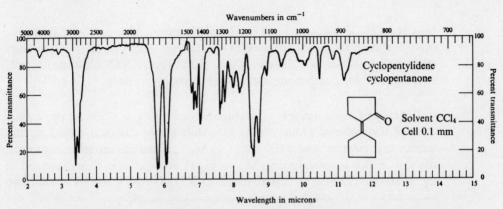

Fig. 5.39 Effect of conjugation on the position of carbonyl absorption and on the intensity of the olefinic stretching.

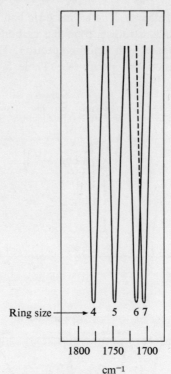

Ring size ——▶ 4   5   6 7

1800   1750   1700

cm⁻¹

Fig. 5.40 Effect of ring size on the position of carbonyl absorption.

The effect of unsaturation depends on the position of attachment of the unsaturated group. In the case of phenyl or olefinic conjugation with the ester

carbonyl (—CH=CH—$\overset{\overset{\textstyle O}{\|}}{C}$—) the carbonyl band is shifted to lower frequency, 1720 cm⁻¹ (5.81μ). However, in nonconjugated vinyl-type esters

(—CH=CH—O—$\overset{\overset{\textstyle O}{\|}}{C}$—), such as aromatic esters, the carbonyl stretching band is shifted to higher frequencies, near 1760 cm⁻¹ (5.68μ). Other correlations are shown in Tables 5.14 and 5.15. Figure 5.43 illustrates typical ester spectra for comparison with other carbonyl spectra.

Acyl and aroyl halides. Substitution of a halogen atom on the carbon atom of the carbonyl group results in a shift of the carbonyl stretching frequency to a position near 1800 cm⁻¹ (5.56μ). When unsaturation is present, the shift is not so pronounced; the carbonyl absorption is then observed in the 1780- to 1750-cm⁻¹ region (5.62 to 5.71μ). Aroyl halides exhibit two

Fig. 5.41 Typical spectra of carboxylic acids. Note the position of the carbonyl stretching band as a function of structure.

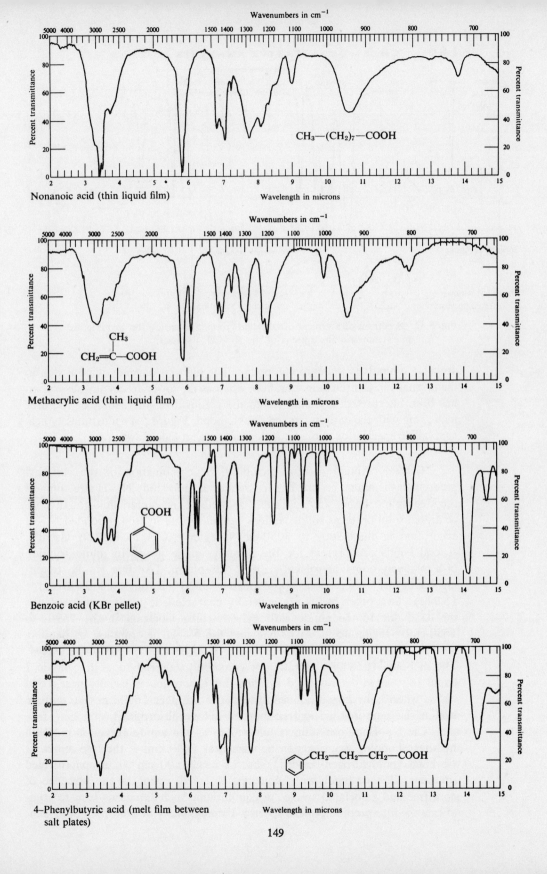

Nonanoic acid (thin liquid film)

Methacrylic acid (thin liquid film)

Benzoic acid (KBr pellet)

4-Phenylbutyric acid (melt film between salt plates)

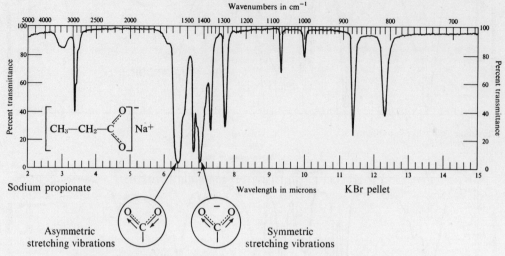

Fig. 5.42   Spectrum of a typical carboxylate group. Shown are the asymmetric and symmetric absorptions of the $R—CO_2^-$ species.

absorption bands in the carbonyl region. The higher-frequency band is due to the normal $C\!\!=\!\!O$ stretching vibration, whereas the lower-frequency absorption has been interpreted as being due to the conjugative interaction of the aromatic ring with the carbon-oxygen double bond. Figure 5.44 illustrates typical acid halide spectra for aliphatic and aromatic acid halide systems.

Amides.   Amide spectra exemplify the combination of the carbonyl group with the amino group. The techniques used to study N—H stretching of the free amino group are applicable as well to the amido linkage. In concentrated solution or as solids, amides exhibit typical hydrogen-bonded N—H absorption in the 3200- to 3050-cm^{-1} region (3.13 to 3.28μ). Usually, several bands are present for the primary amide group in dilute solution of a relatively nonpolar solvent such as chloroform. Two free N—H stretching bands are observed at approximately 3500 (2.86μ) and 3400 cm^{-1} (2.94μ). Two other bands are generally characteristic of the amido group: the band due to the amide carbonyl stretching vibration in the 1690- to 1650-cm^{-1} region (5.92 to 6.06μ) and the N—H deformation or bending absorption between 1640 and 1600 cm^{-1} (6.10 and 6.25μ, respectively). The carbonyl stretching vibration is commonly referred to as the amide I band. In nonhydrogen-bonded systems this absorption is usually near 1690 cm^{-1}, whereas hydrogen-bonded absorptions are near 1650 cm^{-1} (compare similar shifts on bonded and nonbonded ketone absorption).

The N—H deformation is referred to as the amide II vibration. With hydrogen bonding the vibration appears near 1640 cm^{-1}; the free amide II vibration (nonhydrogen-bonded) absorbs near 1600 cm^{-1}. In concentrated solutions, all four bands are frequently observed, owing to the presence of both free and associated species in equilibrium. Such situations tend to complicate the interpretation of the spectra. Usually, study of both the dilute solu-

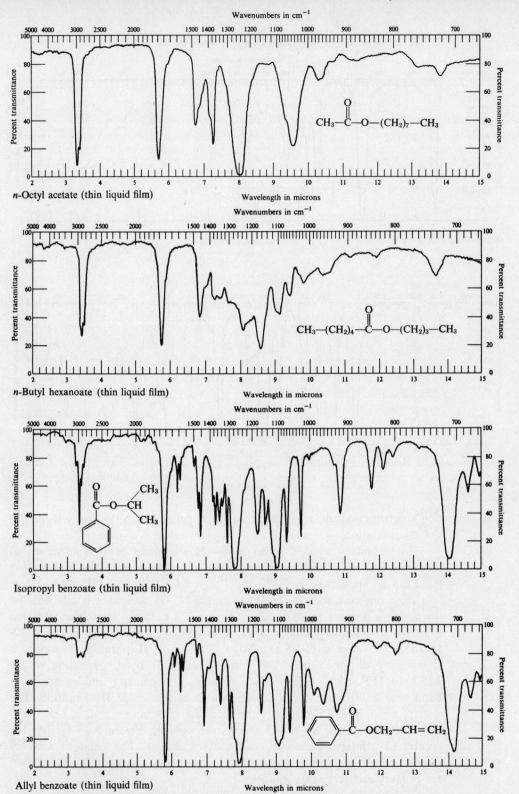

Fig. 5.43 Typical spectra of esters. Note the position of the carbonyl stretching band as a function of structure.

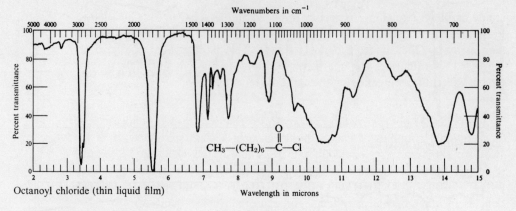

Octanoyl chloride (thin liquid film)

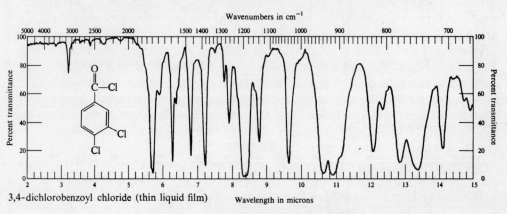

3,4-dichlorobenzoyl chloride (thin liquid film)

Fig. 5.44 Typical spectra of acid chlorides.

tion spectrum and the solid spectrum (KBr pellet or mull) greatly facilitates the interpretation.

In secondary amides, a single N—H stretching band is observed at 3440 cm^{-1} (2.91μ) in dilute solution. The hydrogen-bonded N—H stretching band usually appears in the 3300-cm^{-1} region (3.03μ). It is difficult to ascertain from the examination of the associated N—H stretching bands whether the amide is primary or secondary. The amide I carbonyl stretching vibration is similar in secondary amides to the primary amides, absorbing in the 1680- to 1655-cm^{-1} region (5.95 to 6.04μ). The amide II vibration, however, is significantly displaced from the primary amide II band, appearing in the 1550- to 1530-cm^{-1} region (6.45 to 6.54μ). Secondary amides exhibit a band near 1300 cm^{-1} (7.69μ), referred to as the amide III vibration. The tertiary amide group shows only the carbonyl stretching vibration near 1650 cm^{-1} (6.06μ), since no N—H groups are present. Figure 5.45 typifies the spectra of primary, secondary, and tertiary amides. The enlarged view of the N—H region illustrates the N—H absorption bands in dilute solution for primary and secondary amides.

Table 5.14 in the preliminary discussion summarizes the shift of the amide carbonyl stretching frequency in cyclic amides (lactams). One characteristic feature of cyclic amides is the observation that in rings having less than nine members, the amide II band is absent. This is illustrated in Fig. 5.46. Table 5.15 summarizes the characteristic amide vibrations and indicates the typical effects of conjugation on the carbonyl band position.

Anhydrides and peroxides. Anhydrides give rise to two bands because of vibrational coupling of two carbonyl groups. These bands absorb in the 1860- to 1800-cm^{-1} region (5.38 to 5.56μ) and in the 1800- to 1750-cm^{-1} region (5.56 to 5.71μ). The bands are usually separated by approximately 60 cm^{-1} (0.2μ in this region of the spectrum). The influence of conjugation, as in other carbonyl systems, shifts the anhydride bands to lower frequencies (longer wavelengths). The lower-frequency band absorbs in the region of the corresponding ester or lactone. The relative intensities of the two bands vary, depending upon whether the anhydride is cyclic or linear, as shown in Fig. 5.47. In the linear anhydride, the higher-frequency band is more intense than the lower-frequency absorption. The reverse is true for the cyclic anhydrides. In cyclic materials in which the C=O group is part of a five-membered ring, the influence of ring strain causes a shift to higher frequencies for the C=O absorption band. Anhydrides also show strong bands due to the C—O—C stretching vibration. In open-chain materials this C—O—C band is located in the 1175- to 1045-cm^{-1} region (8.51 to 9.57μ). In cyclic materials involving ring strain, it is located in the 1310- to 1210-cm^{-1} region (7.64 to 8.27μ); absence of a strong band in this region is useful as evidence against a strained-ring structure. The presence of a strong band in these regions does not necessarily indicate the presence of an anhydride, as other groups also absorb strongly in this region.

Symmetrical diacyl peroxides (aliphatic and aromatic) exhibit a double band resulting from vibrational coupling of the carbonyl stretching vibrations. This system is completely analogous to the coupled anhydride bands. The intensities of the coupled bands can be used to distinguish between anhydrides and diacyl peroxides. In linear anhydrides, the higher-frequency band is stronger and sharper than the lower-frequency band. The situation is reversed in diacyl peroxides. Unsymmetrical diacyl peroxides exhibit the same coupled bands, but the positions of the absorption bands are at slightly higher wavelengths.

Summary. Table 5.15 summarizes the absorption characteristics of carbonyl-containing compounds. Where possible, Table 5.15 has been constructed for easy reference in terms of absorption bands appearing from high-frequency to low-frequency regions. Groups having two carbonyl bands are listed on the basis of the position of the band of highest frequency. Where conjugative effects or other factors change the absorption position, they are listed as subgroups under the normal aliphatic case rather than as separate entries in Table 5.15.

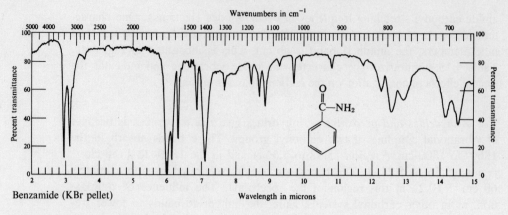

Benzamide (KBr pellet)

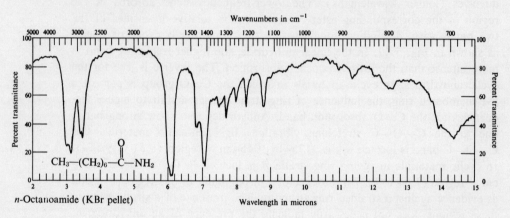

n-Octanoamide (KBr pellet)

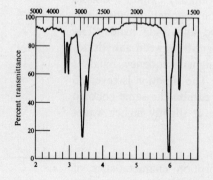

Spectrum of the primary amide group (R—C—NH₂) in dilute CHCl₃ solution. Note the clarity of the asymmetric and symmetric N—H stretching bands and the amide I and II bands.

Fig. 5.45 Spectral

5.4.6 Nitro, nitroso, and related N—O systems

Nitro compounds. The infrared spectra of a variety of nitroalkanes are characterized by a very strong —NO₂ asymmetric stretching band between 1615 and 1540 cm⁻¹ (6.19 and 6.49μ, respectively) and a strong symmetric stretching band between 1390 and 1320 cm⁻¹ (7.20 and 7.58μ,

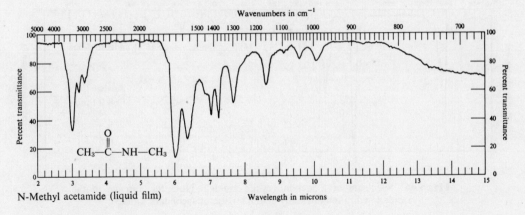

N-Methyl acetamide (liquid film)

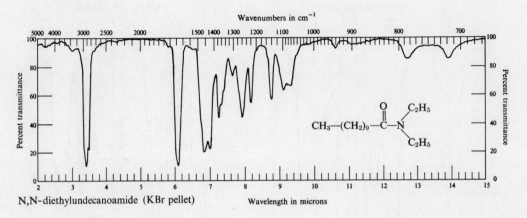

N,N-diethylundecanoamide (KBr pellet)

Spectrum of the secondary amide group (R—C—NH—R′) in dilute
||
O

CHCl₃ solution. Note the clearly defined N—H stretching band and the amide I band. Also, the position of the amide II band is clearly different from the primary amide absorption.

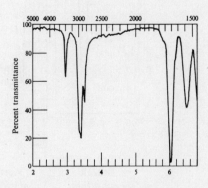

characteristics of amides.

respectively). The simplest nitroalkane (nitromethane) has been thoroughly investigated. Frequencies associated with the C—NO₂ group fundamentals have been assigned and are summarized in Table 5.16.

In more complex molecules, the C—N stretching band will not be observed because other more intense structural bands appear in this region. Splitting of the —NO₂ bands as a result of vibrational interactions will some-

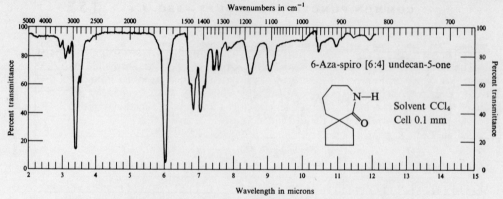

Fig. 5.46 Spectrum of a lactam (cyclic amide). Note the absence of the amide II vibration normally characteristic of secondary amides.

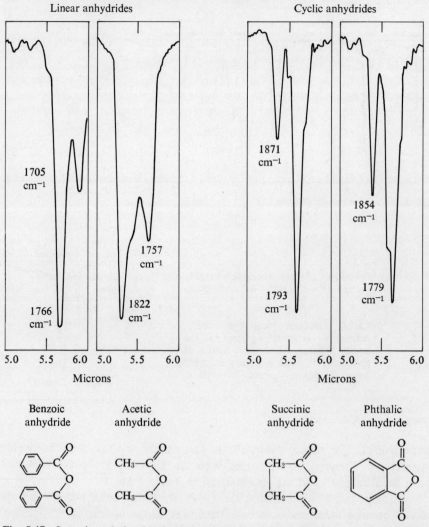

Fig. 5.47 Intensity relationship between coupled carbonyl vibrations in linear and cyclic anhydrides.

Table 5.15.   Summary of the Absorption Characteristics of Carbonyl-containing Compounds

The stretching frequencies of the carbonyl group ($v_{C=O}$) are correlated by the position of absorption of the saturated carbonyl compound in dilute nonpolar solvent (carbon tetrachloride or carbon disulfide). Generally these frequencies are referred to as the standard $v_{C=O}$ frequencies for a particular functional group type. All shifts are correlated to these frequencies.

Functional Group	Frequency (cm^{-1})	Wavelength (μ)	Remarks
Standard $v_{C=O}$			
Anhydrides $\left(\begin{smallmatrix} O & & O \\ \parallel & & \parallel \\ -C & -O- & C- \end{smallmatrix}\right)$	1830–1810	5.46–5.53	Asymmetric stretching, C=O (symmetric at 1770–1750 cm^{-1})
Peroxides $\left(\begin{smallmatrix} O & & & O \\ \parallel & & & \parallel \\ -C & -O- & -O- & C- \end{smallmatrix}\right)$	1820–1780	5.49–5.62	Asymmetric stretching, C=O (symmetric at 1796–1769 cm^{-1})
Acid Halides $\left(\begin{smallmatrix} O \\ \parallel \\ -C-X \end{smallmatrix}\right)$	1810–1790	5.53–5.59	C=O stretching
Acids $\left(\begin{smallmatrix} O \\ \parallel \\ -C-OH \end{smallmatrix}\right)$	1770–1750	5.65–5.71	Monomeric stretching, C=O
Esters $\left(\begin{smallmatrix} O \\ \parallel \\ -C-O- \end{smallmatrix}\right)$	1745–1725	5.73–5.80	C=O stretching
Aldehydes $\left(\begin{smallmatrix} O \\ \parallel \\ -C-H \end{smallmatrix}\right)$	1735–1715	5.76–5.83	C=O stretching
Ketones $\left(\begin{smallmatrix} O \\ \parallel \\ -C- \end{smallmatrix}\right)$	1720–1710	5.81–5.85	C=O stretching
Amides $\left(\begin{smallmatrix} O \\ \parallel \\ -C-NH_2 \end{smallmatrix}\right)$	1700–1680	5.88–5.95	C=O stretching "amide I band"
Anhydrides *Linear* $\begin{smallmatrix} O & & O \\ \parallel & & \parallel \\ R-C & -O- & C-R \end{smallmatrix}$ (Aliphatic)	1830–1810	5.46–5.53	C=O asymmetric stretching (strong)
	1770–1750	5.65–5.71	C=O symmetric stretching (weaker than asymmetric stretching band)

Table 5.15—Cont.

Functional Group	Frequency (cm^{-1})	Wavelength (μ)	Remarks
$R-\overset{\overset{O}{\|\|}}{C}-O-\overset{\overset{O}{\|\|}}{C}-R$ (Vinyl or aromatic)	1795–1775	5.57–5.63	C=O asymmetric stretching (strong)
	1735–1715	5.76–5.83	C=O symmetric stretching (weaker than asymmetric stretching band)
Cyclic 6-membered ring	1810–1790	5.53–5.59	C=O asymmetric stretching (weaker than symmetric stretching band)
	1760–1740	5.68–5.75	C=O symmetric stretching (strong)
5-membered ring	1875–1855	5.33–5.39	C=O asymmetric stretching (weaker than symmetric stretching band)
	1795–1775	5.57–5.63	C=O symmetric stretching (strong)
Other Cases Maleic anhydride	1850 1790	5.41 5.59	C=O asymmetric stretching (weaker than 1790-cm^{-1} symmetric stretch)
Phthalic anhydride	1850 1770	5.41 5.65	C=O asymmetric stretching (weaker than 1770-cm^{-1} symmetric stretch)
Peroxides $R-\overset{\overset{O}{\|\|}}{C}-O-O-\overset{\overset{O}{\|\|}}{C}-R$ (aliphatic)	1820–1811	5.49–5.52	C=O asymmetric stretching (strong)
	1796–1784	5.57–5.61	C=O symmetric stretching (weaker than asymmetric stretching band)
$R-\overset{\overset{O}{\|\|}}{C}-O-O-\overset{\overset{O}{\|\|}}{C}-R$ (aromatic)	1805–1780	5.54–5.62	C=O asymmetric stretching (strong)
	1794–1769	5.57–5.65	C=O symmetric stretching (weaker than asymmetric stretching band)

Table 5.15—Cont.

Functional Group	Frequency (cm^{-1})	Wavelength (μ)	Remarks
Acid Halides $\underset{\text{(aliphatic)}}{\overset{\displaystyle \overset{O}{\|}}{R-C-Cl}}$	1810–1790	5.53–5.59	C=O stretching $\overset{\displaystyle \overset{O}{\|}}{C-F}$ shifted to higher frequencies; $\overset{\displaystyle \overset{O}{\|}}{C-Br(I)}$ shifted to lower frequencies
$\underset{\text{(aromatic or unsaturated)}}{\overset{\displaystyle \overset{O}{\|}}{R-C-Cl}}$	1780–1750	5.62–5.71	C=O stretching (strong)
Acids $\underset{\text{(aliphatic)}}{\overset{\displaystyle \overset{O}{\|}}{R-C-OH}}$	1765–1750	5.67–5.71	C=O stretching of nonhydrogen-bonded species (variable in intensity in solution, depending on concentration)
	1720–1710	5.81–5.85	C=O stretching of acid dimer (most commonly observed band)
	3000–2500	3.33–4.00	Broad, complex band structure of O—H stretching and combination bands (characteristic)
	Near 3550 Near 1420 Near 1250	2.82 7.04 8.00	O—H stretching monomer bands due to coupling of in-plane bending of O—H and C—O stretching of the dimer (CH$_2$ bendings overlap 1420-cm^{-1} band)
	900–860	11.15–11.65	Broad, medium intensity band; O—H out-of-plane bending of acid dimer (characteristic)

Table 5.15—Cont.

Functional Group	Frequency (cm^{-1})	Wavelength (μ)	Remarks
α-halogen substituent	Shift of +10–20	Approx. 0.05	Values for α-bromo and α-chloro (α-fluoro about +50 cm^{-1})
R—C(=O)—OH (aromatic)	1730–1710	5.78–5.85	C=O stretching of the monomeric species
	1700–1680	5.88–5.95	C=O stretching in the acid dimer
R—C(=O)—O$^-$ (acid salts)	1610–1550	6.21–6.45	Asymmetric stretching of CO_2^- group (strong)
	Near 1400	7.14	Symmetric stretching of CO_2^- group (strong)
Esters R—C(=O)—O—R' (R and R' aliphatic)	1735	5.76	C=O stretching (strong)
	1275–1185	7.85–8.44	C—O—C asymmetric stretch
	1160–1050	8.62–8.70	C—O—C symmetric stretch (both are strong bands, the higher frequency band is usually more intense than the C=O stretching band; position is usually indicative of ester type)
Ester Types (C—O—C)			
(a) Formates	Near 1185 Near 1160	8.44 8.62	
(b) Acetates	Near 1245 665–635 615–580	8.03 15.04–15.75 16.26–17.24	
(c) Propionates	1275 1200–1190 1080 1020 810	7.84 8.33–8.40 8.47 9.80 12.35	

Table 5.15—Cont.

Functional Group	Frequency (cm^{-1})	Wavelength (μ)	Remarks
(d) *n*-Butyrates	1255	7.97	
	1190	8.40	
	1100	9.09	
(e) Isobutyrates	1260	7.93	
	1200	8.33	
	1160	8.62	
	1080	9.26	
(f) Isovalerates	1195	8.37	
	1285–1265	7.78–7.90	
α-halogen substituent	Shift of +10–40	Approx. 0.1–0.15	Shift depends on electronegativity of the halogen and stereochemistry
$\begin{matrix} O \\ \parallel \\ R{-}C{-}OR' \end{matrix}$ (where R is vinyl or aromatic)	1725–1715	5.80–5.83	C=O stretching (shifted by conjugation)
	1300–1250	7.69–8.00	C—O—C asymmetric stretching
	1200–1050	8.33–9.52	C—O—C symmetric stretching
$\begin{matrix} O \\ \parallel \\ R{-}C{-}OR' \end{matrix}$ (where R' is vinyl or aromatic)	1765–1755	5.67–5.70	C=O stretching (strong)
	1690–1650	5.92–6.06	C=C stretching in vinyl cases (enhanced intensity)
	Near 1210	8.26	C—O—C asymmetric stretching (very strong)
$\begin{matrix} O \\ \parallel \\ R{-}C{-}OR' \end{matrix}$ (where R and R' are aromatic)	1735	5.76	C=O stretching vibration
Benzoates (C—O—C)	1310–1240	7.64–8.06	Asymmetric and symmetric C—O—C stretching
	1150–1080	8.70–9.26	
Cyclic (cf. Table 5.14) 6-membered ring	1735	5.76	C=O stretching vibration (shifts with conjugation with C=O or ester O—C as in aliphatic cases)

Table 5.15—Cont.

Functional Group	Frequency (cm⁻¹)	Wavelength (μ)	Remarks
5-membered ring	1770	5.65	$C=O$ stretching (shifts with conjugation to 1785 cm⁻¹ and split, 1755 band is present; conjugation with ester O—C shifts $C=O$ stretching to 1880 cm⁻¹
Phthalates	1780–1760	5.62–5.68	$C=O$ stretching, 1780 cm⁻¹ in nonpolar solvents; 1760 cm⁻¹ in polar solvents
	1130–1110	8.85–9.01	Asymmetric and symmetric C—O—C stretching, (strong)
	1075–1065	9.30–9.39	

Aldehydes

O
‖
R—C—H
(aliphatic)

	1725–1715	5.80–5.83	$C=O$ stretching, (strong)
	2820	3.55	C—H stretching (overlapped with other C—H stretching bands)
	2720	3.67	C—H stretching-*characteristic* (used to distinguish aldehyde from ketone)

O
‖
R—C—H
(aromatic)

	Near 1700	5.88	$C=O$ stretching (shifting due to conjugation with aromatic ring)

O
‖
R—C—H
(α,β-unsaturated)

	Near 1685	5.94	$C=O$ stretching (shifted by conjugation; extended conjugation shifts the band to 1675 cm⁻¹)

Ketones

O
‖
R—C—R
(aliphatic)

	1720–1710	5.81–5.85	$C=O$ stretching (nonpolar solvent; shifts lower in polar media)
	Near 1100	9.09	C—C—C bending and C—C stretching of

O
╱╱
C—C   linkage
╲
C

Table 5.15—Cont.

Functional Group	Frequency (cm^{-1})	Wavelength (μ)	Remarks
R—C(=O)—R' (where R' is aromatic)	Near 1690	5.93	C=O stretching (shifted by conjugation)
R—C(=O)—R' (where R and R' are aromatic)	Near 1665	6.01	C=O stretching (shifted by conjugation)
Conjugation α,β-unsaturation:	Near 1675	5.97	C=O stretching vibration
(—CH=CH—C(=O)—)	1650–1600	6.06–6.25	C=C stretching (enhanced intensity)
Extended or crossed: (—CH=CH—CH=CH—C(=O)—) *or* (—CH=CH—C(=O)—CH=CH—)	Near 1665	6.01	C=O stretching vibration
Cyclopropyl: (▷—C(=O)—)	Near 1695	5.90	C=O stretching vibration
α-halogen substituent	Shifts +0 to 25	Approx. 0.05	Depends on electronegativity and stereochemistry
Two halogens (αα or αα')	Shifts +0 to 45	Approx. 0.1	
R—C(=O)—R (cyclic; cf. Table 5.14)			
4-membered ring	1780	5.62	All bands shift approximately 20 cm^{-1}
5-membered ring	1745	5.73	(0.05μ) on conjugation
6-membered ring	1715	5.83	
7-membered ring or larger	1705	5.87	
Diketones —C(=O)—C(=O)—	1720–1705	5.81–5.87	C=O stretching vibration

Table 5.15—Cont.

Functional Group	Frequency (cm^{-1})	Wavelength (μ)	Remarks
$\overset{\text{O}}{\underset{}{\|}}\quad\overset{\text{O}}{\underset{}{\|}}$ —C—CH$_2$—C—	1720–1705	5.81–5.87	C=O stretching vibration
	1640–1540	6.00–6.49	Conjugated chelate

Amides

O‖ R—C—NH$_2$ (aliphatic)	1690–1650	5.92–6.06	The "amide I" band C=O stretching (1690 cm^{-1} free, and 1650 cm^{-1} when hydrogen-bonded)
	3550–3420	2.82–2.92	Asymmetric N—H stretching
	3450–3320	2.90–3.01	Symmetric N—H stretching
	(3200–3050)	(3.12–3.28)	Hydrogen-bonded N—H
	1640–1600	6.10–6.25	The "amide II" band, NH$_2$ bending
	1420–1405	7.04–7.12	The "amide III" band, C—N stretching
O‖ R—C—NH—R (aliphatic)	1680–1640	5.95–6.10	The "amide I" band, C=O stretching
	Near 3440	2.91	N—H stretching
	(Near 3300)	(3.03)	Hydrogen-bonded N—H stretching
	1570–1530	6.37–6.54	The "amide II" band.
	1300–1260	7.69–7.94	The "amide III" band
O‖ R—C—NR$_2$ (aliphatic)	Near 1650	6.06	The "amide I" band; since no N—H is present amide II and III bands are absent

Table 5.15—Cont.

Functional Group	Frequency (cm^{-1})	Wavelength (μ)	Remarks
Conjugation:			
(Vinyl and aromatic)	Shifts +15	Approx. 0.05	
$\left(\begin{array}{c} \text{O} \\ \| \\ \text{R—C—N—CH=CH—} \text{ or} \\ \text{O} \\ \| \\ \text{—CH=CH—C—N} \end{array}\right)$			
α-halogen substituent	Shifts +5 to +50	Approx. 0.1	Depending on electro-negativity and stere-ochemistry
O $\|$ R—C—NH—R (cyclic; cf. Table 5.14)			
4-membered ring	1745	5.73	All bands shift approx.
5-membered ring	1700	5.88	15 cm^{-1} (0.05μ) on
6-membered ring	1677	5.96	conjugation (no
7-membered ring	1675	5.97	amide II band pres-ent in 4- to 9-mem-bered lactams)

times be observed in the more complex nitroalkanes. Vibrational interaction also occurs with methyl groups attached to the same carbon atom as the nitro group. Nitro groups also may cause shifts in the characteristic bands of other groups attached to the same carbon atom. For example, in α-nitro-ketones both the carbonyl stretching and the —NO$_2$ asymmetric stretching bands are shifted to higher frequencies.

Conjugated nitroalkenes exhibit —NO$_2$ asymmetric stretching bands be-tween 1500 and 1505 cm^{-1} (6.67 and 6.65μ, respectively) and —NO$_2$ sym-metric stretching bands in the 1360- to 1335-cm^{-1} region (7.36 and 7.49μ). The exact frequencies of these bands depend on the nature of the substituents present on the olefinic carbons. In nitroalkenes the —NO$_2$ symmetric stretch-

Table 5.16. C—NO$_2$ Group Fundamental Vibration Assignments in Nitromethane

Vibration	Frequency (cm^{-1})	Wavelength (μ)
NO$_2$ asymmetric stretching	1570	6.37
NO$_2$ symmetric stretching	1380	7.25
C—N stretching	918	10.89
NO$_2$ in-plane bending	656	15.24
NO$_2$ out-of-plane bending	615	16.26
CNO bending	480	20.83

ing band is almost as intense as the —NO$_2$ asymmetric, whereas in nitro-alkanes it is only about one-quarter as strong. There is no definite assignment for the C—N stretching mode in nitroalkenes. The nitro group appears to have little effect upon the frequency of the characteristic olefinic C—H and C=C bands. However, the C=C stretching absorption is intensified in α- and β-nitro olefins. Also, the =C—H stretching and wagging bands are intensified when the nitro group is on the same carbon atom as the olefinic hydrogen.

The —NO$_2$ asymmetric stretching band in aromatic nitro compounds is observed in the 1548- to 1508-cm^{-1} region (6.46 to 6.63μ) and the —NO$_2$ symmetric stretching band in the region from 1356 to 1340 cm^{-1} (7.37 to 7.46μ). The frequency of the C—N stretching absorption band in aromatic nitro compounds is not known. Figure 5.48 illustrates the spectral characteristics of both aliphatic and aromatic nitro compounds. The consistency of the asymmetric and symmetric stretching frequencies is summarized in Table 5.17.

Table 5.17.   Consistency of the Positions of Absorption of the Asymmetric and Symmetric —NO$_2$ Stretching Vibrations

Compound	Asymmetric Stretching* Vibration		Symmetric Stretching† Vibration	
	Frequency (cm^{-1})	Wavelength (μ)	Frequency (cm^{-1})	Wavelength (μ)
Nitromethane	1570	6.37	1380	7.25
Nitroethane	1558	6.42	1368	7.31
2-Nitropropane	1553	6.44	1361	7.35
1-Nitropentane	1553	6.44	1383	7.23
1-Nitrocyclohexane	1553	6.44	1361	7.35
2-Nitroethanol	1555	6.43	1370	7.30
1,2,-Dinitrobutane	1567	6.38	1383	7.23
6-Nitrocamphene	1527	6.55	1361	7.35
Nitrobenzene	1529	6.54	1353	7.39
m-Dinitrobenzene	1548	6.46	1353	7.39
p-Chloronitrobenzene	1527	6.55	1350	7.41
p-Nitrophenol	1524	6.56	1346	7.43
p-Nitroaniline	1508	6.63	1340	7.46
p-Nitrobenzoylchloride	1536	6.51	1351	7.40
p-Nitrotoluene	1524	6.56	1341	7.40
m-Nitrotoluene	1531	6.53	1355	7.38
m-Nitrobenzaldehyde	1541	6.49	1357	7.37

* Position is affected by electrical environment.
† Position is affected by the ability to conjugate with unsaturation (i.e., planarity).

Investigation of infrared spectra of nitro compounds reveals information concerning:

1. The electron-donating capacity of the structure attached to the nitro group (wavelength of the —NO$_2$ asymmetric stretching band).

2. The presence of negative substituents on the α-carbon or on the same

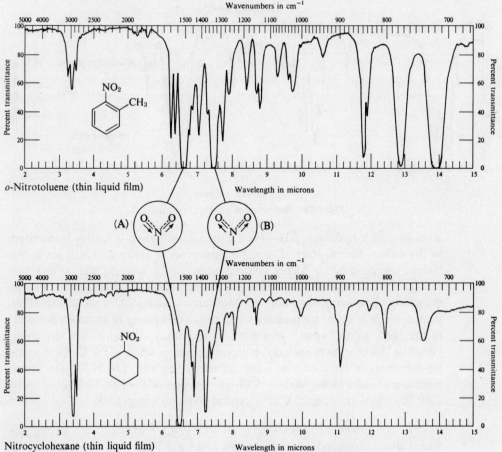

o-Nitrotoluene (thin liquid film)

Wavelength in microns

(A) (B)

Nitrocyclohexane (thin liquid film)

Wavelength in microns

Fig. 5.48 Typical spectra of nitro compounds.

unsaturated system as that attached to the nitro group (difference between the wavelengths of the —NO₂ symmetric and asymmetric stretching bands).

3. The extent of conjugation of the nitro group with the attached structure (relative intensities of the NO₂ symmetric and asymmetric stretching frequencies).

4. Presence of structures having two or more nitro or methyl groups, or both, on the same carbon atom (splitting of the 1370-cm⁻¹ band, 7.30µ).

5. The presence of a negative group attached to a CH₂ (shift of the 1450-cm⁻¹ band to 1430 cm⁻¹, 6.90 to 7.00µ).

Nitroso compounds and oximes. The nitroso group, C—N=O, exhibits a strong N—O stretching frequency in the 1600- to 1500-cm⁻¹ region (6.25 to 6.67µ). The position of the band is affected by substituent groups in much the same manner as with the carbonyl group. For example, aromatic nitroso compounds exhibit the —N=O stretching band near 1500 cm⁻¹ (6.67µ), whereas *t*-aliphatic nitroso compounds absorb near 1550 cm⁻¹ (6.45µ).

In carbon compounds where the nitroso group is situated on a carbon

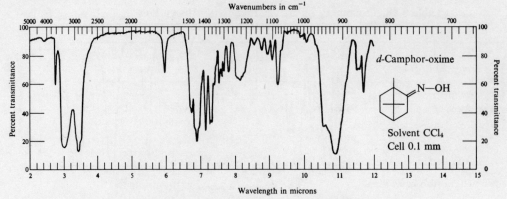

Fig. 5.49   Spectrum of a typical oxime.

atom bearing a hydrogen, CH—N=O, the nitroso group is readily isomerized to the oxime, C=N—OH. This interconversion is easily detected, since the nitroso compounds are highly colored compounds, whereas the oximes are usually white crystalline substances. The oximes exhibit a characteristic O—H stretching vibration in the 3650- to 3500-cm^{-1} region (2.74 to 2.86μ). This band appears at lower frequencies when the —OH group is hydrogen-bonded. In the 1685- to 1650-cm^{-1} region (5.94 to 6.06μ), a weak C=N stretching vibration absorbs. As in carbonyl compounds, the position of the C=N stretching frequency in cyclic oximes is influenced by ring size. The N—O stretching vibration absorbs in the 960- to 930-cm^{-1} region (10.42 to 10.75μ). Figure 5.49 illustrates the spectrum of a typical oximino compound.

Nitrate esters.   Nitrate esters (R—O—NO$_2$) exhibit very strong infrared absorption bands at 1640 (6.10μ) and 1285 cm^{-1} (7.78μ), which are due to NO$_2$ asymmetric and symmetric stretching vibrations; a broader, weaker band near 855 cm^{-1} (11.30μ) due to N—O stretching; and a band of medium intensity near 690 cm^{-1} (14.49μ) due to the NO$_2$ bending vibration. Nitrate esters are easily identified even in mixtures with large amounts of other polar compounds because of the strength of the nitrate ester bands.

Typical correlations for nitro compounds and related substances are summarized in Table 5.18.

5.4.7   Halogen-containing compounds

Carbon-fluorine vibrations.   The presence of a single fluorine atom in a molecule usually results in the appearance of an intense absorption band in the 1100- to 1020-cm^{-1} region (9.09 to 9.80μ). With further fluorine substitution this frequency rises and splits into two bands due to symmetric and asymmetric vibrations. In more complex molecules having a large proportion of fluorine, very intense absorption occurs over the 1400- to 1050-cm^{-1} region (7.15 to 9.52μ). In fully fluorinated hydrocarbons the spectra are very complex, giving rise to a series of very intense bands in the 1360- to 1090-cm^{-1} region (7.36 to 9.18μ).

Table 5.18. Summary of the Characteristic Absorptions of Nitro, Nitroso, and Related N—O Systems

Functional Group	Frequency (cm⁻¹)	Wavelength (μ)	Remarks
C—NO₂ (nitro) aliphatic	1615–1540	6.19–6.49	Asymmetric —NO₂ stretching vibration (very strong)
	1390–1320	7.20–7.58	Symmetric —NO₂ stretching vibration (very strong)
olefinic	1500–1505	6.67–6.65	Asymmetric stretching vibration (intense)
	1360–1335	7.36–7.49	Symmetric stretching vibration (intense)
aromatic	1548–1508	6.46–6.63	Asymmetric stretching vibration (intense)
	1356–1340	7.37–7.46	Symmetric stretching vibration
	Near 870	11.49	C—N stretching vibration (difficult to assign in aromatic nitro compounds)
C—N=O (nitroso)	1600–1500	6.25–6.67	Shifts similar to those observed for carbonyl compounds
C=N—OH (oxime)	3650–3500	2.74–2.86	O—H stretching vibration (at lower frequencies when hydrogen bonded)
	1685–1650	5.94–6.06	C=N stretching vibration weak unless conjugated; position influenced by ring strain (cf. Table 5.14 for similar C=O shifts)
	960–930	10.42–10.75	N—O stretching vibration
N → O (N- oxide) Aliphatic N → O	970–950	10.31–10.53	N—O stretching vibration (intense)
Aromatic N → O (Pyridine N- oxides)	1300–1200	7.69–8.33	N—O stretching vibration (intense); shifting due to conjugation (N⁺=O); hydrogen bonding shifts band to lower frequencies (10–20 cm⁻¹)
R—O—NO₂ (nitrate esters)	1640–1620	6.10–6.17	Asymmetric —NO₂ stretching vibration (intense)
	1300–1250	7.69–8.00	Symmetric —NO₂ stretching vibration (intense)
	870–855	11.49–11.70	N—O stretching vibration
	Near 690	14.49	NO₂ bending vibration

Carbon-chlorine vibrations. The C—Cl stretching absorption frequency is observed in the 745- to 695-cm^{-1} region (13.42 to 14.39μ). Compounds containing more than one chlorine atom will exhibit asymmetric and symmetric absorption bands. Interaction with other groups will shift the frequency to as high as 840 cm^{-1} (11.90μ). Complex molecules having a large number of chlorine atoms will exhibit a very intense fundamental and, usually, a medium-intensity band in the 1510- to 1480-cm^{-1} region (6.62 to 6.76μ), assigned as the first overtone.

Carbon-bromine and carbon-iodine vibrations. The stretching motion of the C—Br bond is found in the 600- to 500-cm^{-1} region (16.7 to 20.0μ). This frequency shifts to a higher region for molecules having more than one bromine atom and is then observed as two separate absorption bands. Only a limited number of molecules having C—I bonds has been investigated. Indications are that the stretching absorptions of the C—I bond is observed in the 500- to 200-cm^{-1} region (20.0 to 50.0μ).

Typical spectra of halogenated (chlorine-containing) materials are exemplified in Sec. 4.2.1. Table 5.19 summarizes the characteristic frequencies of halogenated compounds.

Table 5.19. Summary of Characteristic Carbon-Halogen Absorptions

Functional Group	Frequency (cm^{-1})	Wavelength (μ)	Remarks
C—F	1250–960	8.00–10.42	Stretching vibration
—CF$_2$ and CF$_3$	1350–1200	7.41–8.33	Asymmetric stretching vibration
	1200–1080	8.33–9.26	Symmetric stretching vibration
=C—F	1230–1100	8.13–9.09	Stretching vibration
—C—F	1120–1010	8.93–9.90	Stretching vibration
C—Cl	830–500	12.04–20.0	Stretching vibration
	1510–1480	6.62–6.76	Overtone of stretching vibration
—C—Cl$_2$	845–795	11.83–12.58	Asymmetric stretching vibration
	620	16.13	Symmetric stretching vibration
C—Br*	667–290	14.99–34.5	Stretching vibration
C—I*	500–200	20.0–50.0	Stretching vibration

* The reader should note that C—Br and C—I fundamental stretching absorptions are not usually observed in the 2 to 16μ region of the infrared spectrum.

5.4.8 Summary of common functional-group absorptions. From study of the previous sections related to the common functional groups and the included typical spectra, the overall shapes of the spectra of various types of compounds and the positions of particular bands of common functional groups can now be visualized. For ready reference, Fig. 5.50 summarizes the correlations discussed in Secs. 5.3 and 5.4.

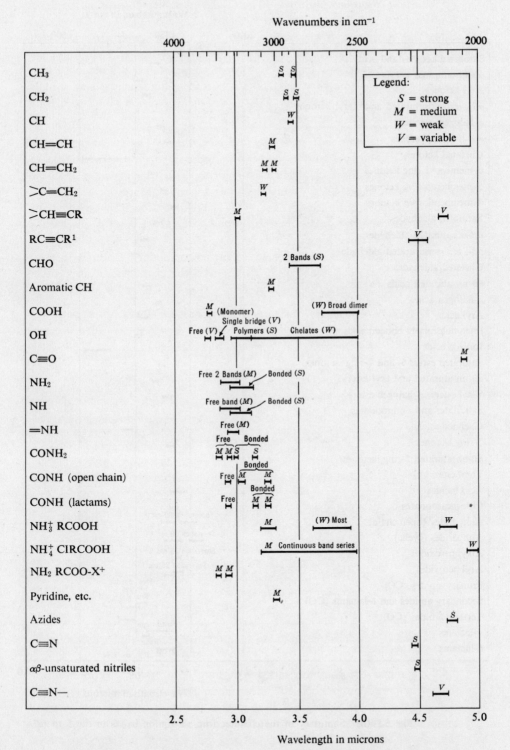

Fig. 5.50(A) Summary of the characteristic absorption bands in the 2.5 to 5μ region (4000 cm⁻¹ to 2000 cm⁻¹) due to the more common functional groups.

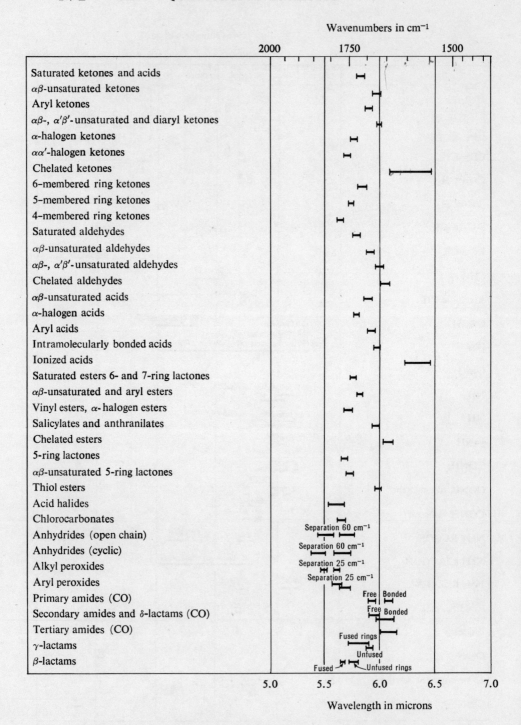

Fig. 5.50(B) Summary of the characteristic absorption bands in the 5 to 6.7μ

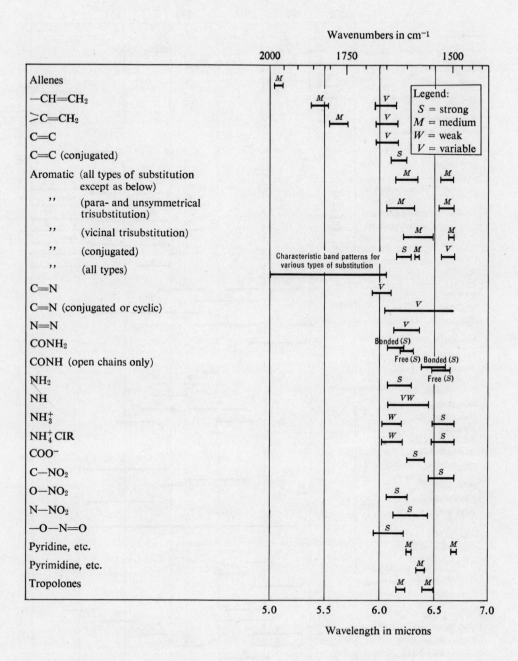

Wavenumbers in cm⁻¹

Legend:
S = strong
M = medium
W = weak
V = variable

Wavelength in microns

region (2000 cm⁻¹ to 1500 cm⁻¹) due to the more common functional group.

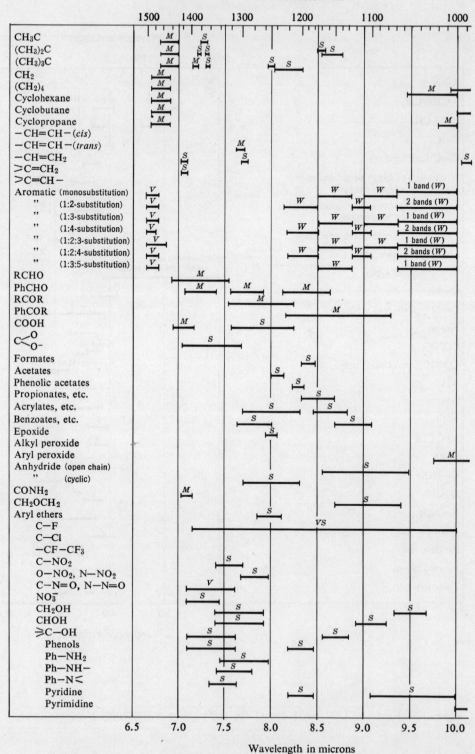

Fig. 5.50(C) Summary of the characteristic absorption bands in the 6.7 to 16μ

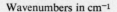
Wavenumbers in cm⁻¹

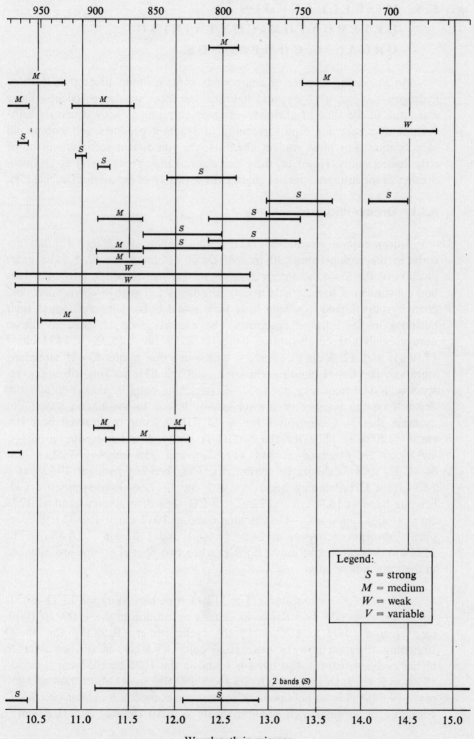

region (1500 cm⁻¹ to 625 cm⁻¹) due to the more common functional groups.

5.5 MISCELLANEOUS HETEROATOM-CONTAINING ORGANIC COMPOUNDS

An increasing number of compounds contain atoms other than carbon, hydrogen, oxygen, nitrogen, and halogen. As these substances occupy more and more of the time of chemists, infrared correlations with structural units become necessary for rapid screening of reaction products and compound identification. For most student chemists, the subsequent sections will be of only limited utility. However, these correlations may prove useful as an introduction to the infrared spectral changes of a variety of heteroatom substances.

5.5.1 Organo-silicon compounds

Silicon-carbon vibrations. The silicon-carbon stretching vibration absorbs in the region from 890 to 690 cm^{-1} (11.24 to 14.49μ). The exact position of the Si—C vibration depends on the nature of the particular carbon substituent. Characteristic absorption bands for methyl, ethyl, vinyl, and phenyl groups linked to silicon have been found to be quite constant in their positions in the infrared spectrum. The methyl group attached to silicon always exhibits three absorption bands at 2959 cm^{-1} (3.38μ), 1421 cm^{-1} (7.08μ), and 1263 cm^{-1} (7.92μ), which are due to the C—H stretching vibration, the C—H bending vibration, and the CH$_2$ rocking vibration, respectively. The frequency of the Si—C stretching band in methyl compounds depends on the number of methyl groups linked to the silicon atom. For example, the Si—C absorption for the Si(CH$_3$)$_2$ group is observed near 800 cm^{-1} (12.50μ), while for the Si(CH$_3$)$_3$ group, two bands due to Si—C vibrations are observed at 844 (11.85μ) and 756 cm^{-1} (13.22μ). The Si—C$_2$H$_5$ group exhibits an asymmetric CH$_3$ bending band at 1462 cm^{-1} (6.84μ); a CH$_2$ bending band at 1412 cm^{-1} (7.08μ); a symmetric CH$_3$ bending band at 1377 cm^{-1} (7.26μ); a CH$_2$—Si deformation band at 1238 cm^{-1} (8.08μ); and a C—C stretching band at 1012 cm^{-1} (9.88μ). Silicon-phenyl absorptions appear at 1429 (7.00μ) and 1126 cm^{-1} (8.88μ). The 1126-cm^{-1} band is split into a doublet when two phenyl groups are attached to the same silicon atom.

Silicon-oxygen vibrations. The Si—O stretching vibration in (R$_2$SiO)$_n$ types of compounds gives rise to an intense absorption in the 1100- to 1000-cm^{-1} region (9.09 to 10.0μ). In the cyclic trimer (R$_2$SiO)$_3$, the Si—O stretching vibration absorbs near 1020 cm^{-1} (9.80μ); in the tetramer or higher cyclic structures, this band is found in the 1075 to 1055-cm^{-1} region (9.30 to 9.48μ). Disiloxanes (R$_3$Si)$_2$O exhibit the Si—O absorption at 1050 cm^{-1} (9.52μ). Linear polymeric silicon-oxygen compounds exhibit two Si—O vibrations of approximately equal intensity at 1080 (9.26μ) and 1020 cm^{-1}

(9.80μ). In all cases, the Si—O vibration is observed as an extremely intense, broad absorption band.

When the oxygen atom of the Si—O group is attached to a carbon atom Si—O—CH₃, the Si—O stretching vibration absorbs near 1090 cm⁻¹ (9.18μ). When the carbon substituent is an ethyl group the 1090-cm⁻¹ band is split into a doublet.

Silicon-hydrogen vibrations.   The silicon-hydrogen stretching vibration is observed as a sharp, intense absorption band near 2200 cm⁻¹ (4.55μ). Compare the spectrum in Fig. 5.51 with those in Sec. 5.4.1 for other materials absorbing in the 4 to 5μ region. It is clearly seen from this comparison that spectral differentiation of the Si—H vibration from other absorptions in this region can be made readily. The exact frequency of the Si—H stretching vibration depends upon the nature and type of the remaining substituents on the silicon atom. The Si—H bending vibration absorbs as an intense band near 860 cm⁻¹ (11.63μ).

Hydroxyl vibrations.   When silicon compounds contain the hydroxyl group attached to Si, hydroxylic absorption occurs in very nearly the same region as that previously discussed for alcohols and phenols. A means of differentiation for the C—OH and Si—OH groups is the examination of the O—H deformation band. The C—OH deformation occurs near 1050 cm⁻¹ (9.52μ), whereas the Si—OH deformation absorbs in the 870- to 820-cm⁻¹ region $(11.49$ to $12.19\mu)$.

Table 5.20 summarizes the characteristic absorptions for organo-silicon compounds.

5.5.2   Organo-sulfur compounds

Sulfur-hydrogen vibrations.   Organic substances possessing the S—H group absorb weakly in the 2600- to 2550-cm⁻¹ region $(3.85$ to $3.92\mu)$ be-

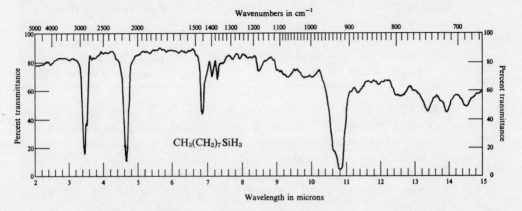

Fig. 5.51   Spectrum of *n*-octyl silane.

Table 5.20. Typical Absorption Characteristics of Organo-Silicon Compounds

Functional Group	Frequency (cm⁻¹)	Wavelength (μ)	Remarks
SiH	2230–2150	4.48–4.65	Stretching vibration
	890–860	11.24–11.63	Bending vibration
SiOH	3390–3200	2.95–3.13	OH stretching vibration
	870–820	11.49–12.20	OH bending vibration
Si—O—	1110–1000	9.01–10.00	Si—O stretching vibration (very intense, broad)
Si—O—Si (disiloxanes)	1053	9.50	Si—O stretching vibration (very intense, broad)
Si—O—Si (linear)	1080	9.26	Si—O stretching vibration of
	1025	9.76	approx. equal intensity
Si—O—Si (cyclic trimer)	1020	9.80	Si—O— stretching vibration
Si—O—Si (cyclic tetramer)	1082	9.24	Si—O— stretching vibration
Si—OCH₃	1090–1050	9.18–9.52	Si—O— stretching vibration
Si OC₂H₅	1090	9.18	Intense doublet; if Si—O—Si
	1085	9.22	is present, this doublet is overlapped
Si—C	890–690	11.24–14.49	Si—C stretching
Si—CH₃	1260	7.93	CH₃ rocking mode (sharp and intense)
	794	12.60	Si—C stretching
Si(CH₃)₂	1260	7.93	CH₃ rocking mode (intense, broad, and characteristic)
	820–800	12.21–12.50	Si—C stretching
Si(CH₃)₃	1260	7.93	CH₃ rocking vibration
	840	11.90	Characteristic of the Si(CH₃)₃
	755	13.25	grouping
Si—C₆H₅	1632	6.13	C≕C stretching vibration
	1428	7.00	C—C— ring stretching vibration (sharp, intense)
	1125	8.89	Intense band, which appears as doublet for Si(C₆H₅)₂

cause of the S—H stretching vibration. Since the S—H group enters into very weak hydrogen bonds, the S—H stretching absorption does not shift to the same extent as the hydroxyl stretching band. On examining spectra in the liquid state and in dilute solutions, only a small shift of the S—H stretching absorption due to association is observed. Since this is a weakly absorbing vibration, the S—H absorption is generally not detected in very thin cells.

Carbon-sulfur vibrations. The C—S stretching absorption is also extremely weak, appearing in the 700- to 590-cm^{-1} region (14.28 to 16.95μ). The position of this absorption band is dependent on the nature of the sulfur and carbon atom substituents. However, since the linkage is weakly absorbing and other carbon groups exhibit skeletal vibrations in this region, the C—S absorption has only very limited practical application in spectral interpretation. When the C—S bond is conjugated with adjacent unsaturated linkages such as vinyl or phenyl, the stretching absorption is observed near 590 cm^{-1} (16.95μ). The intensity of the C—S stretching vibration is increased significantly by conjugation, but since the absorption is usually beyond 16μ, the band is not observed in the normal spectrum. It should be noted that C—Cl absorptions occur in the same region as these C—S absorptions (Sec. 5.4.7). When both are present in the same molecule, care must be exercised in assigning absorption bands to particular groups. When a phenyl ring is attached directly to the sulfur atom, the C—S stretching vibration absorbs near 700 cm^{-1} (14.28μ). Thioethers exhibit a C—S stretching band, which if more accurately assigned should be analogous to the ether C—O—C vibration, namely, C—S—C. The thioether stretching vibration absorbs in the 695- to 655-cm^{-1} region (14.39 to 15.27μ).

The C=S (thiocarbonyl) stretching vibration absorbs in the 1200- to 1050-cm^{-1} region (8.33 to 8.69μ) and the shifts observed for the absorption within this region closely parallel those discussed in Sec. 5.4.5 for carbonyl compounds. In molecules having the C=S group attached to a nitrogen atom (thioamides) the stretching frequency is observed at higher frequencies (1405 to 1290 cm^{-1}, 7.12 to 7.75μ). When chlorine is attached directly to the carbon atom of the C=S linkage, the C=S stretching vibration is shifted to the 1235- to 1225-cm^{-1} region (8.10 to 8.16μ).

Sulfur-oxygen vibrations. The sulfur-oxygen stretching vibration for the S=O group absorbs in the 1080- to 1000-cm^{-1} region (9.26 to 10.00μ). The absorption band is very intense and relatively constant in position. Conjugation, for example, has little effect on the position of the stretching absorption. Sulfoxides in solution absorb between 1065 and 1040 cm^{-1} (8.59 and 8.77μ). In the solid state, only a slight frequency shift is observed.

Sulphones have the SO_2 group as part of their structure and, as a typical vibrating unit of three atoms, exhibit an asymmetric and symmetric stretching vibration. These vibrations absorb in the 1340- to 1300-cm^{-1} region (7.46 to 7.69μ) and the 1160- to 1135-cm^{-1} region (8.62 to 8.81μ), respectively. Conjugation does not seem to have any effect on the position of these frequencies. Likewise, hydrogen bonding produces very small shifts, pointing to the consistency of band positions for this functional group.

Sulfonyl chlorides (—SO_2Cl) have a halogen atom directly attached to the sulfur atom of the SO_2 linkage. Sulfonamides (—SO_2NH_2) have the amino group substituted analogously. Both functional group types exhibit asymmetric and symmetric SO_2 vibrations. These absorptions appear at higher

Table 5.21.   Characteristic Absorption Bands Due to the More Common Sulfur-Containing Linkages

Functional Group	Frequency (cm^{-1})	Wavelength (μ)	Remarks
—S—H			
Alkyl —SH	2600–2550	3.85–3.92	S—H stretching vibration
Aryl —SH	2560–2550	3.91–3.92	S—H stretching vibration
—C—S	700–590	14.28–16.95	C—S stretching vibration (extremely weak)
CH$_3$—S—	700–685	14.28–14.60	C—S stretching vibration
—CH$_2$—S—CH$_2$—	695–655	14.39–15.27	C—S—C stretching vibration
\CH—S—/	630–600	15.87–16.67	C—S stretching vibration
Phenyl —S— or C=C—S—	Near 590	16.95	CH— stretching vibration (increased intensity due to conjugation)
C=S	1200–1050	8.33–9.52	C=S stretching (strong) shifts similar to C=O (Table 5.15)
Cl—C=S	1235–1225	8.10–8.16	C—S stretching
\N—C=S/	1405–1290	7.12–7.75	Analogous to "amide I" band (Table 5.15)
S—O			
S—O	900–700	11.11–14.28	S—O stretching vibration (intense)
S=O	1080–1000	9.26–10.00	S=O stretching vibration (intense)
—SO$_2$	1340–1300	7.46–7.69	Asymmetric stretching vibration (intense)
	1160–1135	8.62–8.81	Symmetric stretching vibration (intense)
Common Types			
R\ /S=O R (sulfoxide)	1060–1040	9.43–9.62	Shifts to lower cm^{-1} values when conjugated or hydrogen-bonded (10–20 cm^{-1})
RSO$_2$R	1340–1300	7.46–7.69	Asymmetric stretching
(sulfone)	1160–1135	8.62–8.81	Symmetric stretching
RSO$_2$—N/\	1370–1330	7.30–7.52	Asymmetric stretching

Table 5.21—Cont.

Functional Group	Frequency (cm⁻¹)	Wavelength (μ)	Remarks
(sulfonamide)	1180–1160	8.47–8.62	Symmetric stretching
R—SO₂—Cl	1385–1340	7.22–7.46	Asymmetric stretching
(sulfonylchlorides)	1185–1160	8.44–8.62	Symmetric stretching
R—SO₂̄ OH	1250–1160	8.00–8.62	Asymmetric stretching
(sulfonic acids)	1080–1000	9.26–10.00	Symmetric stretching
	700–610	14.28–16.39	S—O stretching
R—SO₂—OR	1420–1330	7.04–7.52	Asymmetric stretching
(sulfonates)	1200–1145	8.33–8.73	Symmetric stretching

frequencies, however, than do those observed for the sulfones. The asymmetric vibration absorbs in the 1385- to 1340-cm⁻¹ region (7.22 to 7.46μ), whereas the symmetric absorption band appears in the 1185- to 1160-cm⁻¹ region (8.44 to 8.62μ). In sulfonic acids, the S=O linkage possesses considerable single-bond character due to the —SO₃H structural unit. Three absorption bands are observed for the sulfonic acid group. As would be expected, the highest-frequency vibration is at lower frequency than is the asymmetric absorption band of the corresponding sulfone. The three bands absorb in the following regions; 1250 to 1160 cm⁻¹ (8.00 to 8.62μ), 1080 to 1000 cm⁻¹ (9.26 to 10.00μ), and 700 to 610 cm⁻¹ (14.29 to 16.39μ). Of the three bands, the highest-frequency band is the most intense. This absorption is often split into a number of closely spaced bands.

Table 5.21 summarizes the characteristic absorption bands present in the more common organo-sulfur compounds.

5.5.3 Organo-phosphorus compounds

Phosphorus-hydrogen vibrations. Since the phosphorus atom is much heavier than hydrogen, the atomic motions associated with these vibrations are mainly confined to the hydrogen atoms. Hence, in compounds containing the P—H group, the stretching and bending frequencies are almost independent of the remainder of the molecule and will be observed in the 2325- to 2425-cm⁻¹ region (4.30 to 4.12μ) and the 1250- to 950-cm⁻¹ region (8.00 to 10.53μ). In compounds containing organic units (i.e., R—P—H), only one band will be observed in the P—H stretching region, and the P—H bending motion in the molecule will appear as a very weak band.

Phosphorus-oxygen vibrations. There are two types of phosphorus-oxygen vibrations that must be considered, namely, the P=O or P⁺—O⁻ vibration and the P—O—R vibration, where R is alkyl or aryl. The stretching vibration of the P=O group absorbs as a strong band in the 1315- to 1180-

cm⁻¹ region (7.60 to 8.49μ). It is interesting to note that because of the size of the phosphorus atom, the absorption band arising from the P=O stretching vibration seems to be independent of the type of compound and the size of other substituent groups. Apparently the only factor influencing the position of the P=O absorption is the number of electronegative substituents, phosphonic and phosphinic acids being excluded from this generalization. In both acid types the P=O stretching band and the hydroxyl stretching bands are shifted to lower frequencies as a result of hydrogen bonding. Also, both bands (P=O and O—H) are very broad absorptions. The analogous P=S vibration appears in the 800- to 650-cm⁻¹ region (12.50 to 15.38μ) as a relatively weak absorption band.

The P—O—R absorption is an intense and broad band between 1100 and 950 cm⁻¹ (9.00 and 10.53μ, respectively). When the R group is a methyl group, the P—O—C absorption is a strong, sharp band at 1050 cm⁻¹ (9.52μ). In addition, a second weak, but sharp, band appears near 1190 cm⁻¹ (8.40μ). The characteristic symmetric methyl absorption at 1379 cm⁻¹ (7.25μ) for normal carbon-containing substances is absent. Higher alkyl groups absorb in the same region (1050 cm⁻¹) and usually have a second medium-intensity band (similar to the 1190-cm⁻¹ band) near 1165 cm⁻¹ (8.59μ). In the case of an aromatic-carbon substituent (P—O— phenyl) the P—O—C absorption is observed at lower frequencies (in the region of 950 to 875 cm⁻¹, 10.53 to 11.43μ).

Hydroxyl vibrations. The stretching vibration of the hydroxyl group in phosphorus compounds should be expected near 3000 cm⁻¹ (3.35μ). Hydrogen bonding of P—OH groups in oxygenated phosphorus systems is very strong, and a very broad absorption in the 2600-cm⁻¹ (3.85μ) region is the only band observed for the P—OH hydroxyl stretching vibration. The hydroxyl bending band has not been assigned with certainty because of hydrogen-bonding effects. However, a broad band, presumably the O—H bending absorption, does appear in the 1050-cm⁻¹ (9.52μ) region. Most organo-phosphorus compounds possess strong absorption in this region, and therefore the bending vibration is of little value in spectral interpretation.

Table 5.22 summarizes the characteristic absorptions arising from correlations derived from some of the more common organo-phosphorus compounds.

5.5.4 Organo-metallic compounds. The absorption spectra of several cyclopentadienyl metal compounds have been investigated. The ferrocene molecule $(C_5H_5)_2Fe$ and substituted ferrocenes have been rather extensively examined, and one may conclude that the C_5H_5 metal types of compounds are characterized by the following assigned frequencies: a normal C—H stretching absorption near 3075 cm⁻¹ (3.25μ); a medium-intensity band due to the C—C stretching vibration at 1430 cm⁻¹ (7.00μ); strong bands at 1110 and 1005 cm⁻¹ (9.01 and 9.95μ, respectively) due to an asymmetric ring-breathing mode and a C—H bending mode, respectively; and a strong absorption

Table 5.22. Summary of Characteristic Absorptions Attributed to Organo-Phosphorus Compounds

Functional Group	Frequency (cm⁻¹)	Wavelength (μ)	Remarks
P—H	2425–2325	4.12–4.30	P—H stretching vibration sharp (medium intensity)
	1250–950	8.00–10.53	P—H bending (very weak)
P=O	1315–1180	7.60–8.49	P=O stretching vibration (strong; position affected by the number of electronegative substituents)
P=S	800–650	12.50–15.38	P=S stretching vibration (weak absorption)
P—O—C	1100–950	9.00–10.53	Where C = CH_3, strong sharp band at 1050 cm⁻¹ (9.52μ); a sharp weak band near 1190 cm⁻¹ (8.40μ) also present due to P—O stretching (higher alkyls absorb similarly)
			Where C = phenyl, a strong band is present in the 950- to 875-cm⁻¹ (10.53 to 11.42μ) region
P—OH	Near 2600	3.85	Hydrogen-bonded —OH stretching (strong, very broad absorption)
	Near 1050	9.52	O—H bending

near 825 cm⁻¹ (12.12μ) assigned to the C—H out-of-plane vibration. Cyclopentadienyl metal compounds also exhibit a series of three or more very weak bands in the 1750- to 1615-cm⁻¹ region (5.71 to 6.19μ). These bands have been ascribed to overtones. No metal-to-carbon link absorption has been conclusively ascertained. A striking characteristic of disubstituted ferrocene structures is that the absorption bands at 1110 (9.01μ) and 1005 cm⁻¹ (9.95μ) are completely absent. This is not the case, however, in the spectra of monosubstituted ferrocene structures, where these bands are still observed. Fulvene metal, benzene metal, and related compounds possess similar characteristic absorptions.

Metallic carbonyl compounds have been extensively investigated. Such compounds are characterized by very intense bands in the 2050- to 1750-cm⁻¹ region (4.88 to 5.71μ). The spectral characteristics observed in this region depend on the complexity of the metal-carbonyl compound. Generally terminal carbonyls give rise to absorption bands near the high-frequency end of the 2050- to 1750-cm⁻¹ region. Bridged carbonyl groups exhibit characteristic strong absorption bands near 1800 cm⁻¹ (5.56μ).

Similar correlations have been established for metal-cyano compounds. The metal-cyano compounds exhibit absorption frequencies attributable to both terminal C≡N groups and bridged C≡N groups. Terminal C≡N vibrations give rise to absorptions near 2065 cm^{-1} (4.84μ) and the bridged C≡N vibration is found near 2130 cm^{-1} (4.69μ).

Table 5.23 summarizes the general frequency assignments for a number

Table 5.23.   Characteristic Absorptions of Several Organo-Metallic Systems

Functional Group	Frequency (cm^{-1})	Wavelength (μ)	Remarks
(C$_5$H$_5$)-metal compounds	3075	3.25	C—H stretching mode
	1750–1615	5.71–6.19	3–6 very weak bands; overtone of ring rotational mode
	1430	6.99	C—C vibration
	1110*	9.01*	Asymmetric ring breathing mode (sharp and intense)
	1005*	9.95*	C—H bending vibration (sharp and intense)
	825	12.12	Probably CH out-of-plane mode (very strong and broad)
Metallic-carbonyl compounds	2050–1750	4.88–5.71	CO vibrations
	2050–1875	4.88–5.33	Terminal CO modes
	1875–1750	5.33–5.71	Bridge CO vibrations
Metallic-cyano compounds	2065	4.84	Terminal C≡N stretching mode
	2130	4.70	Bridge C≡N stretching mode

* Absent in disubstituted systems.

of the more common organo-metallic compounds. Coordination compounds resulting from the association of a metal ion with such organic substances as acetylacetone have been omitted from the present discussion, as have carboxylate salts. In principle, these will generally follow the trends expected from earlier discussions.

5.6   INFRARED SPECTRAL CHARACTERISTICS OF INORGANIC COMPOUNDS

In the routine work of the chemist it is not unlikely that inorganic samples will be examined spectrophotometrically. At first glance, the resulting spectrum may appear to be quite different from those presented up to this point. Typical carbon-hydrogen absorptions will be completely absent, and the spectrum will possess a relatively small number of broad bands. It is the purpose of the present brief discussion to introduce the important elements found in inorganic spectra, with the hope that the reader will correlate a number of the discrete regions of absorption to parallel and augment his familiarity with the characteristic regions of absorptions appearing in organic substances.

The application of the infrared method to the examination of inorganic substances is a relatively recent development. The spectral analysis of inorganic compounds was severely curtailed because of the difficulties in obtaining suitable sample preparation techniques. In recent years, extensive investigation of the spectral characteristics of inorganic compounds, using the Nujol mull, pressed pellet technique, and polyethylene cells (for studies in the long wavelength region), has yielded valuable information concerning group correlations. From the examination of a large number of inorganic compounds, it was apparent that particular anions absorbed in certain rather narrow regions of the infrared spectrum. From these observations it was clear that such correlations were useful in establishing qualitative identifications.

5.6.1 Types of vibrations in solids. In ionic solids composed of monoatomic ions, such as sodium chloride, potassium bromide, and cesium iodide, the only vibrations are those vibrations of individual ions in which the movements are related to the nearest neighboring ions. Such a system can be thought of as a three-dimensional array of balls for individual ions and springs representing the forces holding the ionic array together. A motion within such a system is referred to as a lattice vibration. The resulting spectral bands are broad, and as the atomic weights of the atoms increase, these vibrations appear at successively lower energies (longer wavelengths, lower frequencies). Such lattice vibrations are responsible for the long-wavelength cutoff in transmission of alkali halide crystals (cf. Chap. 3).

In contrast, a solid containing a polyatomic ion will exhibit, in addition to lattice vibrations of the type described for monoatomic ions, motions of the polyatomic unit with respect to neighboring ions (rotatory movements) and vibrations within the polyatomic ion unit. These vibrations of the polyatomic unit are very much similar to vibrations occurring in organic substances and, as the reader has probably already deduced, are characteristic of the particular type of ion (i.e., all carbonate anions or sulfate anions should have characteristic vibrations regardless of the cation present, although the cation may cause a small shift in the position of the absorption).

Molecular solids, such as organic acid dimers, should have parallel analogs in inorganic systems; e.g., where two or more inorganic molecules are held together by hydrogen bonds or van der Waals' forces. Here, again, vibrations should be of two types: the lattice type due to stretchings and bendings of the weak associative bonds, and internal modes of vibration due to movements of atoms within the inorganic molecule. Such substances are clearly analogous to organic systems.

Finally, certain inorganic materials should exist as a single large molecular unit, similar to an organic polymer. Such a system would be exemplified by quartz, in which the entire atomic array is joined in three dimensions by Si—O—Si covalent bonds. By analogy to the organo-silicon compounds described in Sec. 5.5.1, such substances would be expected to exhibit characteristic bands in the infrared region.

5.6.2   Qualitative correlations in the 2 to 16μ region.   In the spectrum of sodium sulfate (Fig. 5.52), two bands are characteristic of the sulfate ion ($SO_4^=$) and appear within reasonably narrow ranges. A strong, broad band absorbs in the 1130- to 1080-cm^{-1} region (8.85 to 9.26μ) and a less intense absorption appears in the 680- to 610-cm^{-1} region (14.71 to 16.39μ). Similarly in the spectrum of potassium nitrate (Fig. 5.52), two bands are characteristic for the nitrate ion (NO_3^-). A very strong absorption appears in the 1380- to 1350-cm^{-1} region (7.25 to 7.41μ) and a sharp, less intense band in the 840- to 815-cm^{-1} region (11.90 to 12.27μ). These bands seem to be quite independent of the cation present. From comparison of the third spectrum in Fig. 5.52 (that of lead nitrate) with that of potassium nitrate, it can be seen that small shifts do occur within the narrow regions characteristic of the nitrate group (i.e., KNO_3 exhibits bands at 1380 (7.25μ) and 824 cm^{-1} (12.14μ), whereas $Pb(NO_3)_2$ has bands at 1373 (7.29μ) and 836 cm^{-1} (11.96μ).

No correlation of the particular cation to the position of these absorptions has been possible, although it is clear that shifts are to be anticipated. The different charges and radii of the various cations would be expected to produce different electrical environments about a particular cation, affecting the vibrational frequencies of the anionic polyatomic unit. Also, differences in symmetry should result in a similar environmental change. Different positive ions in many cases produce different crystalline arrangements. Moreover, a similar result, with perhaps even greater effect on the vibrational frequencies of polyatomic ions, would be expected with varying extent and type of hydration.

In certain instances a good correlation has been observed for the position of an anionic absorption band and the cation present. Such a relationship has been established for the 11 to 12μ band in anhydrous carbonates. As expected, increasing the mass of the cation shifts the band to lower frequencies (longer wavelengths). This correlation is illustrated in Fig. 5.53.

Variations in inorganic spectra.   In actual practice the chemist may obtain from an inorganic substance spectra that do not completely resemble the spectrum recorded in the literature. Two spectra recorded in the same laboratory from different samples also may show variations significant enough to cause doubt concerning the similarities between the two samples. There are several possible reasons for observations of these types: presence of impurities, crystal orientation in the radiant beam, polymorphism and hydration phenomena.

Figure 5.54 indicates a sample of sodium cyanide as examined in Nujol. The regions labeled with the asterisk are absorptions due to the Nujol. The

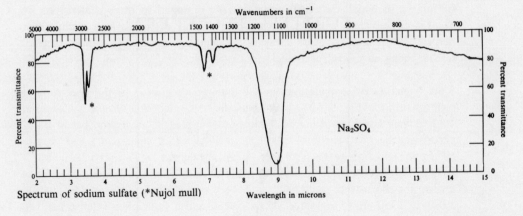

Spectrum of sodium sulfate (*Nujol mull)

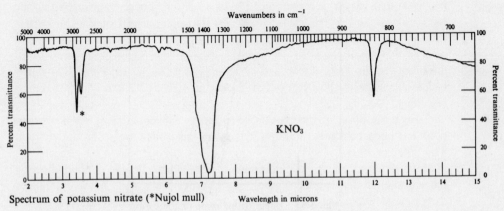

Spectrum of potassium nitrate (*Nujol mull)

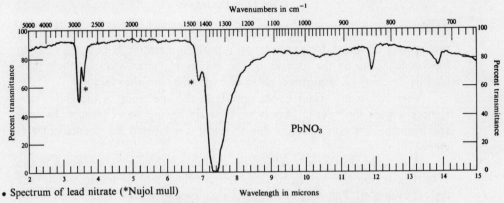

• Spectrum of lead nitrate (*Nujol mull)

Fig. 5.52   Typical spectra of inorganic anions.

arrows indicate bands not due to the cyanide ion. The spectrum immediately below that of sodium cyanide is the absorption curve of sodium carbonate, recorded as a Nujol mull. The similarity between the sodium carbonate bands and the impurity bands in the sodium cyanide spectrum is quite apparent. In spectra such as those in Fig. 5.54, care must be exercised in attempting to

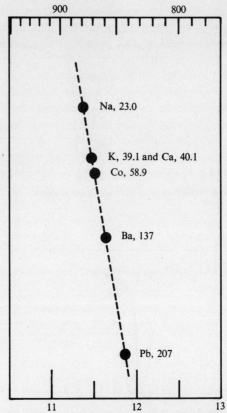

Fig. 5.53 Effect of the mass of the cation on the position of absorption in carbonates in the 11 to 12μ region.

correlate the bands in an experimentally obtained curve with reported literature spectra obtained, for example, on a purified material. It is much safer to base conclusions on the identity of the spectrum, rather than on their non-identity, because of impurities, water of hydration, or other factors.

Very frequently water bands appear in the spectrum of inorganic substances. Figure 5.55 exemplifies typical spectra having water present. In each spectrum the absorption bands due to water are labeled for convenient reference.

A number of inorganic substances exhibit no absorption spectrum in the 2 to 16μ region. Nickel hydroxide, ferric oxide, and mercuric sulfide are typical examples. The only absorptions that appear in their spectra are those due to water and hydroxyl bands.

5.6.3 Correlations of inorganic substances with the far-infrared spectra. Using a spectrophotometer equipped with a cesium bromide prism or a suitable filter-grating system, it is possible to examine absorptions beyond 16μ. As pointed out earlier, the vibrational energy decreases with increasing mass.

Therefore this region should be useful for the examination of low-energy vibrations occurring in both organic (particularly organo-metallic) and inorganic substances. An example of this approach has been the extension of correlations beyond 16μ in an effort to obtain further characteristic bands for inorganic ions. With presently available instrumentation, it is possible to examine the spectra of materials as far out in this region as 40μ (250 cm^{-1}). In such instances, Nujol can be used as a suspending agent for mulling samples, but sodium chloride must be replaced by a crystal material transparent in this region (i.e., CsBr or similar optical material with a long-wavelength cutoff). Considerable success in the examination of inorganic materials in the far-infrared region has been obtained using cells constructed of organic polymers such as polyethylene, which show no appreciable absorptions in this region.

Figure 5.56 typifies the spectra obtained from inorganic substances in the entire region from 4000 to 250 cm^{-1} (2.5 to 40μ).

5.6.4 Summary of inorganic correlations.

The utility of the correlations of characteristic frequencies of inorganic anions is quite obvious. The exami-

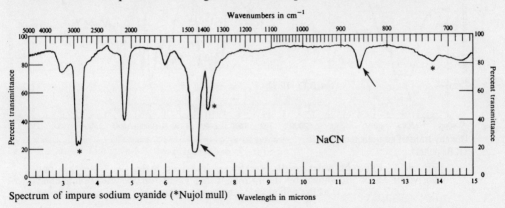

Spectrum of impure sodium cyanide (*Nujol mull)   Wavelength in microns

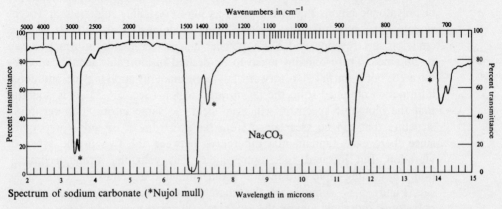

Spectrum of sodium carbonate (*Nujol mull)   Wavelength in microns

Fig. 5.54 Example of the effect of impurities on the recorded spectrum of inorganic materials.

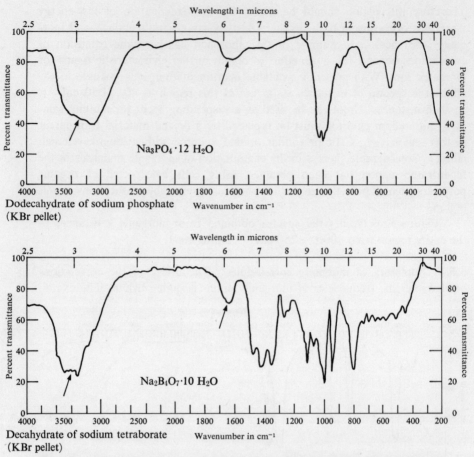

Dodecahydrate of sodium phosphate
(KBr pellet)

Decahydrate of sodium tetraborate
(KBr pellet)

Fig. 5.55 Effect of water on the spectra of inorganic materials. Note that only the water bands are shown by the arrows. Other effects on the absorption bands of the polyatomic ion are not indicated.

nation of the spectrum can yield, by comparison with known samples, identities of polyatomic anions that are present as pure crystalline materials or (occasionally) in some mixtures. By employing other analytical methods such as emission spectroscopy and X-ray powder analyses, valuable information can be obtained. There remains much to be desired in inorganic identification by infrared, but a partial step forward has been made in applying the additional information obtained from the far-infrared region (Sec. 5.6.3). It is doubtful that the inorganic spectrum will ever yield the same information regarding structure that can be ascertained from the spectrum of organic compounds, since there exist fundamental differences between the two in the types of vibration. But infrared spectrophotometry has valuable, although limited, utility in gaining rapid information about inorganic materials.

Figure 5.57 summarizes the characteristic frequencies established for polyatomic inorganic ions in the 3600- to 300-cm^{-1} region.

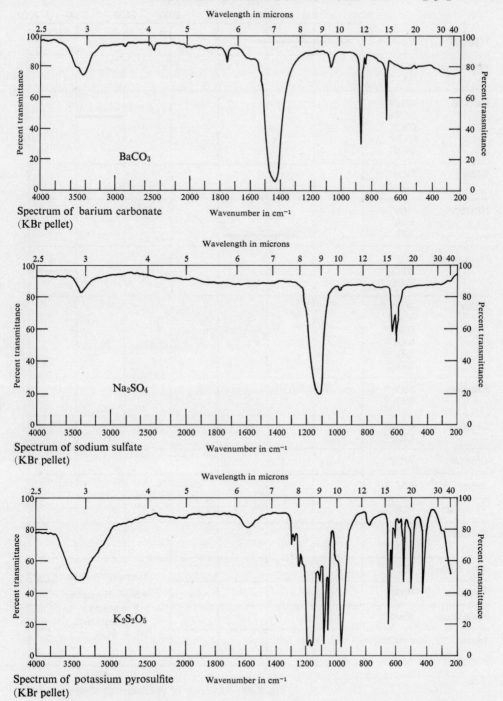

Spectrum of barium carbonate
(KBr pellet)

Spectrum of sodium sulfate
(KBr pellet)

Spectrum of potassium pyrosulfite
(KBr pellet)

Fig. 5.56 Typical spectra of inorganic substances over the 4000 to 250 cm^{-1} region.

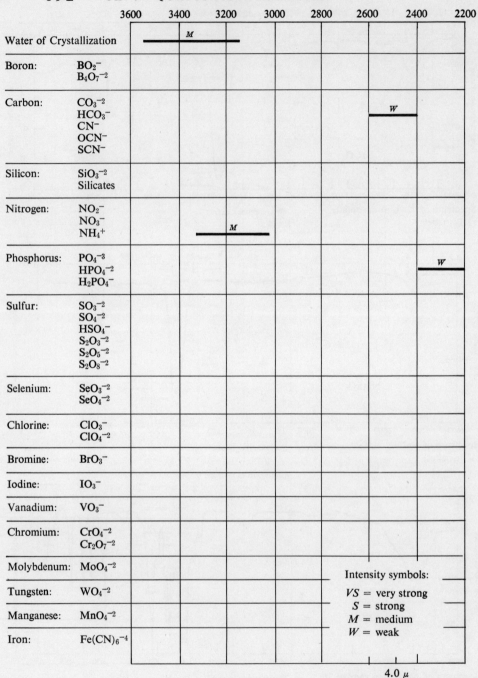

Fig. 5.57   Summary of characteristic absorption bands

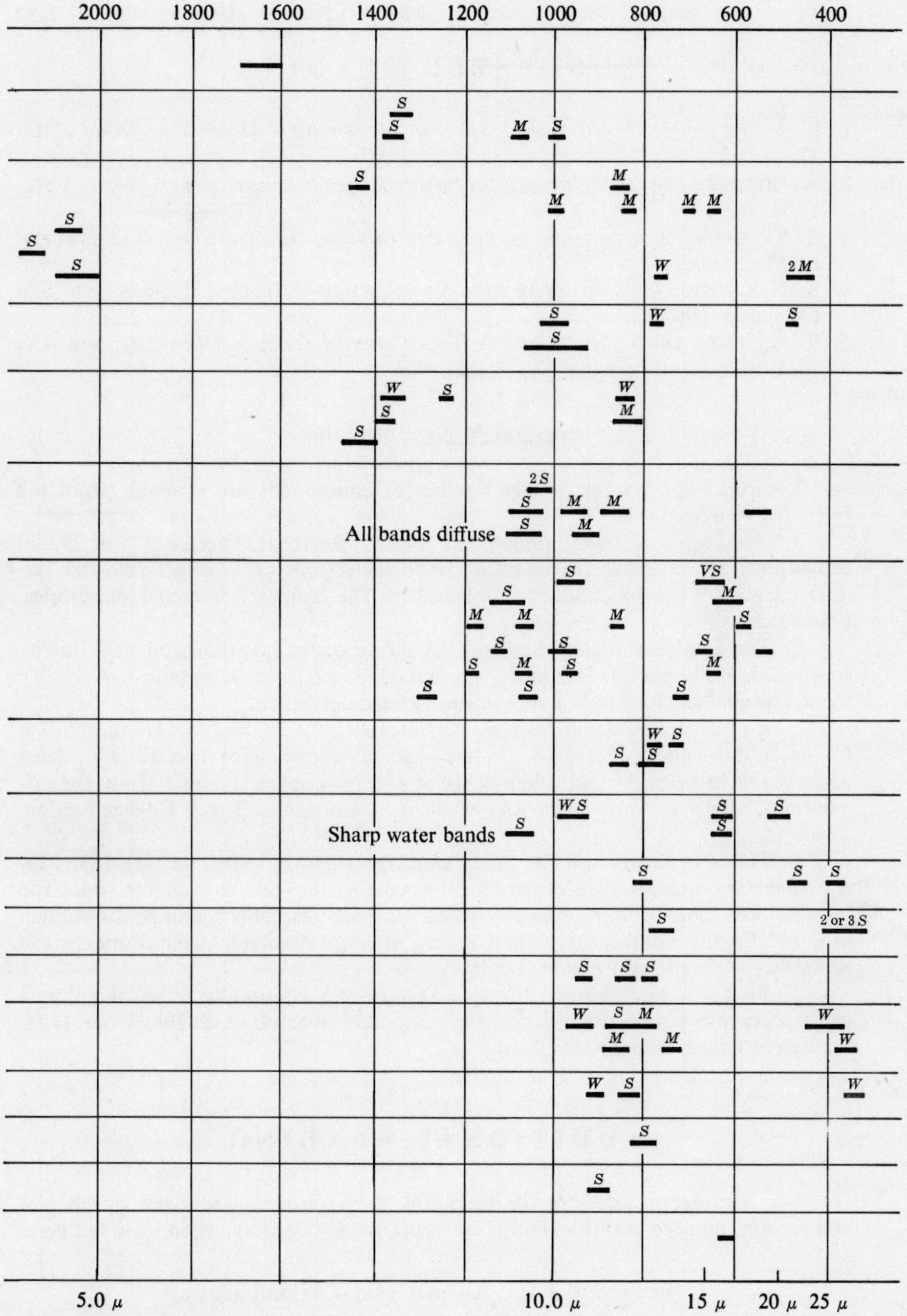

2000   1800   1600   1400   1200   1000   800   600   400

S
S

M   S

S

M   M
M

S   M   M   M

S   S   2 M

W

S   W   S
S

W   S   W
S   M

S

2 S
S   M   M
S   M
S

S   VS
M   M   M
M   S

M   M   M   S
S   S   S   M
S   M   S   S
S   S

W S
S   S

W S   S   S
Sharp water bands   S   S
S

S   S   S

S   2 or 3 S

S   S   S

W   S   M   W
M   M   W

W   S   W

S

S

All bands diffuse

5.0 μ   10.0 μ   15 μ   20 μ 25 μ

of inorganic materials in the 3600 to 300 cm⁻¹ region.

SUGGESTED READING

1. L. J. BELLAMY, *The Infrared Spectra of Complex Molecules.* Wiley, New York, 1958.
2. W. BRUGEL, *An Introduction to Infrared Spectroscopy.* Wiley, New York, 1962.
3. A. D. CROSS, *Introduction to Practical Infrared Spectroscopy.* Buttersworth, London, 1960.
4. K. NAKANISHI, *Infrared Absorption Spectroscopy—Practical.* Holden-Day, San Francisco, 1962.
5. R. N. JONES AND C. SANDORFY in *Techniques of Organic Chemistry,* Vol. IX, ed. W. West. Interscience, New York, 1956.

Spectral Source Materials

Reference spectra for a large number of compounds are available from the following sources:

1. *The Sadtler Research Laboratory Series.* Reference spectra of over 25,000 compounds are available. In addition, small collections of near-infrared and far-infrared spectra can be obtained. Published by The Sadtler Research Laboratories, Philadelphia, Pa.

2. *The Coblentz Society Spectra.* A group of several thousand high-quality spectra, carefully chosen for purity of compound, etc., can be obtained. Available from The Sadtler Research Laboratories, Philadelphia, Pa.

3. *American Petroleum Institute Research Project 44, and the Manufacturing Chemists Association Research Project.* Standard reference spectra are issued periodically in infrared and other fields of spectroscopy. Available from Department of Chemistry, Agricultural and Mechanical College of Texas, College Station, Texas.

4. *The Documentation of Molecular Spectroscopy—Spectra* (DMS). Infrared spectra and coded information for needle sorting of the available series can be obtained. The coding system is based on basic skeletal features, substituent groups, and the number of carbon atoms present. Available from Buttersworth Scientific Publications, London, England.

5. *An Index to Published Infrared Spectra.* A continuing series of volumes referencing the publication of specific compound spectra. Available from H.M. Stationery Office, London, England.

ADDITIONAL READING

For convenient access to the literature, the references are given by chapter and section, number and title. Only representative articles have been included here.

Section 5.3.1:   Alkanes and Cycloalkanes

C. F. H. ALLEN, T. DAVIS, W. J. HUMPHLETT, AND D. W. STEWART, *J. Org. Chem.,* **22** (1957), 1291.
P. BARCHEWITZ AND R. CHABBAL, *J. Phys. Radium,* **12** (1951), 637.
J. J. BRAUNHOLTZ, E. A. V. EBSWORTH, F. G. MANN, AND N. SHEPPARD, *J. Chem. Soc.* (1958), 2780.

L. H. BRIGGS AND L. D. COLEBROOK, *Anal. Chem.*, **29** (1957), 904.

J. K. BROWN, N. SHEPPARD, AND D. M. SIMPSON, *Trans. Roy. Soc. (London)*, **A247** (1954), 35.

R. CHABBAL AND P. BARCHEWITZ, *J. phys. radium*, **12** (1951), 701.

A. R. H. COLE AND R. N. JONES, *J. Opt. Soc. Am.*, **42** (1952), 348.

A. R. H. COLE, *Chem. & Ind. (London)* (1953), 946.

A. R. H. COLE, *J. Chem. Soc.* (1954), 3807, 3810.

J. J. FOX AND A. E. MARTIN, *Proc. Roy. Soc. (London)*, **A167** (1938), 257.

J. J. FOX AND A. E. MARTIN, *Proc. Roy. Soc. (London)*, **A175** (1940), 208.

S. A. FRANCIS, *J. Chem. Phys.*, **18** (1950), 861.

S. A. FRANCIS, *J. Chem. Phys.*, **19** (1951), 942.

H. B. HENBEST, G. D. MEAKINS, B. NICHOLLS, AND A. A. WAGLAND, *J. Chem. Soc* (1957), 1462.

R. D. HILLS AND G. D. MEAKINS, *J. Chem. Soc.* (1958), 760.

R. N. JONES, A. F. McKAY, AND R. G. SINCLAIR, *J. Am. Chem. Soc.*, **74** (1952), 2575.

J. M. MARTIN, R. W. B. JOHNSTON, AND M. J. O'NEAL, *Spectrochim Acta*, **12** (1958), 12.

H. L. McMURRAY AND V. THORNTON, *Anal. Chem.*, **24** (1952), 218.

B. NOLIN AND R. N. JONES, *J. Am. Chem. Soc.*, **75** (1953), 5626.

E. K. PLYLER AND N. ACQUISTA, *J. Research NBS*, **43** (1949), 37.

A. POZEFSKY AND N. P. COGGESHALL, *Anal. Chem.*, **23** (1951), 1611.

H. PRIMAS AND Hs. H. GUNTHARD, *Helv. Chim. Acta.*, **36** (1953), 1659, 1791.

R. S. RASMUSSEN, *J. Chem. Phys.*, **16** (1948), 712.

J. D. ROBERTS AND V. C. CHAMBERS, *J. Am. Chem. Soc.*, **73** (1951), 5030.

N. SHEPPARD, *J. Chem. Phys.*, **16** (1948), 690.

N. SHEPPARD AND D. M. SIMPSON, *Quart. Revs. (London)*, **7** (1953), 19.

S. E. WIBERLEY AND S. C. BUNCE, *Anal. Chem.*, **24** (1952), 623.

N. WRIGHT AND M. J. HUNTER, *J. Am. Chem. Soc.*, **69** (1947), 803.

Section 5.3.2: Alkenes

K. ALDER AND H. VON BRACHEL, *Ann.*, **608** (1957), 195.

J. L. H. ALLAN, G. D. MEAKINS, AND M. C. WHITING, *J. Chem. Soc.* (1955), 1874.

H. C. ALLEN, JR., AND E. K. PLYER, *J. Chem. Soc.*, **80** (1958), 2673.

B. BAK AND D. CHRISTENSEN, *Spectrochim. Acta.*, **12** (1958), 355.

D. BARNARD, *J. Chem. Soc.* (1950), 915.

M. I. BATUEV, A. S. ONISHCHENKO, A. V. MATVEEVA AND N. I. ARONOVA, *Dokl. Akad. Nauk S.S.S.R.*, **132** (1960), 581.

L. J. BELLAMY AND R. L. WILLIAMS, *J. Chem. Soc.* (1958), 2463.

S. BRODERSAW AND LANGSETH, *J. Mol. Spectroscopy*, **3** (1959), 114.

D. CHAPMAN AND R. J. TAYLOR, *Nature*, **174** (1954), 1011.

W. H. T. DAVISON, *Chem. & Ind. (London)*, (1957), 131.

R. HEILMAN, C. DE GAUDEMARIS, AND P. ARNAUD, *Compt. rend. Acad. sci., Paris*, **242** (1956), 2953.

H. B. HENBEST, G. D. MEAKINS, B. NICHOLLS, AND R. A. L. WILSON, *J. Chem. Soc.* (1957), 997.

R. E. KITSEN, *Anal. Chem.*, **25** (1953), 1470.

Section 5.3.3: Aromatics

R. N. BAPAT, *Indian J. Phys.*, **33** (1959), 295.

J. BOMSTEIN, **25** (1953), 512.

W. BRUHN AND R. MECKE, *Z. Elektrochem.*, **62** (1958), 441.

A. CABANA, J. L. PATENANDE, C. SANDORFY, AND P. M. G. BAVIN, *J. Phys. Chem.*, **64** (1960), 1941.

C. G. CANNON AND G. B. B. M. SUTHERLAND, *Spectrochim. Acta*, **4** (1951), 373.

M. MARGOSHES AND V. A. FASSEL, *Spectrochim. Acta*, **7** (1955), 14.

W. J. POTTS, *Anal. Chem.*, **27** (1955), 1027.

D. H. WHIFFEN, *Spectrochim. Acta*, **7** (1955), 253.

C. W. YOUNG, R. B. DuVALL, AND N. WRIGHT, *Anal. Chem.*, **23** (1951), 709.

Section 5.4.1: Triple-bonded and Cumulative Multiple-bonded Groups

C. F. H. ALLEN, T. DAVIS, W. J. HUMPHLETT, AND D. W. STEWART, *J. Org. Chem.*, **22** (1957), 1291.

F. BOHLMANN AND H. SINN, *Chem. Ber.*, **88** (1955), 1869.

P. E. B. BUTLER, D. R. EATON, AND H. W. THOMPSON, *Spectrochim. Acta*, **13** (1958), 223.

G. L. CALDOW AND H. W. THOMPSON, *Spectrochim. Acta*, **13** (1958), 212.

E. FAHR, *Ann.*, **617** (1958), 11.

D. G. I. FELTON AND S. F. D. ORR, *J. Chem. Soc.* (1955), 487.

N. S. HAM AND J. B. WILLIS, *Spectrochim. Acta*, **6** (1960), 279.

N. S. HAM AND J. B. WILLIS, *Spectrochim. Acta*, **6** (1960), 393.

H. HOYER, *Chem. Ber.*, **89** (1956), 2677.

J. P. JESSON AND H. W. THOMPSON, *Spectrochim. Acta*, **13** (1958), 217.

R. E. KITSON AND N. E. GRIFFITH, *Anal. Chem.*, **24** (1952), 334.

G. D. MEAKINS AND R. L. MOSS, *J. Chem. Soc.* (1957), 993.

R. A. NYQUIST AND W. J. POTTS, *Spectrochim. Acta*, **16** (1960), 419.

P. SENSI AND G. G. GALLO, *Gazz. Chim. Ital.*, **85** (1955), 224.

P. SENSI AND G. G. GALLO, *Gazz. Chim. Ital.*, **85** (1955), 235.

M. W. SKINNER AND H. W. THOMPSON, *J. Chem. Soc.* (1955), 487.

C. L. STEVENS AND J. C. FRENCH, *J. Am. Chem. Soc.*, **75** (1953), 657.

C. L. STEVENS AND R. J. GASSER, *J. Am. Chem. Soc.*, **79** (1957), 6057.

K. B. WHETSEL, G. F. HAWKINS, AND F. E. JOHNSON, *J. Am. Chem. Soc.*, **78** (1956), 3360.

J. H. WOTIZ AND D. E. MANCUSO, *J. Org. Chem.*, **22** (1957), 207.

P. YATES, B. L. SHAPIRO, N. YODA, AND J. FUGGER, *J. Am. Chem. Soc.*, **79** (1957), 9755.

Section 5.4.2: Alcohols and Phenols

J. A. ANDERSON AND W. D. SEYFRIED, *Anal. Chem.*, **20** (1948), 998.

A. W. BAKER, *J. Am. Chem. Soc.*, **80** (1958), 3598.

A. W. BAKER, *J. Phys. Chem.*, **62** (1958), 744.

A. W. BAKER AND A. T. SHULGIN, *J. Am. Chem. Soc.*, **80** (1958), 5358.

P. M. G. BAVIN AND W. J. CANADY, *Can. J. Chem.*, **35** (1957), 1555.

W. BECKERING, *J. Phys. Chem.*, **65** (1961), 206.

L. J. BELLAMY AND H. E. HALLAM, *Trans. Faraday Soc.*, **55** (1959), 220.

P. M. BOLL, *Acta Chem. Scand.*, **12** (1958), 1777.

T. L. BROWN, *J. Am. Chem. Soc.*, **80** (1958), 6489.

T. L. BROWN, J. M. SANDRI, AND H. HART, *J. Phys. Chem.*, **61** (1957), 698.

T. CAIRNS AND G. EGLINTON, *Nature*, **196** (1962), 535.

G. CHIURDOGLU, A. CARDOU, AND W. MASSCHELEIN, *Bull. Soc. Chim. Belges*, **68** (1960), 29, 154, 484.

W. C. COBURN, JR., AND E. GRUNWALD, *J. Am. Chem. Soc.*, **80** (1958), 1318.

A. R. H. COLE, P. R. JEFFERIES, AND G. T. A. MULLER, *J. Chem. Soc.* (1959), 1222.

A. R. H. COLE, G. T. A. MULLER, D. W. THORNTON, AND R. L. S. WILLIX, *J. Chem. Soc.* (1959), 1218.

A. EMS AND F. E. MURRAY, *Can. J. Chem.,* **35** (1957), 170.

M. ST. C. FLETT, *Spectrochim. Acta,* **10** (1957), 21.

A. FURST, H. H. KUHN, R. SCOTONI, JR., AND H. GUNTHARD, *Helv. Chim. Acta,* **35** (1952), 951.

K. U. INGOLD, *Can. J. Chem.,* **38** (1960), 1092.

K. U. INGOLD, *Can. J. Chem.,* **40** (1962), 111.

K. U. INGOLD AND D. R. TAYLOR, *Can. J. Chem.,* **39** (1960), 471.

K. U. INGOLD AND D. R. TAYLOR, *Can. J. Chem.,* **39** (1961), 481.

S. JULIA, D. VARECH, T. CURER, AND H. H. GUNTHARD, *Helv. Chim. Acta,* **43** (1960), 1623.

A. NICKON, *J. Am. Chem. Soc.,* **79** (1957), 243.

N. A. PUTTNAM, *J. Chem. Soc.* (1960), 486.

N. A. PUTTNAM, *J. Chem. Soc.* (1960), 5100.

P. VON R. SCHLEYER, D. S. TRIFAN, AND R. BACSKAI, *J. Am. Chem. Soc.,* **80** (1958), 6691.

P. VON R. SCHLEYER, C. WINTER, D. S. TRIFAN, AND R. BACSKAI, *Tetrahedron* (Letters) No. 14 (1959), 1.

D. D. SHREWSBURY, *Spectrochim. Acta,* **16** (1960), 1244.

A. V. STUART AND G. B. B. M. SUTHERLAND, *J. Chem. Phys.* (1956), 24, 559.

R. WEST, *J. Am. Chem. Soc.,* **81** (1959), 1614.

J. J. WREN AND R. M. LENTHEN, *J. Chem. Soc.* (1961), 2557.

H. H. ZEISS AND M. TSUTSUI, *J. Am. Chem. Soc.,* **75** (1953), 897.

Section 5.4.3: Ethers and Related Functional Groups

J. A. ANDERSON AND W. D. SEYFRIED, *Anal. Chem.,* **20** (1948), 998.

E. D. BERGMANN AND S. PINCHAS, *Rec. Trav. Chim.,* **71** (1952), 161.

J. BOMSTEIN, *Anal. Chem.,* **30** (1958), 544.

M. L. BREY AND P. TARRANT, *J. Am. Chem. Soc.,* **79** (1957), 6533.

L. H. BRIGGS, L. D. COLEBROOK, H. M. FALES, AND W. C. WIDMAN, *Anal. Chem.,* **29** (1957), 904.

C. R. EDDY, M. E. WALL, AND K. M. SCOTT, *Anal. Chem.,* **25** (1953), 266.

HS. H. GUNTHARD, H. HEUSSER, AND A. FURT, *Helv. Chim., Acta,* **36** (1953), 1900.

H. B. HENBEST, G. D. MEAKINS, B. NICHOLLS, AND A. A. WAGLAND, *J. Chem. Soc.* (1957), 1462.

H. B. HENBEST, G. D. MEAKINS, B. NICHOLLS, AND K. J. TAYLOR, *J. Chem. Soc.* (1957), 1459.

A. KIRRMANN AND R. CHANCEL, *Bull. Soc. Chim. France* (1954), 1338.

Y. MIKAWA, *Bull. Chem. Soc. Japan,* **29** (1959), 110.

M. NORISADA AND T. NAKAGAWA, *J. Pharm. Soc. (Japan),* **79** (1959), 177.

W. A. PATTERSON, *Anal. Chem.,* **26** (1954), 823.

K. J. SAX, W. S. SAARI, C. L. MAHONEY, AND J. M. GORDON, *J. Org. Chem.,* **25** (1960), 1590.

H. TSCHAMLER AND R. LEUTNER, *Monatsh.,* **83** (1952), 1502.

Section 5.4.4: Amines, Imines, and Ammonium Salts

D. A. BARR AND R. N. HASZELDINE, *J. Chem. Soc.* (1955), 4169.

L. J. BELLAMY AND R. L. WILLIAMS, *Spectrochim. Acta,* **9** (1957), 341.

J. BELLANATO, *Spectrochim. Acta,* **16** (1957), 1344.

C. BRISSETTA AND C. SANDORFY, *Can. J. Chem.,* **38** (1960), 34.

S. Califano and R. Moccia, *Gazz. Chim. Ital.,* **87** (1957), 805.

B. Chenon and C. Sandorfy, *Can. J. Chem.,* **36** (1958), 1181.

L. K. Dyall, *Spectrochim. Acta,* **17** (1961), 291.

J. Fabian and M. Legrand, *Bull. Soc. Chim. France* (1956), 1461.

J. Fabian, M. Legrand, and P. Poirier, *Bull. Soc. Chim. France* (1956), 1499.

V. C. Farmer and R. H. Thomson, *Spectrochim. Acta,* **16** (1960), 559.

H. H. Freedman, *J. Am. Chem. Soc.,* **83** (1961), 2900.

A. N. Hambly and J. Bonnyman, *Australian J. Chem.,* **11** (1958), 529.

R. A. Heacock and L. Marion, *Can. J. Chem.,* **34** (1956), 1782.

R. D. Hill and G. D. Meakins, *J. Chem. Soc.* (1958), 760.

P. J. Krueger, *Nature,* **194** (1962), 1077.

P. J. Krueger, *Can. J. Chem.,* **41** (1963), 363.

S. F. Mason, *J. Chem. Soc.* (1958), 3619.

A. G. Moritz, *Spectrochim. Acta,* **16** (1960), 1176.

A. G. Moritz, *Spectrochim. Acta,* **17** (1961), 365.

A. G. Moritz, *Spectrochim. Acta.,* **18** (1962), 671.

A. G. Moritz, *Nature,* **195** (1962), 800.

M. Oki and K. Mutai, *Bull. Chem. Soc., Japan* (1960), 784.

W. J. Orville-Thomas, A. E. Parsons, and C. P. Ogden, *J. Chem. Soc.* (1958), 1047.

P. L. Pickard and G. W. Polly, *J. Am. Chem. Soc.,* **76** (1954), 5169.

M. A. Salimov and V. M. Tatevskii, *Proc. Acad. Sci. U.S.S.R., Phys. Chem. Sect.,* **112** (1957), 141.

J. N. Scheinker, E. M. Peresleni, and G. I. Bras, *J. Phys. Chem. (U.S.S.R.),* **29** (1955), 518.

J. E. Stewart, *J. Chem. Phys.,* **30** (1959), 1259.

P. J. Stone, J. C. Craig, and H. W. Thompson, *J. Chem. Soc.* (1958), 52.

W. B. Wright, Jr., *J. Org. Chem.,* **24** (1959), 1362.

Section 5.4.5: Carbonyl Compounds

R. A. Abramovitch, *Can. J. Chem.,* **37** (1959), 361.

N. H. E. Ahlers, R. A. Brett, and N. G. McTaggart, *J. Appl. Chem.,* **3** (1953), 433.

G. Allen, P. S. Ellington, and G. D. Meakins, *J. Chem. Soc.* (1960), 1909.

N. L. Allinger, J. Allinger, L. A. Freiberg, R. F. Czaja, and N. A. Lebel, *J. Am. Chem. Soc.,* **82** (1960), 5876.

C. L. Angell, P. J. Krueger, R. Lauzon, L. C. Leitch, K. Noack, R. J. D. Smith, and R. N. Jones, *Spectrochim. Acta,* **12** (1959), 926.

L. B. Archibald and A. D. E. Pullin, *Spectrochim. Acta,* **12** (1958), 34.

R. P. Bauman and E. Thomson, *J. Opt. Soc. Am.,* **53** (1963), 202.

L. J. Bellamy, B. R. Connelly, A. R. Philpotts, and R. L. Williams, *Z. Elektrochem.,* **64** (1960), 563.

L. J. Bellamy and R. L. Williams, *J. Chem. Soc.* (1957), 4294.

L. J. Bellamy and R. L. Williams, *Trans. Faraday Soc.,* **55** (1959), 14.

M. L. Bender and J. Figueras, *J. Am. Chem. Soc.,* **75** (1953), 6304.

E. Billeter, Th. Turer, and Hs. H. Sunthard, *Helv. Chim. Acta,* **40** (1957), 2046.

S. Bratoz, D. Hodzi, and N. Sheppard, *Spectrochim. Acta,* **8** (1961), 249.

C. J. W. Brooks, G. Eglinton, and J. F. Morman, *J. Chem. Soc.* (1961), 661.

F. V. Brutcher, T. Roberts, S. J. Barr, and N. Pearson, *J. Am. Chem. Soc.,* **78** (1956), 1507.

R. D. Campbell and N. H. Cromwell, *J. Am. Chem. Soc.,* **79** (1957), 3456.

C. G. Cannon, *Mikrochim. Acta* (1958), 555.

C. G. Cannon, *J. Chem. Phys.,* **24** (1956), 491.

C. Castinel, G. Chiurdoglu, M. L. Josien, J. Lascombe, and E. Vanlenduyt, *Bull. Soc. Chim. France* (1958), 807.

R. Cetina and J. L. Mateos, *J. Org. Chem.*, **25** (1960), 704.

A. R. H. Cole and A. J. Michell, *J. Chem. Soc.* (1959), 2005.

A. R. H. Cole and R. L. S. Willix, *J. Chem. Soc.* (1959), 1212.

P. J. Cornish and D. Chapman, *J. Chem. Soc.* (1957), 1746.

W. G. Dauben and W. W. Epstein, *J. Org. Chem.*, **24** (1959), 1595.

L. Eberson, *Acta. Chem. Scand.*, **13** (1959), 224.

S. A. Francis, *J. Chem. Phys.*, **19** (1951), 942.

J. P. Freeman, *J. Am. Chem. Soc.*, **80** (1958), 5954.

D. L. Glusker and H. W. Thompson, *Spectrochim. Acta*, **6** (1954), 434.

F. Gonzalez-Sanchez, *Combustibles*, **16** (1956), 129.

W. Gordy, *J. Chem. Phys.*, **8** (1940), 516.

R. R. Hampton and J. E. Newell, *Anal. Chem.*, **21** (1949), 914.

R. Heilmann, P. Traynard, and R. Glenat, *Compt. rend. Acad. sci., Paris*, **242** (1956), 2953.

H. B. Heubest, G. D. Meakins, and T. I. Wrigley, *J. Chem. Soc.* (1958), 2633.

R. N. Jones, C. L. Angell, T. Ito, and R. J. D. Smith, *Can. J. Chem.*, **37** (1959), 2007.

M. L. Josien and C. Castinel, *Bull. Soc. Chim. France* (1958), 801.

M. L. Josien and J. Lascombe, *J. Chim. Phys.*, **52** (1955), 162.

G. J. Karabatsos, *J. Org. Chem.*, **25** (1960), 315.

A. R. Katritzky, A. M. Mouro, J. A. T. Beard, D. P. Dearnaley, and N. J. Earl, *J. Chem. Soc.* (1958), 2182.

A. R. Katritzky and S. Oksne, *Spectrochim. Acta.*, **17** (1961), 1286.

J. Loscombe, P. Grange, and M. L. Josien, *Bull. Soc. Chim. France* (1957), 773.

N. J. Leonard and F. H. Owens, *J. Am. Chem. Soc.*, **80** (1958), 6039.

H. Luther and W. Stein, *Z. Elektrochem.*, **60** (1956), 1115.

R. Mecke and E. Funck, *Z. Elektrochem.*, **60** (1956), 1124.

R. Mecke and K. Noack, *Spectrochim. Acta*, **12** (1958), 391.

R. Mecke and K. Noack, *Chem. Ber.*, **93** (1960), 210.

F. A. Miller and G. L. Carlson, *J. Am. Chem. Soc.*, **79** (1950), 3995.

H. H. Morris and R. H. Young, jr., *J. Am. Chem. Soc.* **79** (1957), 3408.

F. E. Murray and S. Sundaram, *Can. J. Chem.*, **39** (1961), 1625.

K. Noack, *Spectrochim. Acta*, **18** (1962), 697.

N. Ogata, *Bull. Chem. Soc. (Japan)*, **34** (1961), 248.

M. Oki and M. Hirota, *Bull. Chem. Soc. (Japan)*, **34** (1961), 374.

J. Overent and J. R. Scherer, *Spectrochim. Acta*, **16** (1960), 773.

S. Pinchas, D. Samuel, and M. Weiss-Broday, *J. Chem. Soc.* (1961), 1688.

S. Pinchas, D. Samuel, and C. Weiss-Broday, *J. Chem. Soc.* (1961), 2382.

S. Pinchas, D. Samuel, and C. Weiss-Broday, *J. Chem. Soc.* (1961), 2666.

S. Pinchas, D. Samuel, and C. Weiss-Broday, *J. Chem. Soc.* (1961), 3063.

C. N. R. Rao and R. Venkatarghavan, *Spectrochim. Acta*, **18** (1962), 273.

R. S. Rasmussen and R. R. Brattain, *J. Am. Chem. Soc.*, **71** (1949), 1073.

R. S. Rasmussen, D. D. Tunnicliff, and R. R. Brattain, *J. Am. Chem. Soc.*, **71** (1949), 1068.

G. Salomon, C. J. Schoonveldt, and J. H. L. Zweers, *Rec. Trav. Chim.*, **79** (1960), 313.

D. S. Sarkadi and J. D. De Boer, *Rec. Trav. Chim.*, **76** (1957), 628.

W. M. Schubert and W. A. Sweeney, *J. Am. Chem. Soc.*, **77** (1955), 4172.

H. W. Thompson, R. W. Needhan, and D. Jameson, *Spectrochim. Acta*, **9** (1957), 208.

F. Wenzel, V. Schiedt, and F. L. Breusch, *Z. Naturf.*, **126** (1957), 71.

T. V. Yakovleva, A. G. Maslennikova, and A. A. Petrov, *Optika i Spektroskopiya*, **10** (1961), 131.

Section 5.4.6: Nitro, Nitroso, and Related N—O Systems

P. M. BOLL, *Acta. Chem. Scand.,* **12** (1958), 1777.

Z. BUCZKOWSKI AND T. URBANSKI, *Spectrochim. Acta,* **18** (1962), 1187.

S. CALIFANO AND W. LUTTKE, *Z. Phys. Chem.,* **6** (1956), 83.

R. CARDINAND, *Bull. Soc. Chim. France* (1960), 634.

R. A. G. CARRINGTON, *Spectrochim. Acta,* **16** (1960), 1279.

C. P. CONDUIT, *J. Chem. Soc.* (1959), 3273.

L. K. DYALL, *Spectrochim. Acta,* **17** (1961), 291.

J. C. EARL, R. J. W. LE FEVRE, A. G. PULFORD, AND A. WALSH, *J. Chem. Soc.* (1951), 2207.

B. FRANCK, H. HORMANN, AND S. SCHIEBE, *Chem. Ber.,* **90** (1957), 330.

P. A. GIGUERE AND D. CHIN, *Can. J. Chem.,* **39** (1961), 1214.

D. HADZI, *J. Chem. Soc.* (1956), 2725.

R. N. HASZELDINE AND J. JANDER, *J. Chem. Soc.* (1954), 691.

N. KORNBLUM, H. E. UNGNADE, AND R. A. SMILEY, *J. Org. Chem.,* **21** (1956), 377.

W. H. LUNN, *Spectrochim. Acta,* **16** (1960), 1088.

W. LUTTKE, *Z. Elektrochem.,* **61** (1957), 302.

W. LUTTKE, *Z. Elektrochem.,* **61** (1957), 976.

R. MATHIS-NOEL, R. WOLF, AND F. GALLIS, *Compt. rend. Acad. sci., Paris,* **242** (1956), 1873.

A. PALM AND H. WERBIN, *Can. J. Chem.,* **32** (1954), 858.

R. R. RANDLE AND D. H. WIFFEN, *J. Chem. Soc.* (1952), 4153.

H. SHINDO, *Pharm. Bull. (Japan),* **7** (1959), 407.

H. SHINDO, *Pharm. Bull. (Japan),* **7** (1959), 791.

J. TROTTER, *Can. J. Chem.,* **37** (1959), 1487.

W. R. VAUGHAN AND G. K. FINCH, *J. Org. Chem.,* **21** (1956), 1201.

Section 5.4.7: Halogen-containing Compounds

J. BURDON AND D. H. WHIFFEN, *Spectrochim. Acta,* **12** (1958), 139.

C. P. CJASCENKA, *Optika i Spektroskopiya,* **11** (1961), 192.

D. W. DAVIDSON AND H. J. BERNSTEIN, *Can. J. Chem.,* **33** (1955), 1226.

A. R. KATRITSKY AND J. M. LAGOWSKI, *J. Chem. Soc.* (1960), 2421.

P. KLAEBOE, J. J. LOTHE, AND K. LUNDE, *Acta. Chem. Scand.,* **10** (1956), 1465.

P. KLAEBOE, J. J. LOTHE, AND K. LUNDE, *Acta. Chem. Scand.,* **11** (1957), 1677.

E. T. MCBEE AND D. L. CHRISTMAN, *J. Am. Chem. Soc.,* **77** (1955), 755.

F. A. MILLER AND C. H. WILKENS, *Anal. Chem.,* **24** (1952), 1253.

J. R. NIELSEN, H. H. CLAASEN, AND D. C. SMITH, *J. Chem. Phys.,* **18** (1950), 485.

J. R. NIELSEN, C. Y. LIANG, D. C. SMITH, AND M. ALPERT, *J. Chem. Phys.,* **21** (1953), 1070.

H. W. THOMPSON AND P. TARKINGTON, *Trans. Faraday Soc.,* **42** (1946), 432.

Section 5.5.1: Organo-Silicon Compounds

R. C. FINCH AND H. POST, *J. Org. Chem.,* **24** (1959), 969.

M. E. GRENOBLE AND P. J. LAUNER, *Appl. Spectroscopy,* **14** (1960), 85.

M. C. HARVEY AND W. H. NEBERGALL, *Appl. Spectroscopy,* **16** (1962), 12.

M. C. HARVEY, W. H. NEBERGALL, AND J. S. PEAKE, *J. Am. Chem. Soc.,* **76** (1954), 4555.

R. N. KMISELEY, V. A. FASSEL, AND E. E. CONRAD, *Spectrochim. Acta,* **13** (1959), 651.

H. KRIEGSMANN, *Z. Elektrochem.*, **62** (1958), 1033.
H. KRIEGSMANN, *Z. Elektrochem.*, **61** (1957), 1088.
H. KRIEGSMANN, *Z. Anorg. Chem.*, **294** (1958), 113.
H. KRIEGSMANN, *Z. Anorg. Chem.*, **299** (1959), 78.
H. KRIEGSMANN, *Z. Anorg. Chem.*, **299** (1959), 138.
H. KRIEGSMANN, *Z. Elektrochem.*, **64** (1960), 541.
H. KRIEGSMANN, *Z. Elektrochem.*, **64** (1960), 848.
H. KRIEGSMANN AND H. BEYER, *Z. Anorg. Chem.*, **311** (1961), 180.
H. KRIEGSMANN AND H. CLAUSS, *Z. Anorg. Chem.*, **300** (1959), 210.
H. KRIEGSMANN AND G. ENGELHARDT, *Z. Anorg. Chem.*, **310** (1961), 320.
H. KRIEGSMANN AND K. LICHT, *Z. Electrochem,* **62** (1958), 1163.
H. KRIEGSMANN AND K. H. SCHOWTKA, *Z. Phys. Chem.*, **209** (1958), 261.
M. MARGOSHES AND V. A. FASSEL, *Anal. Chem.*, **27** (1955), 351.
L. D. NASIAK AND H. POST, *J. Org. Chem.*, **24** (1959), 489.
A. L. SMITH, *Spectrochim. Acta,* **16** (1960), 87.
A. L. SMITH AND N. C. ANGELOTTI, *Spectrochim. Acta,* **15** (1959), 412.
H. W. THOMPSON, *Spectrochim. Acta,* **16** (1960), 238.
T. V. YAKOVLEVA, A. A. PETROV, AND M. D. STANDNICUK, *Optika i Spektroskopiya,* **11** (1961), 588.
C. W. YOUNG, P. C. SERVAIS, C. C. CURRIE, AND M. J. HUNTER, *J. Am. Chem. Soc.,* **70** (1948), 3758.

Section 5.5.2: Organo-Sulfur Compounds

R. N. BAPAT, *Indian J. Phys.,* **33** (1959), 295.
L. J. BELLAMY, *The Organic Chemistry of Sulfur Compounds,* N. Kharasch, ed. New York, The Pergamon Press, 1961, pp. 47–56.
G. GEISELER AND N. O. BENDENAGEL, *Z. Elektrochem.*, **63** (1959), 1140.
H. HARRY-SZMANT, *J. Am. Chem. Soc.,* **78** (1956), 454.
R. N. HASZELDINE AND J. M. KIDD, *J. Chem. Soc.* (1955), 2901.
A. R. KATRITZKY AND R. A. JONES, *J. Chem. Soc.* (1960), 4497.
G. MALEWSKI AND H. J. WEIGMANN, *Spectrochim. Acta,* **18** (1962), 725.
D. PLANT, D. S. TARBELL, AND C. WHITEMAN, *J. Am. Chem. Soc.,* **77** (1955), 1572.
C. N. R. RAO AND R. VENKATARGHAVAN, *Spectrochim. Acta,* **18** (1962), 541.
A. SIMON AND D. KUNATH, *Z. Anorg. Chem.*, **308** (1961), 321.
A. SIMON AND D. KUNATH, *Z. Anorg. Chem.*, **311** (1961), 203.
S. SIMON AND D. KUNATH, *Chem. Ber.*, **94** (1961), 1776.

Section 5.5.3: Organo-Phosphorus Compounds

L. J. BELLAMY AND L. BEECHER, *J. Chem. Soc.* (1952), 475.
L. J. BELLAMY AND L. BEECHER, *J. Chem. Soc.* (1952), 1701.
J. R. FERRARO, *Appl. Spectroscopy,* **17** (1963), 12.
L. C. THOMAS AND R. A. CHITTENDEN, *Chem. & Ind.,* (*London*) (1961), 1913.
L. C. THOMAS AND R. A. CHITTENDEN, *J. Opt. Soc. Am.,* **52** (1962), 829.

Section 5.5.4: Organo-Metallic Compounds

C. C. BARRACLOUGH, J. LEWIS, AND R. S. NYHOLM, *J. Chem. Soc.* (1961), 2582.
G. BOR, *Spectrochim. Acta,* **18** (1962), 817.
F. A. COTTON, A. D. LIEHR, AND G. WILKINSON, *J. Inorg. Nucl. Chem.,* **1** (1955), 175.
F. A. COTTON AND R. R. MONCHAMP, *J. Chem. Soc.* (1960), 1882.

W. F. EDGELL, C. MAGEE, AND G. GALLUP, *J. Am. Chem. Soc.,* **78** (1956), 4185.

R. D. FISCHER, *Chem. Ber.,* **93** (1960), 165.

R. A. FRIEDEL, I. WENDER, S. L. SHUFLER, AND H. W. STERNBERG, *J. Am. Chem. Soc.,* **77** (1955), 3951.

H. P. FRITZ, *Chem. Ber.,* **92** (1959), 780.

H. P. FRITZ, W. LUTTKE, H. STAMMREICH, AND R. FORNERIS, *Chem. Ber.,* **92** (1959), 3246.

T. S. PIPER AND G. WILKINSON, *J. Inorg. Nucl. Chem.,* **3** (1956), 104.

R. K. SHELINE, *J. Am. Chem. Soc.,* **72** (1950), 5761.

R. K. SHELINE, *J. Am. Chem. Soc.,* **73** (1951), 1615.

R. K. SHELINE AND K. S. PITZER, *J. Am. Chem. Soc.,* **72** (1950), 1107.

R. G. SNYDER, *Spectrochim. Acta,* **15** (1959), 807.

Section 5.6: Inorganic Compounds

C. C. ADDISON AND B. M. GATEHOUSE, *Chem. & Ind. (London)* (1958), 464.

C. C. ADDISON AND B. M. GATEHOUSE, *J. Chem. Soc.* (1960), 613.

D. E. C. CORBRIDGE, *J. Appl. Chem.,* **6** (1956), 456.

J. R. FERRARO, *J. Inorg. Nucl. Chem.,* **10** (1959), 319.

J. R. FERRARO, *J. Inorg. Nucl. Chem.,* **15** (1960), 365.

J. R. FERRARO, *J. Mol. Spectroscopy,* **4** (1960), 99.

B. M. GATEHOUSE, S. E. LIVINGSTONE, AND R. S. NYHOLM, *J. Chem. Soc.* (1957), 4222.

B. M. GATEHOUSE AND J. COMYNS, *J. Chem. Soc.* (1958), 3965.

B. M. GATEHOUSE, S. E. LIVINGSTONE, AND R. S. NYHOLM, *J. Chem. Soc.* (1958), 3137.

J. M. HUNT, M. P. WISHERD, AND L. D. BONHAM, *Anal. Chem.,* **22** (1950), 1478.

J. M. HUNT AND D. S. TURNER, *Anal. Chem.,* **25** (1953), 1169.

J. LECOMPTE, *Anal. Chim. Acta.,* **2** (1948), 727.

J. LECOMPTE, *Cahiers Phys.,* **17** (1943), 1.

F. MILLER AND C. H. WILKINS, *Anal. Chem.,* **24** (1952), 1253.

F. MILLER AND G. L. CARLSON, *Spectrochim. Acta,* **16** (1960), 135.

S. MIZUSHIMA AND J. V. QUAGLIANO, *J. Am. Chem. Soc.,* **75** (1953), 4870.

D. F. PEPPARD AND J. R. FERRARO, *J. Inorg. Nucl. Chem.,* **10** (1959), 275.

6

Quantitative Analysis

In recent years infrared spectroscopy has become more and more familiar to the chemist as a routine qualitative tool for functional-group analysis (Chap. 5). The utility of measurements in this spectral region for the quantitative analysis of mixtures should nevertheless not be underestimated. In many cases, infrared spectral measurements can be made rapidly and quantitatively. As in other spectrophotometric methods of analysis, such as ultraviolet and visible spectrophotometry, the requirements for the analysis of a mixture of compounds rests solely on the presence of a unique, reasonably strong, absorption band for each component that is not interfered with by other components in the total sample. Generally, solid, liquid, or gaseous phase analyses can be performed by the application of infrared methods. Since an overwhelming number of the problems confronting the chemist requiring infrared spectrophotometry can be handled in solution, this chapter will deal almost exclusively with solution methods.

Briefly, quantitative determination of a specific component in a mixture is accomplished by comparison of the intensity of a unique absorption band with the same infrared band from the pure component under conditions of known concentration. Thus, if the band being measured is not interfered with by other components of the mixture (i.e., each component has a specific absorption band that is not overlapped by absorptions as the result of other species being present), the concentration of each component in the mixture can be determined from a single infrared spectrum. This is rarely the case, however, and precise quantitative analyses require a somewhat more careful treatment. For mixtures in which the absorption of a minor component is known to contribute only slightly to the absorption of the analytical band for the component being determined, a comparison should be made of the extent of these absorptions, with the accuracy necessary in the analysis. For example, if the analysis requires distinction between samples containing 42% of component A or 45% of component A, and the contribution by a second component is small (measured by the ratio of absorbances of pure A and pure B at the wavelength being studied), then the contribution of B to the accuracy of the analysis will be insignificant. Corrections, therefore, for the absorbance of B need not be made.

In any analysis, to conserve his time and effort, the chemist should be familiar with the accuracy dictated by the problem, prior to undertaking the extensive analytical measurements. In situations where a highly accurate measurement is required, the analyst should be certain that the infrared spectrophotometer itself is suitable for the particular determination. Since the ultimate accuracy of the quantitative determination will be dependent upon the spectrophotometer, it remains to the chemist to determine if his particular analysis can best be performed by the infrared method or perhaps by some other equally rapid method such as gas chromatography. The student-reader should be particularly careful in this regard when tracing methods of analysis for specific mixtures through the original literature. Many of the multicomponent analyses published in the mid-1940s through the late 1950s, using the infrared method, have been discarded for newer, more accurate techniques. These methods, such as gas chromatography, rely heavily on infrared spectroscopy for identification purposes rather than for quantitative measurement of concentration.

6.1 THE RELATIONSHIP BETWEEN INFRARED RADIATION REACHING THE DETECTOR AND SAMPLE CONCENTRATION: THE BEER-LAMBERT LAW

Since all spectrophotometric methods record the relative light intensity reaching the detector or the percent transmission of the incident radiation through the sample, a relationship between the radiation reaching the detector and the concentration of the component in solution is necessary before a quantitative analysis can be performed. This relationship is generally known as the Beer-Lambert law (it is sometimes referred to as the Beer-Bouguer law, or simply Beer's law).

If one considers the passage of an incident beam of radiation through a cell as shown in Fig. 6.1, we can let I represent the amount of radiation passing through a square centimeter of cell area per second. If we consider a small differential segment of the total cell, db, the decrease in the amount of radiation $-dI$ passing across db will be proportional to the amount of radiation per second per square centimeter (I) available for absorption, and to the

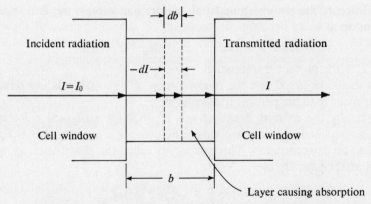

Fig. 6.1 Decrease in radiant energy as a result of absorption.

number of molecules capable of absorption of radiation in a square centimeter of the segment. Since the number of molecules capable of absorption per square centimeter of the segment is proportional to the concentration of absorbing molecules, c, and to db, then $-dI$, the *absorbed* radiation, should equal the product of the concentration c, segment length db, and the amount of radiation per square centimeter, I. In equation form, this can be summarized by

$$-dI = a'cI \cdot db \qquad (6.1)$$

where a' is a proportionality factor whose value depends on the absorbing molecule at a particular frequency (and, of course, the units used to express c and b). The physical meaning of a' should be clear to the reader. If one considers an actual spectrum of a substance, it is clear that a' can vary with each given wavelength value; therefore, with c and b held constant, the curve obtained is a record of the change of this coefficient with wavelength.

If one integrates Eq. 6.1 to find the total decrease in the intensity of the incident radiation, Eq. 6.1 becomes

$$\int_{I_0}^{I} \frac{dI}{I} = -\int a'cdb = -a'c \int_0^b db$$

Therefore

$$\log_e \frac{I}{I_0} = -a'cb \qquad (6.2)$$

Since logarithms to the base 10 are normally used in analytical work, Eq. 6.2 becomes

$$\log_{10} \frac{I}{I_0} = -abc \qquad (6.3)$$

where the absorptivity a is defined as $a'/\log_e 10$. The Beer-Lambert relationship is usually expressed in the form of Eq. 6.3. In this equation I represents the infrared energy transmitted by the solution and I_0 represents the total energy of the incident beam. Therefore the term I/I_0 represents the percent transmission of the absorbing material, and we can express the Beer-Lambert relationship as

$$\log T = -abc \qquad \text{or} \qquad \log 1/T = abc$$

where T is the percent transmission.

It should be noted that the concentration of a substance is *not* related in a linear manner to the percent transmission.

Actually the chemist does not use Eq. 6.3 for analytical calculations; rather, a simplified equation is obtained by defining a quantity that is linearly related to the concentration. This quantity is called the absorbance, A, and is defined mathematically as

$$A = -\log \frac{I}{I_0} = -\log T = \log \frac{1}{T}$$

Therefore the Beer-Lambert expression becomes

$$A = abc \tag{6.4}$$

The absorbance A is a quantity measurable directly from the spectrophotometer simply by using an absorbance scale rather than a transmission scale, as shown in Fig. 6.2.

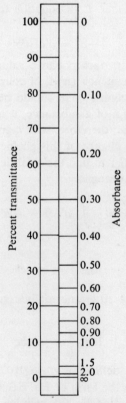

Fig. 6.2 Comparison of absorbance and transmission scales.

6.2 DEVIATIONS FROM THE
BEER-LAMBERT RELATIONSHIP

When the plot of the absorbance A versus the concentration c is a straight line, the substance is said to follow the Beer-Lambert law. However, many compounds do not yield straight-line relationships when plotted in this fashion. In such cases a "working curve" is used to correct for the deviation of the concentration from the linear relationship. Figure 6.3 indicates three examples of nonideal behavior. In most cases the deviation (case B, Fig. 6.3) is caused by chemical or physical interaction between molecules in solution. Hydrogen bonding, ion-pair formation, solvation, decomposition, and other chemical reactions may take place, causing an anomalous change in concentration of one of the components as the concentration of the mixture is changed. Physical interactions of polar molecules in solution are also important. As the concentration is increased in the case of polar molecules, a variation in the absorptivity usually occurs, again producing variations in the Beer-Lambert law.

Deviations from the Beer-Lambert relationship nearly always become significant at high concentrations. Therefore deviations from the law experimentally are more frequent than one might have expected. Any experimental situation in which the absorbance is not equal to the product of cell length, concentration, and absorptivity represents a deviation from the law.

In some cases, deviations are caused by instrumental parameters or background absorption. Where necessary, these instrumental effects can be compensated for by instrument adjustments or correction factors. However, in the case of chemical and physical interactions, if the sample mixture-solvent system cannot be widely varied because of solubility problems, a working curve must be constructed over the nonlinear portion of the curve. In case A, Fig. 6.3, or over a limited and almost linear range in cases B and C, the Beer-Lambert equation can be modified to include the added absorbance A_x:

$$A = A_x + abc \qquad (6.5)$$

6.2.1 The working curve. Figure 6.4 illustrates a working curve for a typical analysis where the Beer-Lambert relationship is not followed for a single-component analysis. The single component can be measured readily from its unique spectral-band position. For such routine analyses, this method has very distinct advantages over direct calculation methods based on the Beer-Lambert law. It is clear from the manner in which the working curve is constructed that it is as close a measure of the behavior of the compound in solution as it is possible to obtain experimentally. Therefore it should be expected that this method would be quite accurate. For the student-reader, the following example may be useful in gaining some idea of how to perform a simple, one-component analysis: A series of solutions of cyclohexanone in cyclohexane gave values for absorbance as a function of concentration, as

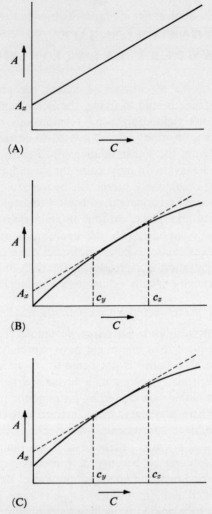

Fig. 6.3 Examples of absorbance versus concentration curves that do not strictly follow the Beer-Lambert relationship over a wide range (non-ideal behavior). (A) Compound follows the Beer-Lambert relationship plus background absorption; $A = A_x + abc$. (B) Compound exhibits nonlinear behavior. The equation in (A) is followed only over a limited range (c_y to c_z). (C) Combination of (A) and (B). The equation of (A) is followed only over a limited range (c_y to c_z).

shown in Table 6.1. From these data, the working curve shown in Fig. 6.4 was constructed. This curve was utilized in the analysis of a series of samples resulting from the oxidation of cyclohexanol to cyclohexanone with potassium permanganate. Since the background absorption from the residual, unreacted

Table 6.1.   Typical Set of Standards Used in Preparing a Working Curve for a Single Component Analysis

(*Analysis of Cyclohexanone in Cyclohexane*)

Concentration (g/l)	Absorbance* (5.83μ band)
5	0.190
10	0.244
15	0.293
20	0.345
25	0.390
30	0.444
35	0.487
40	0.532
45	0.562
50	0.585

* Cell-path length 0.096 mm.

alcohol was found to be insignificant, the analysis proved to be rapid and reproducible.

In practice, it makes little or no difference whether a working curve is completely linear. Unfortunately, for very accurate analyses of multicomponent mixtures where overlapping of absorption bands occurs, this method is not applicable, and more sophisticated methods must be used (see Sec. 6.3 for examples).

6.3   MEASUREMENT OF THE ABSORBANCE

Instrumentally speaking, two general methods employing peak heights for quantitative determination are in practice. The first utilizes the scanning of the spectrum by either a single- or double-beam spectrophotometer and measuring the band absorbance by the "base-line" method. The second is similar to the technique frequently employed in the ultraviolet-visible region. The absorbance of the sample in solvent is measured at fixed wavelength; the cell is then filled only with solvent and the absorbance is again determined, to obtain the solvent-blank absorbance correction. This technique is commonly referred to as the "cell-in-cell-out" method. Both methods give a value for the absorbance A directly.

The chemist is normally confronted with an analysis that can be performed under scanning conditions. Therefore, although he should be familiar with both methods of obtaining absorbance values, the following section will deal solely with the "base-line" method. More detailed treatment can be obtained by consulting one or more of the reference works listed at the end of the chapter under "Suggested Reading."

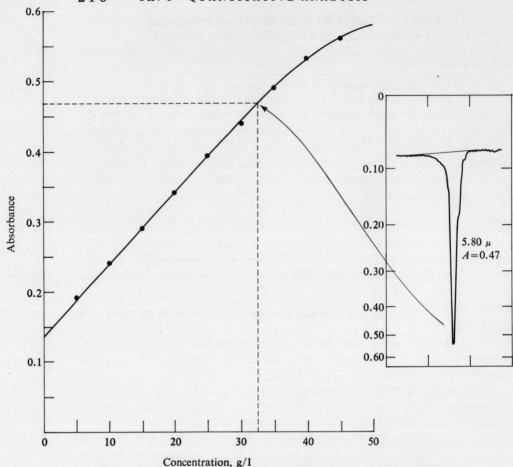

Fig. 6.4 Construction of a typical working curve for the analysis of cyclohexanone in cyclohexane solution. The dashed lines indicate concentration versus absorbance for an unknown mixture exemplified in the inserted spectrum.

6.3.1 The Base-line method. The "base-line" method consists simply of drawing an arbitrarily chosen line to represent the base line of the absorption band. As shown in Fig. 6.5, the representative base line can be drawn in various ways, the choice depending closely on the absorption characteristics of other components in the mixture. The choice of the base line to be drawn is generally tenored by the following considerations:

1. If interfering substances are not present, line 1, Fig. 6.5, is drawn. The assumption made is that the solvent will give this line in the absence of the solute.

2. If an interfering substance is present, a single-point base line can be drawn (lines 2 and 3, Fig. 6.5), depending on whether the interference is on the high- or low-wavelength side of the analytical band being measured.

3. If the interfering band is close to the analytical band, but its effect is

essentially constant over the range of the analysis, line 4, Fig. 6.5, would be applicable.

In all cases the base line drawn is chosen on the basis of the relative reproducibility of the point or points from which the base line is constructed from among the spectra being compared.

The base-line method has a number of advantages that are definitely worthy of note. Foremost among the advantages is the fact that cell absorption and other absorptions not related to the band under scrutiny are minimized. The experimental collection of data is rapid, since a relatively small number of spectral determinations are necessary. In addition to these advantages, under ideal conditions the numerical computations are simple to carry out and are quite rapid.

6.3.2 Typical analyses. In order to exemplify the routine procedures in carrying out a relatively simple analysis, the following examples can be cited. In the first instance, the analysis is carried out simply by the base-line method, assuming that other components have a significant contribution to the observed absorbance value at each specific wavelength. The second example utilizes the data less fully, taking into consideration the fact that only a very small portion of the observed absorbance at the analytical wavelength is due to the other compounds present. In this second case, the simultaneous equations resulting from the strict adherence to the principle of additivity of absorbances is ignored.

The following example will illustrate the details of the procedure utilized in almost any analysis. Although the computation method will vary according to the complexity of the mixture to be analyzed, the procedure used in setting up the data generally follows the procedure outlined here. Figure 5.18 shows the spectra of o-xylene, m-xylene and p-xylene. Figure 6.6 illustrates the spectrum over a limited region of an unknown mixture of o-xylene, m-xylene, and

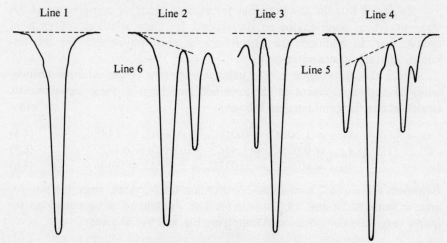

Fig. 6.5   Examples of possible "base-line" constructions.

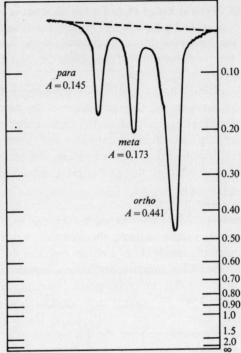

Fig. 6.6 Absorbance data for an unknown mixture of *o*-, *m*-, and *p*-xylene.

p-xylene in cyclohexane solution. Three individual wavelengths were chosen for the analysis: for *o*-xylene, the band at 13.49μ; for *m*-xylene, the band at 13.02μ; and for *p*-xylene, the band at 12.58μ. Each component was examined in cyclohexane solution for any absorbance at the three analytical wavelengths to be used, to determine the concentration of each component in the mixture.

Table 6.2 lists the absorptivities for each of the three components at the three analytical wavelengths as determined for pure solutions of each in cyclohexane. In addition, the absorbance at each wavelength for the unknown mixture is also tabulated.

Since the absorbance of the unknown mixture is the additive absorbances of each component at the specified wavelengths, three simultaneous equations can be formulated as follows:

$$A_{12.58} = 1.506C_p + 0.048C_m + 0.000C_o = 0.145 \qquad (6.6)$$
$$A_{13.02} = 0.025C_p + 1.44C_m + 0.000C_o = 0.173 \qquad (6.7)$$
$$A_{13.49} = 0.032C_p + 0.033C_m + 2.405C_o = 0.441 \qquad (6.8)$$

Equations 6.6 and 6.7 contain no contribution for *o*-xylene, since the absorbance at both 12.58 and 13.02μ is zero. The solution of these equations requires very little computation. Multiplying Eq. 6.6 by 30 gives

$$45.180C_p + 1.44C_m + 0.000C_o = 4.350$$

Table 6.2.   Typical Set of Data for the Analysis of *o*-Xylene
***m*-Xylene, and *p*-Xylene in Cyclohexane Solution**

Wavelength (μ)	Absorptivity* × Cell Length†			Absorbance of Unknown Mixture
	p-xylene	*m-xylene*	*o-xylene*	
12.58	1.506	0.048	0.000	0.145
13.02	0.025	1.440	0.000	0.173
13.49	0.032	0.033	2.405	0.441

* The absorptivities at the specified wavelengths for each component were determined from the Beer-Lambert relationship, $A = abc$; the absorbance A was measured in a cell of known path length (0.1 mm) for each component at a known concentration. For example: For *p*-xylene (0.992 gram in 100 ml of cyclohexane), an absorbance of 1.45 was obtained, using a 0.1-mm cell. Therefore,

$$1.45 = a[9.92 \text{ g/l}(0.01 \text{ cm})]$$
$$a = 14.62$$

† Cell-path length used for all measurements was 0.103 mm.

Subtracting Eq. 6.7 ($0.025C_p + 1.44C_m + 0.000C_o = 0.173$) yields

$$45.155C_p = 4.277$$
$$C_p = 0.095 \text{ g/l}$$

Substituting in Eq. 6.7 the value of the concentration of *p*-xylene (0.095) and solving,

$$C_m = 0.118 \text{ g/l}$$

The values of C_m and C_p when substituted in Eq. 6.8 yield

$$C_o = 0.180 \text{ g/l}$$

Concentrations (by synthesis) of the mixture were 0.096, 0.118, and 0.182 g/l.

By inspection of Table 6.2 the reader can readily see that at each analytical wavelength, the absorbance of one component is significantly greater than the others. In such cases, a direct calculation that ignores the absorbance contribution of the minor components should be made for comparison with the more exact solution. It could well be that the dictates of the problem warrant only an approximate solution. The direct solutions for each component are as follows:

$$A_{12.58} = 1.506C_p = 0.145$$
$$C_p = 0.096 \text{ g/l} \tag{6.9}$$

$$A_{13.02} = 1.440C_m = 0.173$$
$$C_m = 0.120 \text{ g/l} \tag{6.10}$$

$$A_{13.49} = 2.405C_o = 0.441$$
$$C_o = 0.180 \text{ g/l} \tag{6.11}$$

It can be seen that these values do not significantly differ from those obtained from the solution of the simultaneous equations. Although more exact values for the absorptivities and absorbances can be obtained by dividing measured distances, the accuracy of these values is probably no better than ± 0.005 in the units given. For more detailed calculation methods the reader should consult Ref. 1.

6.4   ACCURACY OF INFRARED ANALYSIS

As already implied in Chap. 3, the infrared method should not be expected to give high precision results. The reason for this, assuming that all other experimental errors are minor, lies inherently in the spectrophotometer. The spectrophotometer measures the transmission of radiant infrared energy, but the concentration of a substance in solution is proportional to the absorbance. In order to determine the accuracy of the infrared spectrophotometer, we must know at what point on the transmission scale we have a condition set up such that a small change in absorbance will produce the greatest change in chart deflection. Figure 6.7 shows the change in transmission produced by a 1% change in absorbance as a function of absorbance. The curve has a maximum at an absorbance value of roughly 0.43 and a transmission value of 37%. From simple inspection it is clear the best precision will result when quantitative measurements are made in the 25 to 50% transmission range (0.3 to 0.6 absorbance units). To do this in practice requires the analyst to adjust cell length or concentration. In this region the variation of A is approximately 1% or $\pm 1\%$ of the material being analyzed.

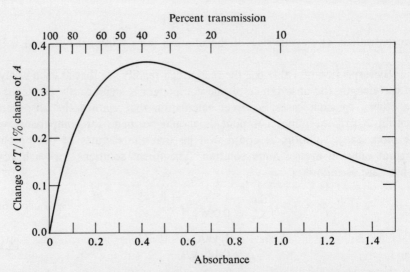

Fig. 6.7   Change in transmission produced by a 1% change in absorbance as a function of absorbance.

6.5 DIFFERENTIAL ANALYSIS

The ultimate accuracy in analytical determinations by infrared spectroscopy is obtained by the differential analysis method, which compares an unknown directly against a reference sample. In the differential method two solutions that are very nearly alike are compared. One of the solutions contains the component being analyzed in known concentration; the other, the unknown solution. Naturally the path lengths of the cells are very carefully matched. It is necessary in using this method that the solutions, when examined alone without reference-beam compensation, should transmit 37% of the incident radiation. In addition, the wavelength selected should be in a region where the solvent has minimal absorption and the sample solution transmits 37%. In order to offset the loss in energy (absorption occurring in both beams of the spectrophotometer), wide slit widths and slow scanning speeds are required. The data so collected are analyzed by the standard methods already discussed, using the Beer-Lambert relationship or a working curve. The differential method can be used with success when two materials absorb closely together and in trace analyses.

6.6 USE OF THE BEER-LAMBERT LAW IN MEASURING PATH LENGTH

In Chap. 4, Sec. 4.2.5, cell path-length measurements were considered for those cells where fringe patterns could be obtained. As an alternate method, the Beer-Lambert expression can be used to determine path lengths. For example, a liquid cell of unknown thickness can be filled with a solvent or solution containing a compound of known absorptivity a. Since the concentration c is known and the absorbance measured directly, the path length b is readily determined by the expression

$$b = \frac{A}{ac} \tag{6.12}$$

A similar technique has been used for the measurement of thin samples of solids such as potassium bromide pellets.

6.7 USE OF INTERNAL STANDARDS: THE RATIO METHOD

As discussed in Chap. 3, numerous difficulties are encountered in obtaining reproducible spectra from solid samples if they cannot be solubilized. In these cases, films, mulls, or pressed disks must be used. These methods have the undesirable characteristic that the path length can not be easily or accurately measured. Quantitative analyses on a relative basis are still possible in a limited number of cases by measuring absorbance ratios.

The ratio of the intensities of two peaks in the same spectrum is measured to eliminate peak-intensity variations. The use of absorbance ratios can be best exemplified as follows: To obtain a suitable peak for comparison purposes, some standard substance, an "internal standard," is introduced into the sample in known concentration. In terms of the Beer-Lambert relationship, the absorbance of the unknown can be designated as

$$A_1 = a_1 b_1 c_1$$

In a similar fashion the absorbance of the internal standard can be expressed as

$$A_2 = a_2 b_1 c_2$$

Since the standard has been placed in the film, mull, or pellet in known amounts, the ratio of the two absorbances is

$$\frac{A_1}{A_2} = \frac{a_1 b_1 c_1}{a_2 b_1 c_2} \tag{6.13}$$

In Eq. 6.13, the values of a_1 and a_2, the absorptivities of the unknown component and the internal standard respectivity, must be known. The value of c_2, the concentration of the internal standard, is known from the preparation of the matrix material (i.e., potassium bromide or mulling agent). The value of b_1, the path length, is constant for the particular sample and can be determined by the method described in Sec. 6.6, using the values of A_2, a_2, and c_2. Since all values except c_1 are known, they can be summed up in a constant, K. Therefore Eq. 6.13 can be expressed simply as

$$\frac{A_1}{A_2} = K c_1 \tag{6.14}$$

By plotting a working curve of the ratio of the absorbances, A_1/A_2, versus several known concentrations of the material to be analyzed, the concentration of the unknown, c_1 can then be determined by reference to the working curve.

The substance used as an internal standard must fulfill several requirements:

1. It should have a relatively small number of peaks so that potential interferences are minimized.

2. It should be stable to heat and insensitive to moisture.

3. It must be available in pure form.

4. It must be capable of being reduced in particle size.

5. If pressed, it must form a clear pellet.

6.8   QUANTITATIVE MEASUREMENTS IN THE STUDY OF REACTION RATES

For organic chemists, one of the most valuable applications of quantitative analysis by infrared spectroscopy is in the determination of the rates of chemical reactions. From our foregoing discussion it is clear that the disappearance of a particular functional group can be accurately measured under certain reaction conditions. If the reacting molecule has a band significantly separated from all others, the kinetics of reaction can be readily evaluated. Perhaps the clearest approach to the method generally employed is to give several simple examples drawn from the recent literature.

Flynn and Nenortas[5] have recently investigated the kinetics of the reaction between phenyl isocyanate and alcohols. The study was instigated as one phase of an effort to resolve the mechanism of the reaction. Their procedure was roughly as follows: The reaction mixture was suspended in a constant-temperature bath. At appropriate time intervals a sample was withdrawn, using a syringe. The sample was transferred to a cell of known thickness and the absorbance of the isocyanate band at 2260 to 2270 cm^{-1} (4.41 to 4.42μ) was measured by slowly scanning the region.

The zero time was taken immediately after the addition of the catalyst. Seven to nine measurements were made during each run of 5 to 7 hr. A calibration curve was prepared by measuring the absorbance versus phenyl isocyanate concentration in benzene; the solution was found to obey the Beer-Lambert law throughout the desired concentration range. From the data obtained, the rate constants were calculated, using the second-order rate equation for reactants present in equimolar amounts.

A similar set of experiments were recorded by Bailey and Fox[6] in an investigation of tautomerism of dialkyl phosphonates. In their study, the deuterium exchange reaction of di-n-butylphosphonate with n-butyl alcohol-D was examined, using infrared techniques. In preliminary experiments it was found that the P—H stretching vibration of the phosphonate was about the same as the O—D stretching vibration (2400 cm^{-1}, 4.17μ). The P—D band at 1770 cm^{-1} (5.65μ) was also interfered with by other absorbing species. The O—H stretching frequency at 2.8 to 3.0μ (3571 to 3333 cm^{-1}) was relatively free of overlapping absorptions from other materials, and this band was used for kinetic evaluation. The Beer-Lambert relationship was evaluated and found essentially linear over the concentration range studied. The reaction was carried out essentially as reported by Flynn and Nenortas[5] in the preceding example. The analysis was made by using a reference compensating cell filled with n-butyl alcohol-D plus the solvent to compensate for any nondeuterated material that might possibly have been present in the deuterated alcohol. This procedure compensated for absorption by any hydroxyl-containing impurities in the reaction medium.

SUGGESTED READING

1. R. P. BAUMAN, *Absorption Spectroscopy*. Wiley, New York, 1962.
2. W. J. POTTS, JR., *Chemical Infrared Spectroscopy, Vol. 1., Techniques*. Wiley, New York, 1963.
3. "Recommended Practices for General Techniques of Infrared Quantitative Analysis," *Am. Soc. Testing Materials, Proc.*, 1959.

4. W. Brugel, *An Introduction to Infrared Spectroscopy.* Wiley, New York, 1962.
5. K. G. Flynn and D. R. Nenortas, *J. Org. Chem.,* **28** (1963), 3527.
6. W. J. Bailey and R. B. Fox, *J. Org. Chem.,* **28** (1963), 531.

ADDITIONAL READING

J. A. Anderson, *Anal. Chem.,* **20** (1948), 801.

J. A. Anderson and W. D. Seyfried, *Anal. Chem.,* **20** (1948), 998.

J. A. Anderson and C. E. Zerwekh, *Anal. Chem.,* **21** (1949), 911.

W. H. Avery and J. R. Morrison, *J. Appl. Phys.,* **18** (1947), 960.

C. C. Bard, T. J. Porro and H. L. Rees, *Anal. Chem.,* **27** (1955), 12.

R. B. Barnes, R. C. Gore, R. W. Stafford, and V. Z. Williams, *Anal. Chem.,* **20** (1948), 402.

H. A. Barnett and A. Bartoli, *Anal. Chem.,* **32** (1960), 1153.

J. C. Bartlet, *Nature,* **180** (1957), 1071.

J. C. Bartlet and J. H. Mahon, *J. Assoc. Offic. Agr. Chemists,* **41** (1958), 450.

M. F. Bell, *Anal. Chem.,* **22** (1950), 1005.

L. J. Bellamy, *J. Appl. Chem.,* **3** (1953), 421.

F. A. Benning, A. A. Ehert, and C. F. Irwin, *Anal. Chem.,* **19** (1947), 867.

A. Berton, *Chim. Anal.,* **38** (1956), 207.

J. Bomstein, *Anal. Chem.,* **25** (1953), 1770.

C. V. Bowen, *J. Assoc. Offic. Agr. Chemists,* **34** (1951), 689F.

K. B. Bradley and W. J. Potts, Jr., *Appl. Spectroscopy,* **12** (1958), 77.

P. E. Braid and J. Leboeuf, *Anal. Chem.,* **29** (1957), 1625.

R. R. Brattain, R. S. Rasmussen, and A. M. Cravath, *J. Appl. Phys.* **14** (1943), 418.

J. R. Brock, *Anal. Chim. Acta,* **27** (1962), 95.

R. S. Browning, S. E. Wiberley, and F. C. Nachol, *Anal. Chem.,* **27** (1955), 7.

C. G. Cannon and I. S. C. Butterworth, *Anal. Chem.,* **25** (1953), 168.

J. Carol, *J. Assoc. Offic. Agr. Chemists,* **38** (1955), 638.

J. Carol, *J. Assoc. Offic. Agr. Chemists,* **43** (1960), 259.

E. Childers and G. W. Struthers, *Anal. Chem.,* **27** (1955), 737.

W. H. Clark, *Anal. Chem.,* **31** (1959), 197.

B. Cleverly, *Anal. Chem.,* **33** (1961), 1621.

R. Cole, *J. Opt. Soc. Am.,* **41** (1951), 38.

G. L. Collier and F. Singleton, *J. Appl. Chem.,* **6** (1956), 495.

A. P. C. Crumming, *J. Appl. Chem.,* **4** (1954), 561.

H. L. Cupples, *Anal. Chem.,* **24** (1952), 1657.

H. L. Cupples, *Anal. Chem.,* **31** (1959), 967.

L. W. Daasch, *Anal. Chem.,* **19** (1947), 779.

G. S. Denisov, *Optika i Spektroskopiya,* **6** (1959), 475.

W. J. Diamond, *Appl. Spectroscopy,* **12** (1958), 10.

W. J. Diamond, *Appl. Spectroscopy,* **13** (1959), 77.

G. Duyckaerts, *Analyst,* **84** (1959), 201.

G. Duyckaerts, *Spectrochim. Acta,* **7** (1955), 24.

G. Fabbri, *Ann. Chim. Roma,* **48** (1958), 310.

F. V. Fair and R. J. Freidrich, *Anal. Chem.,* **27** (1955), 1886.

S. A. Francis, *Anal. Chem.,* **25** (1953), 1466.

R. D. B. Fraser, *J. Opt. Soc. Am.,* **48** (1958), 1017.

R. T. M. Fraser, *Anal. Chem.,* **31** (1959), 1602.

S. K. Freeman, *Anal. Chem.,* **27** (1955), 1268.

S. K. Freeman, *Anal. Chem.,* **29** (1957), 63.

R. A. FRIEDEL, L. PIERCE, AND J. J. McGOVERN, *Anal. Chem.*, **22** (1950), 418.

M. D. GARHART, F. J. WITMER, AND M. A. TAJIMA, *Anal. Chem.*, **24** (1957), 851.

A. T. GIESE AND C. S. FRENCH, *Appl. Spectroscopy*, **9** (1955), 78.

L. GINSBURG AND M. GOODMAN, *Anal. Chem.*, **33** (1961), 1071.

J. H. GOLDSTEIN AND R. A. DAY, JR., *J. Chem. Ed.*, **31** (1954), 417.

R. G. GORE AND J. B. PATBERG, *Anal. Chem.*, **13** (1941), 768.

C. F. HAMMER AND H. R. ROE, *Anal. Chem.*, **25** (1953), 668.

J. C. HAWKES, *J. Appl. Chem.*, **7** (1957), 123.

A. L. HAYDEN, *J. Pharm. Sci.*, **51** (1962), 617.

J. L. JOHNSON, M. F. GROSTIC, AND A. O. JENSEN, *Anal. Chem.*, **29** (1957), 468.

R. W. B. JOHNSTON, W. G. APPLEBY, AND M. O. BAKER, *Anal. Chem.*, **20** (1948), 805.

J. W. KENT AND J. Y. BEACH, *Anal. Chem.*, **19** (1947), 291.

J. J. KIRKLAND, *Anal. Chem.*, **27** (1955), 1537.

J. J. KIRKLAND, *Anal. Chem.*, **29** (1957), 1127.

L. E. KUENTZEL, *Anal. Chem.*, **27** (1955), 301.

H. A. LIEBHAFSKY AND H. G. PFEIFFER, *J. Chem. Ed.*, **30** (1953), 450.

I. R. C. McDONALD, *Nature*, **174** (1954), 703.

I. R. C. McDONALD AND C. C. WATSON, *Anal. Chem.*, **29** (1957), 339.

A. E. MARTIN, *Trans. Faraday Soc.*, **47** (1951), 1182.

J. M. MARTIN, R. JOHNSTON, AND M. J. O'NEAL, *Anal. Chem.*, **26** (1954), 1886.

D. J. MONTGOMERY AND K. F. YOUNG, *J. Chem. Phys.*, **37** (1962), 1056.

J. A. PERRY, *Anal. Chem.*, **31** (1959), 1054.

J. A. PERRY AND G. H. BAIN, *Anal. Chem.*, **29** (1957), 1123.

S. PINCHAS, *Anal. Chem.*, **23** (1951), 201.

R. C. PINKERTON, *J. Chem. Ed.*, **41** (1964), 366.

F. PRISTERA AND M. HALIK, *Anal. Chem.*, **27** (1955), 217.

D. Z. ROBINSON, *Anal. Chem.*, **23** (1951), 273.

D. Z. ROBINSON, *Anal. Chem.*, **24** (1952), 619.

R. C. RUND, *J. Assoc. Offic. Agr. Chemists*, **45** (1962), 524.

E. L. SAIR AND N. O. COGGESHALL, *Anal. Chem.*, **20** (1948), 812.

E. L. SAIR AND R. H. HUGHES, *Anal. Chem.*, **30** (1958), 513.

R. SCHNURMANN AND E. KENDRICK, *Anal. Chem.*, **26** (1954), 1263.

W. D. SEYFRIED AND S. H. HASTINGS, *Anal. Chem.*, **19** (1947), 298.

R. M. SHERWOOD AND F. W. CHAPMAN, JR., *Anal. Chem.*, **32** (1960), 1131.

R. C. SMITH, *Rev. Sci. Inst.*, **34** (1963), 296.

W. C. STEELE AND M. K. WILSON, *ASTM Tech. Publ.* **269** (1959), 185.

W. C. STEELE AND M. K. WILSON, *Spectrochim, Acta,* **17** (1961), 393.

F. C. STRONG, *Anal. Chem.*, **24** (1952), 388.

J. D. STROUPE, *Anal. Chem.*, **22** (1950), 1125.

D. F. SWINEHART, *J. Chem. Ed.*, **39** (1962), 333.

N. R. TENNER, R. W. WALKER, B. ARISON, AND R. P. BUHS, *Anal. Chem.*, **21** (1949), 285.

W. R. WARD AND A. R. PHILPOTTS, *J. Appl. Chem.*, **8** (1958), 265.

W. H. WASHBURN, *Appl. Spectroscopy*, **11** (1957), 46.

W. H. WASHBURN AND E. O. KRUEGER, *J. Am. Pharm. Assoc. Sci. Ed.*, **38** (1949), 623.

W. H. WASHBURN AND M. J. MAHONEY, *Anal. Chem.*, **30** (1958), 1053.

W. H. WASHBURN AND F. A. SCHESKE, *Anal. Chem.*, **29** (1957), 346.

S. E. WIBERLEY, J. W. SPRAGUE, AND J. E. CAMPBELL, *Anal. Chem.*, **29** (1957), 210.

7

The Near-Infrared Region

In recent years chemists have become more and more interested in the region from approximately 0.75 to 2.5μ (13,300 to 4000 cm^{-1}). Studies in this region are certainly not unique or new. However, the application of this region for routine qualitative and quantitative analyses was deterred until recent years, owing to the lack of suitable instrumentation. In fact, much of the early work was carried out using photographic methods for the detection of absorptions of near-infrared radiation. Through these studies it was clearly recognized that this spectral region held the key to the solution of many problems that required a detailed examination of hydrogen stretching vibrations and their overtones.

In 1954, commercial spectrophotometers were capable of examining this region with satisfactory wavelength accuracy and suitable intensity measurement reliability. These instruments possessed monochromators, which employed quartz prisms or gratings for the necessary dispersion of the radiant energy from the source (review Secs. 3.3 and 3.6). In general the transmitted radiation was detected by using a lead sulfide photodetector. Such instruments gave to the chemist the means of examining the near-infrared region rapidly as well as effectively. In most cases these instruments scanned the ultraviolet and visible regions of the spectrum (see Fig. 1.2) as well as the near-infrared region, significantly augmenting the spectral information capabilities of the chemist.

7.1   INSTRUMENTATION

In principle, two types of instruments are available. The first type employs a fused silica prism coupled with a 600 line per millimeter grating in a double-monochromator system. Figure 7.1 illustrates the typical optical path for the prism-grating combination. The source is a tungsten-ribbon filament lamp. The radiant energy from the source is collected by mirrors M_1 and M_2, which focus the radiation through the reference and sample cells, respectively. The beams are rejoined and alternately admitted to the monochromator compartment by the chopper.

In the system shown in Fig. 7.1, the alternating radiant energy is passed through the entrance slit S_1 and dispersed by the grating. After passing through the intermediate slit S_2, the beam is further separated into individual wavelengths by the silica prism of the second monochromator. The narrow band of energies is then passed out of the monochromator section through the exit slit S_3. The radiant energy is then focused onto the lead sulfide photo-

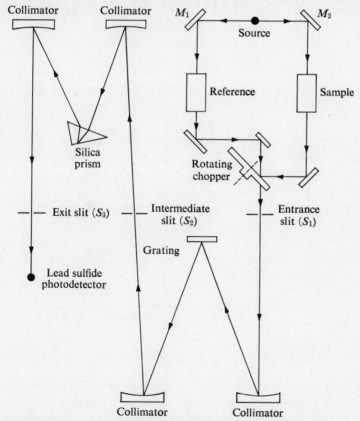

Fig. 7.1   Typical optical path of a prism-grating spectrophotometer utilized in the examination of the near-infrared region.

conductive cell. The signal reaching the cell is amplified and recorded in much the same manner as described in Chap. 3.

˙This system employs a double monochromator. In such a unit all three slits (S_1, S_2, and S_3) are simultaneously adjustable. The arrangement illustrated should be quite familiar to the reader, since it closely parallels the optical path shown in Fig. 3.2. The only real variation is the double monochromator, which is strikingly similar to the optical path illustrated in Fig. 3.11 for the prism-grating spectrophotometer used in the 2 to 16μ region.

The second type of system is shown in Fig. 7.2. This optical arrangement differs from the usual system employed in the normal infrared region, but it is almost identical to the optical system classically used in obtaining spectra in the ultraviolet and visible regions of the spectrum. The radiant energy from the source is passed directly into the monochromator through the entrance slit S_1. The beam is dispersed through the crystal quartz prism and passes out of the monochromator section via the exit slit S_2. The monochromatic beam is passed through a rotating sector mirror and alternately

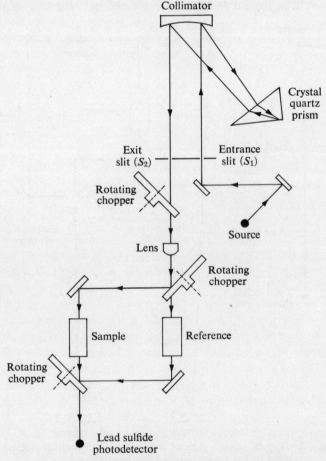

Fig. 7.2 Typical optical path of a prism spectrophotometer for use in the near-infrared region.

focused on the sample and reference cells. The beam transmitted through the cells impinges on the lead sulfide detection system and is amplified and recorded as before. The reader should note particularly that in this system, the sample is not irradiated with the entire energy from the source at the same time as in the arrangements illustrated in Figs. 3.2, 3.11, 3.12, and 7.1. Rather, only a narrow band of energies passes through the sample at any given instant. The crystal quartz prism offers both advantages and disadvantages in the examination of spectral characteristics of compounds in this region. The greatest advantage is that the wavelength range is significantly increased over the prism-grating combination. The major disadvantage is that the dispersion of crystal quartz in the 1.2 to 1.8μ region is poor, and the resolution therefore suffers in this portion of the near-infrared region.

Regardless of the instrumentation employed, some aspects of instrumentation should be emphasized. For good spectral correlations, both qualitative and quantitative, it is important to obtain spectra at known slit widths (i.e., using the same slit program). As in the infrared region between 2 to 16μ (Fig. 3.13), marked differences occur with changes in the slit width. Absorption bands in the near-infrared region are sharp; therefore the narrowest possible slit width is advantageous. Again paralleling the rock salt region, the slit width must be balanced with the inherent noise level in order to produce a satisfactory spectrum. Since water vapor has an effect upon the amount of energy passed through the monochromator in this region, and the lead sulfide detector is influenced by temperature, it is wise to operate such instruments under conditions of relatively constant humidity and temperature. The reader should review Chap. 3 for other comments relating to near-infrared instrumentation.

7.2 TECHNIQUES

The near-infrared region requires much less effort from the analyst than is required in the normal infrared region. The cells generally used are of longer path lengths, so that the problems in path-length determination are greatly simplified. They are constructed from glass or silica with quartz or silica windows (glass or Corex can be used to 2.4μ). Near-infrared cells are considerably more rugged than those used in the normal infrared region, and since they are not affected by water, they can be cleaned much more easily. Also, a number of varied path lengths are available as matched units at far lower cost than are comparable sets of matched sodium chloride cells. Compensation of solvent absorptions can be carried out far more accurately in this region without many of the difficulties encountered in the normal infrared region.

The solvents used for examination of compounds in the 0.75 to 3.0μ region generally parallel those used in the normal infrared region. One exception, however, should be mentioned: those solvents having C—H, O—H, or N—H may be suitable in certain studies in the 2 to 16μ region; in the near-infrared region their utility is greatly diminished because the absorptions of these groups tend to obscure much of the desired information in the spectrum of a particular unknown sample. By far the best general solvent for near-infrared studies is carbon tetrachloride. Since this solvent is transparent throughout this region, it is the preferred solvent for hydroxyl and amino hydrogen-bonding studies. Table 7.1 summarizes the solvents commonly used

Table 7.1.   Common Solvents* Used for Near-Infrared Spectrophotometry

Solvent	Maximum Thickness (cm)	Regions of Solvent Absorption (μ)	(cm⁻¹)
Carbon tetrachloride	10	None	
Carbon disulfide	10	2.21–2.25	4525–4444
	1	None	
Chloroform	10	1.39–1.44	7194–6944
		1.65–1.73	6061–5780
		1.82–1.90	5495–5263
		2.05–2.11	4878–4739
		2.22–3.00	4505–3333
	1	1.68–1.71	5952–5848
		2.32–2.40	4310–4167
		2.65–3.00	3774–3333
Methylene chloride	10	1.15–1.18	8696–8475
		1.37–1.45	7299–6897
		1.63–3.00	6135–3333
	1	1.66–1.74	6024–5747
		2.30–2.41	4348–4149
		2.49–2.72	4016–3676
		2.90–3.00	3448–3333
Dioxane	1	1.70–1.85	5882–5405
		2.20–3.00	4545–3333

* Other solvents such as heptane, benzene, di-*n*-butylether, and acetonitrile are useful in limited regions below 2.2μ in thicknesses from 1 to 10 cm.

in this region. Certain of these should be particularly mentioned. Methylene chloride, an excellent solvent for small ring compounds as well as a good general solvent, can be used with advantage for studies in the 2.7 to 2.9μ region. It is also useful in the region below 2.3μ with a few minor exceptions, when cell paths greater than 2 cm must be used. Carbon disulfide, already familiar as an excellent solvent in the infrared region, exhibits only one band in the near-infrared region at 2.22μ. The spectrum of carbon disulfide is shown in Fig. 7.3.

7.3   SPECTRA-STRUCTURE CORRELATIONS IN THE NEAR-INFRARED REGION

The near-infrared region offers a number of unique potentialities for gaining structural information. It should be recognized from the discussion

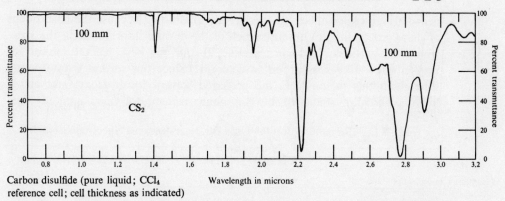

Carbon disulfide (pure liquid; CCl₄ reference cell; cell thickness as indicated)

Fig. 7.3 Near-infrared spectrum of carbon disulfide. (Courtesy Beckman Instruments, Inc.)

in Chap. 5 on qualitative analysis that absorption bands appearing in the region below 3333 cm^{-1} (3.0μ) involve stretching vibrations of hydrogen-containing linkages or combinations of such stretching vibrations with other modes of vibration of the molecule. Of these vibrations, only a few are fundamental vibrations. In general, near-infrared spectra consist of overtone absorptions of a number of fundamentals absorbing in the 3 to 6μ region. Due to this phenomenon, the near-infrared spectrum, from a qualitative viewpoint, is not so characteristic as are the spectra obtained, for example, in the "fingerprint" region. This region should be of greatest utility in the detection and subsequent determination of functional groups that contain unique hydrogen atoms.

As discussed in Chap. 5, aliphatic and aromatic nuclei, as underlying parts of all organic structures, exhibit markedly different infrared absorptions that are useful for interpretative purposes. Indeed, similar correlations can be ascertained in the near-infrared region. Figure 7.4 indicates the typical near-infrared spectrum of an alkane (heptane), a cycloalkane (cyclohexane), and an aromatic substance (benzene). Of particular note are the regions of difference between the two types, the aromatic C—H absorbing again at detectably higher frequencies (shorter wavelengths) than the aliphatic C—H absorptions. Unique hydrogen atoms in such systems as cyclopropanes, epoxide rings, terminal olefins, amines, and alcohol groups can all be distinguished by their characteristic near-infrared spectra. Since the compilation of large numbers of near-infrared spectra will not fulfill the need in gaining structural information, most of the emphasis has been placed on coupling band positions with intensity data. The ease in gaining intensity data and their reliability are definite advantages. Intensity data as a secondary source of information bind qualitative and quantitative information together much more tightly than is possible in the remainder of the infrared region. The reliability of intensity data (if reported, for example, as molar absorptivity in a particular solvent at a certain spectral slit width) can be of definite value. No matter which particular instrument is employed, such data can be transferred reasonably well from one laboratory to another.

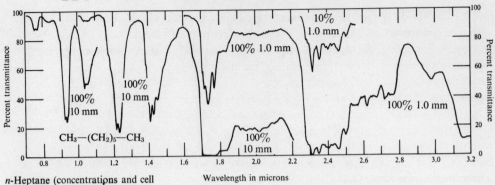

n-Heptane (concentrations and cell thicknesses as indicated; CCl_4 compensating reference cell)

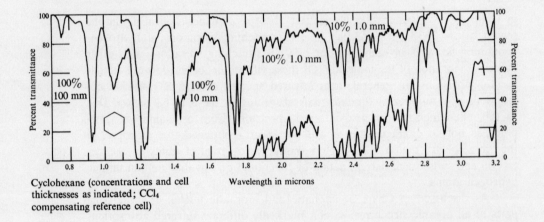

Cyclohexane (concentrations and cell thicknesses as indicated; CCl_4 compensating reference cell)

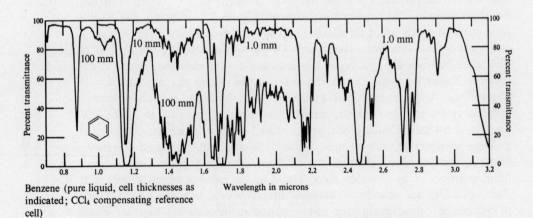

Benzene (pure liquid, cell thicknesses as indicated; CCl_4 compensating reference cell)

Fig. 7.4 Typical near-infrared spectra of alkene, cycloalkane, and aromatic systems common to most organic spectra in this region. (Courtesy Beckman Instruments, Inc.)

7.3.1   Carbon-hydrogen absorptions. All fundamental C—H vibrations, with the exception of the alkyne ≡C—H vibration at about 3.0μ (3333 cm⁻¹), fall outside the near-infrared region. We are concerned, therefore, with combination and overtones almost exclusively. The strongest of these bands, combination bands, appear in the 2.0 to 2.4μ (5000 to 4000 cm⁻¹) region. Overtones appear at 1.6 to 1.8μ (6250 to 5556 cm⁻¹) and 1.1 and 1.2μ (9090 to 8333 cm⁻¹). These are the first and second overtones of the C—H stretching vibrations, respectively. From both qualitative and quantitative viewpoints, particular C—H absorptions are of the greatest importance. In this respect a number of such groups warrant specific comment. These groups are summarized in the sections to follow.

Terminal methylene C—H *absorptions.*   The absorption bands due to terminal methylene groups stand out uniquely. Contrast the absorptions in the spectrum shown in Fig. 7.5 with those in Fig. 7.4 for the alkane and aromatic C—H groups. The two most useful bands in the spectrum in Fig. 7.5 are those in the 2.1μ region (4760 cm⁻¹) and in the 1.6μ region (6250 cm⁻¹). For qualitative purposes the 1.6 region offers some useful data concerning the nature of the substituents on the vinyl group. Vinyl ethers (CH₂=CH—O—) absorb at the shortest wavelength (about 1.615μ), whereas α,β-unsaturated ketones absorb slightly higher (at about 1.620μ). Unsaturated hydrocarbons (see Fig. 7.5) absorb still higher (in the 1.630μ range). It is interesting to note that the absorptivities of compounds of similar structure are almost identical in the 1.6μ region. Because of this, relatively good quantitative determinations can be made for a sample for which no standards are available, by using a compound of related structure.

Vinyl groups (CH₂=CH—) and vinylidene groups $\left(CH_2{=}C{\Big\langle} \right)$ absorb in

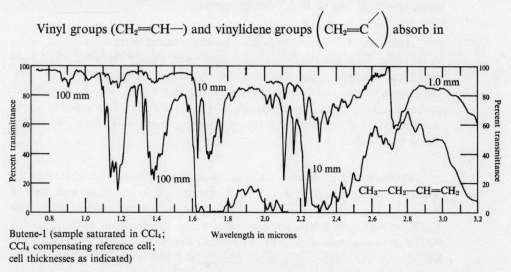

Butene-1 (sample saturated in CCl₄;
CCl₄ compensating reference cell;
cell thicknesses as indicated)

Wavelength in microns

Fig. 7.5 Near-infrared spectrum of butene-1, a typical terminal olefin. (Courtesy Beckman Instruments, Inc.)

the same regions in the near-infrared. In order to distinguish between the two in the 2 to 16μ region, data on the olefinic C—H out-of-plane bending absorptions are necessary. This is a good example of the utility of coupling both types of data for gaining structural information.

Methyne, ≡C—H, *groups.* The methyne carbon-hydrogen stretching vibration can be examined in those instruments capable of reaching to 3.0μ (such as a Beckman DK spectrophotometer). The 3.0μ band and its overtone at 1.53μ are very sharp and characteristic. Although amino groups also absorb in both the 3 and 1.5μ regions, they can be distinguished from the acetylenic compounds on the basis of the differences in absorptivities. Generally the acetylenic C—H overtone has a molar absorptivity of nearly double that of interfering N—H absorptions.

Cis- versus trans- *unsaturated groups.* The problem of *cis* and *trans* unsaturation of the —CH=CH— group can be nicely handled in the near-infrared region, both qualitatively and quantitatively. The *trans* isomers have no definite strong-band structure in this region. However, the *cis* isomer has at least three bands (2.19μ, 2.14μ, and 1.18μ for nonconjugated unsaturated fatty acids). Of these three bands, the band at 2.14μ is extremely useful for both identification and quantitative measurements. The reader should note here that in a molecule containing a number of terminal and *cis* or *trans* linkages, or both *cis* and *trans,* the near-infrared regions offers a wealth of data. The *trans* structure can be determined at 10.34μ in the C—H bending region. However, terminal and *cis* double-bond structures are best measured quantitatively in the near-infrared. Thus the two types of instrumental methods can be highly complementary.

Aldehydic C—H *absorptions.* In the normal infrared regions, aldehydes differ from ketones by only a single band, that of the aldehydic C—H stretching, which is quite characteristic. A band also quite useful for confirmatory evidence can be distinguished in the 2.1 to 2.2μ region. This band, probably arising from a combination of the C—H stretching and the C=O stretching vibrations, is clearly resolved from other C—H vibrations in aliphatic compounds.

Epoxide and cyclopropyl C—H *absorptions.* Figure 7.6 indicates the spectral features of epichlorohydrin. Contrasting this spectrum with that of butene-1 (Fig. 7.5), it will be noted that they are remarkably similar. The bands at 1.65 and 2.20μ are characteristic of the terminal epoxide group. Although in positions similar to absorptions due to the terminal olefins, these absorptions are considerably more intense and also much less complex than the corresponding olefins.

A similar band, shifted to 1.64 and 2.24μ, has been observed in a variety

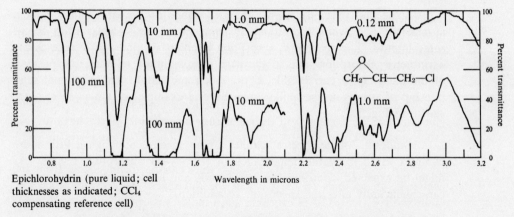

Epichlorohydrin (pure liquid; cell
thickness as indicated; CCl₄
compensating reference cell)

Wavelength in microns

Fig. 7.6 Near-infrared spectrum of epichlorohydrin, a typical epoxide-containing compound. (Courtesy Beckman Instruments, Inc.)

of cyclopropanes. In problems confronting the chemist in which small-ring systems such as cyclopropanes and cyclobutanes are to be distinguished, the C—H absorptions in the near-infrared region offer great promise. Information gained from the near-infrared region, together with the infrared spectrum, is useful in gaining a more complete picture of the structure under examination.

7.3.2 Nitrogen-hydrogen absorptions

Amines. A large amount of investigation carried out has been concerned primarily with both N—H fundamental stretching absorptions and their overtones. The near-infrared spectra of primary, secondary, and tertiary amines are markedly different. Perhaps this is the clearest way to distinguish the three types rapidly in dilute solution, since the fundamental N—H region has two bands between 2.85 and 3.05μ, a doublet in the first overtone region of these two absorptions between 1.45 and 1.55μ, and a single peak at 1.0μ. In contrast, the secondary amines have three single bands in the same regions.

Tertiary amines have no N—H absorptions and therefore no strong near-infrared bands in these regions because of the amino group. From a qualitative viewpoint, studies of these absorptions can usually clearly distinguish the amine type.

From an intensity viewpoint, this region also holds further qualitative information. Often it is not easy to determine the attachment of an amino group to an alkyl or aryl portion of a molecule on the basis of the 2 to 16μ spectral data available. In general, aromatic amines have more intense N—H absorptions by a factor of roughly 20. In addition, primary amines alone give rise to a band at approximately 2.0μ. This band, absent in secondary and tertiary amines, has been assigned to a combination band due to N—H bending and stretching vibrational modes.

In the first overtone region, the two bands of primary amines due to asymmetric and symmetric stretching overtone of the —NH₂ group are of some interest. The symmetric absorption is about six times as intense as the asymmetric absorption, and in the case of substituted anilines, the position of the bands were correlatable to the electronic nature and positional relationship of groups on the aniline ring. Several examples of amine spectra are shown in Fig. 7.7.

Amides. Amide spectra parallel amine spectra, although a little more complex in their overall appearance in the N—H absorption regions. As might be expected, contributions from amide and imide forms of such groups can significantly alter the spectrum. In addition,

$$R-\overset{\overset{\displaystyle O}{\|}}{C}-NH-R \quad \rightleftharpoons \quad R-\overset{\overset{\displaystyle OH}{|}}{C}=N-R$$

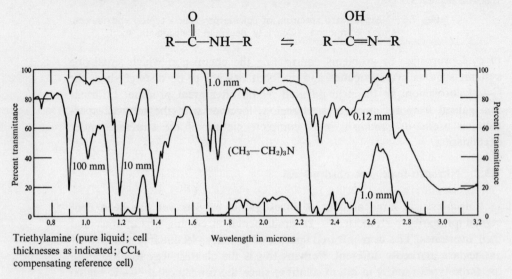

Triethylamine (pure liquid; cell thicknesses as indicated; CCl₄ compensating reference cell)

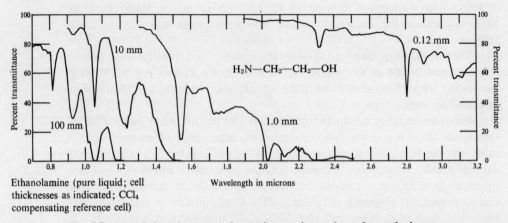

Ethanolamine (pure liquid; cell thicknesses as indicated; CCl₄ compensating reference cell)

Fig. 7.7 Near-infrared spectra of a tertiary amine and a primary hydroxy-amine. (Courtesy Beckman Instruments, Inc.)

the secondary amides can exist in either *cis* or *trans* forms. Both these factors tend to add complexity to the amide N—H absorptions throughout the near-infrared region.

Due to the sensitivity of bands in this region to both intensity and position changes, studies of amine and amide hydrogen bonding are extremely useful. As noted in Chap. 5, Secs. 5.4.4 and 5.4.5, studies of solvent effects on the absorption characteristics of hydrogen-bonded bands, such as the hydroxyl-amino hydrogen-bonded system and the amino-amino hydrogen-bonded unit, can be very valuable in stereochemical conformation studies of structure. Certainly, organic chemists have not yet utilized this region to its fullest extent; the structural information obtainable in alkaloids, peptides, and other natural products, for example, should be given careful consideration.

7.3.3   Oxygen-hydrogen absorptions

Alcohols.   Again, the region from 1 to 3μ embodies the fundamental characteristics of the O—H stretching vibration as well as its overtones. A study of hydrogen bonding is far more easily carried out when using a near-infrared spectrophotometric technique rather than the typical infrared instrumentation. Cell-concentration effects can more easily be changed and modifications made more readily. This is not the case in the 2 to 16μ region studies. In particular the region offers great promise for the examination of molecular interactions of the hydroxyl group with other functional groups within the same molecule (i.e., intramolecular hydrogen bonding, associations, etc.).

As noted in Table 5.10, primary, secondary, and tertiary alcohols are shifted in wavelength from each other. Primary aliphatic alcohol O—H stretching absorption is noted at $2.750 \pm 0.002\mu$; most secondary aliphatic alcohols at $2.760 \pm 0.002\mu$; and the tertiary aliphatic alcohols at $2.766 \pm 0.003\mu$ (dilute carbon tetrachloride solutions). Of greatest interest in the near-infrared region are the unusual effects of various groups on the intensity and position of hydroxyl bands, since these effects in turn lead to a better understanding of structural differences. Figure 7.8 indicates the spectral differences between *n*-octanol and benzyl alcohol in dilute carbon tetrachloride solution. The spectrum of benzyl alcohol appears to have a shoulder at the position expected for primary alcohols (2.750μ). However, the maximum of absorption is at 2.766μ. Such spectra are typical of unsaturated and aromatic alcohols where the hydroxyl group is in a position to interact with the π-electrons of the unsaturated system. Such associations have been extended to other proton acceptors as the acetylene linkage and the cyclopropane ring. Confirmation of such effects is obtainable from variations in the ring substituents of benzyl alcohols. For example, a *p*-nitro group decreases the ring-electron density, and therefore the 2.766μ maximum diminishes in intensity and the 2.750μ shoulder becomes a well-defined, more intense band.

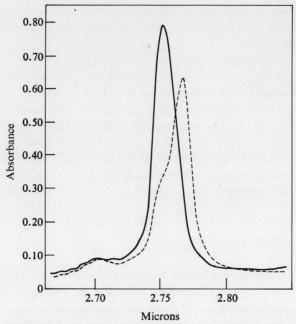

Fig. 7.8 Near-infrared spectra of *n*-octanol and benzyl alcohol in the 2.7 to 2.8μ region. The spectra were recorded in a 1-cm cell. The solid line shows the spectrum of *n*-octanol in carbon tetrachloride solution at a concentration of 0.0013 *M*. The dashed line represents the spectrum of benzyl alcohol in carbon tetrachloride at a concentration of 0.0012 *M*. Contrast the spectra in this region with those of the pure liquids and the 10% solutions for similar alcohols in Fig. 7.9.

Extensive work on the configuration and conformation of alcohols has been reported. The reader is referred to the "Additional Reading" in Chap. 5 and at the end of this chapter for complete details. For exemplification of typical alcohol absorptions in this region, compare the primary, secondary, and tertiary alcohol spectra shown in Fig. 7.9.

Phenols. Phenols have already been treated in some detail in Chap. 5. However, Fig. 7.10 contrasts the positions of a nonhindered alcohol, 4-methylphenol, with a hindered phenol, 2,6-di-*tert*-butyl-4-methylphenol. The effect of steric hindrance is quite apparent in this spectrum.

Ortho-substituted halogen, amino, ether, allyl, hydroxyl, benzyl, and phenyl groups on the phenol ring lead to intramolecular bonding of the hydroxyl groups, and therefore to changes in the absorption of both the fundamental and first overtone absorptions in this region. The frequency differences between the free absorption band and the intramolecular bonded bands are very characteristic of the groups involved. Such data are extremely useful in proof-of-structure studies.

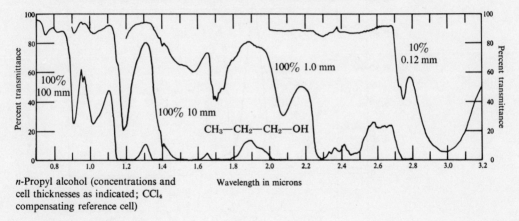

n-Propyl alcohol (concentrations and
cell thicknesses as indicated; CCl₄
compensating reference cell)

Wavelength in microns

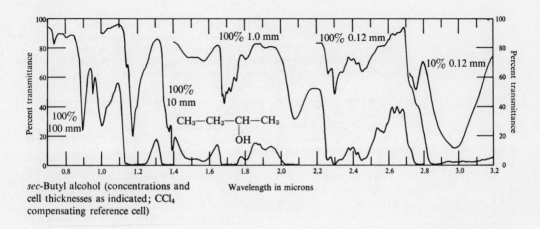

sec-Butyl alcohol (concentrations and
cell thicknesses as indicated; CCl₄
compensating reference cell)

Wavelength in microns

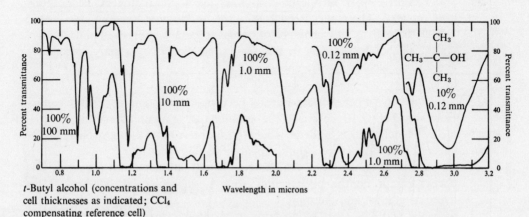

t-Butyl alcohol (concentrations and
cell thicknesses as indicated; CCl₄
compensating reference cell)

Wavelength in microns

Fig. 7.9 Comparison of typical near-infrared spectra of alcohols at concentration levels of 10% to pure liquid samples. Contrast these with the
very dilute spectra in the 2.7 to 2.9μ region shown in Figs. 7.8 and 7.10.
(Courtesy Beckman Instruments, Inc.)

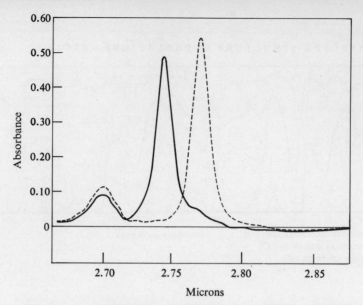

Fig. 7.10 Near-infrared spectra of hindered versus non-hindered alcohols. The spectra were recorded in a 10-cm cell in dilute (0.00026 *M*) carbon tetrachloride solution. The solid line is the spectrum of 2,6-di-*t*-butyl-4-methylphenol, whereas the dashed line is the spectrum of 4-methylphenol. Contrast these spectra with those in Figs. 7.8 and 7.9.

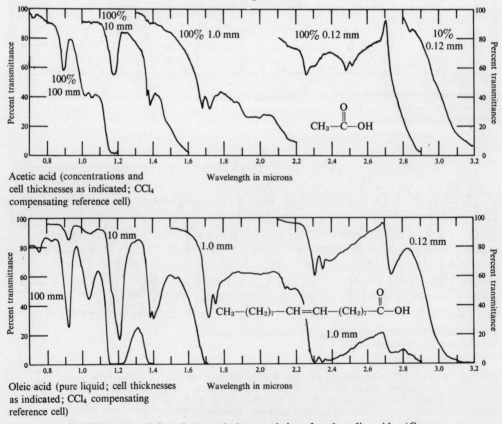

Acetic acid (concentrations and cell thicknesses as indicated; CCl₄ compensating reference cell)

Oleic acid (pure liquid; cell thicknesses as indicated; CCl₄ compensating reference cell)

Fig. 7.11 Near-infrared spectral characteristics of carboxylic acids. (Courtesy Beckman Instruments, Inc.)

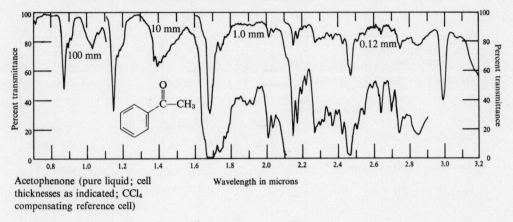

Acetophenone (pure liquid; cell
thicknesses as indicated; CCl₄
compensating reference cell)

Wavelength in microns

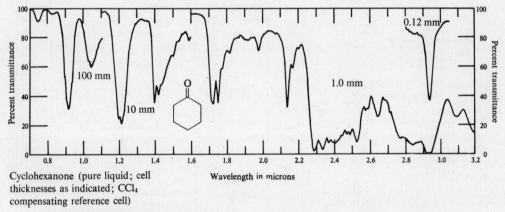

Cyclohexanone (pure liquid; cell
thicknesses as indicated; CCl₄
compensating reference cell)

Wavelength in microns

Fig. 7.12   Typical near-infrared spectra of ketones. Note the first overtone
of the carbonyl stretching vibration at 2.9 to 3.0μ. (Courtesy Beckman
Instruments, Inc.)

Carboxylic Acids.   Figure 7.11 illustrates the spectrum of acetic and
oleic acids in the near-infrared region. Generally, several bands appear in
the 2.7 to 3.0μ region, the number depending on the state of association
of the acid. Because of the monomer-dimer equilibrium in carboxylic acids,
even in dilute solution, the hydroxyl region is of good qualitative value in confirming acid species as present or absent in an unknown sample. In dilute
solution the monomer bands usually appear at roughly 2.8μ, 2.1μ, and 1.45μ
as a result of the O—H stretching fundamental, a combination band, and the
O—H stretching first overtone, respectively.

7.3.4   Carbonyl groups.   Figures 7.12 and 7.14 indicate the near-infrared
spectra of several carbonyl-containing substances. The first overtone of the
carbonyl group appears in the 2.8 to 3.0μ region as a relatively weak but
sharp absorption. Its intensity clearly distinguishes this absorption from other
bands in the region due to hydroxyl and amino groups. It will be noted that

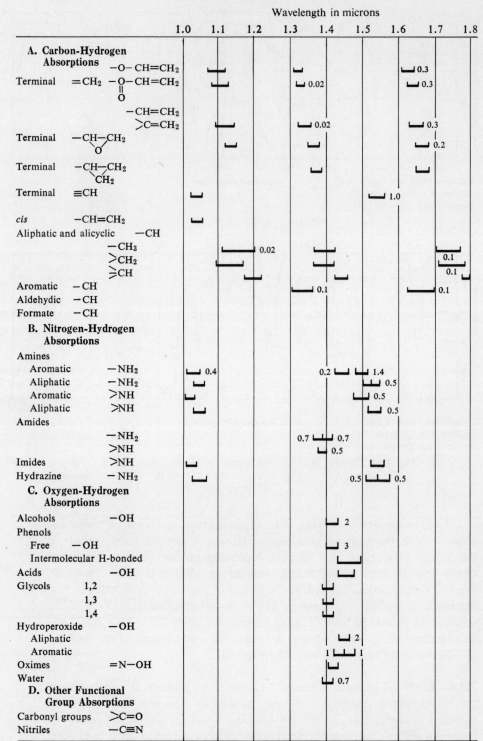

Fig. 7.13 Summary of functional group correlations in the near-infrared

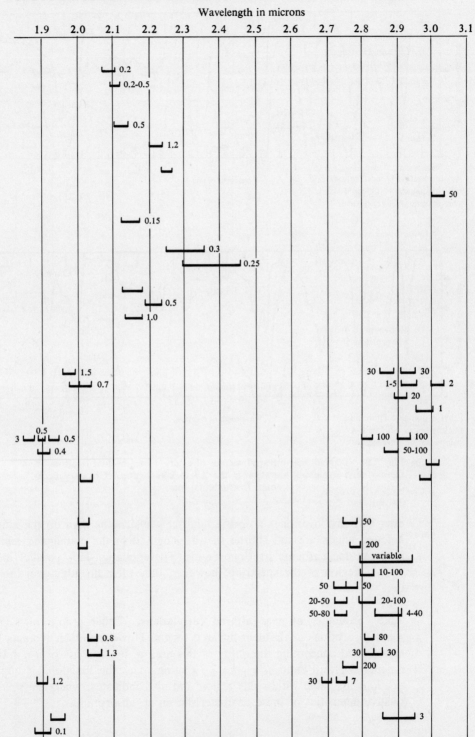

Wavelength in microns

region. Data expressed as position in microns and intensity in molar absorptivity.

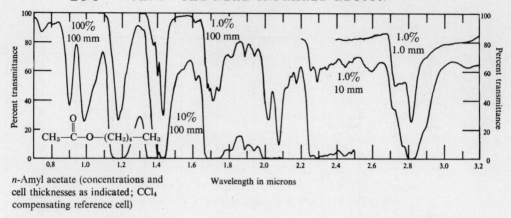

n-Amyl acetate (concentrations and
cell thicknesses as indicated; CCl₄
compensating reference cell)

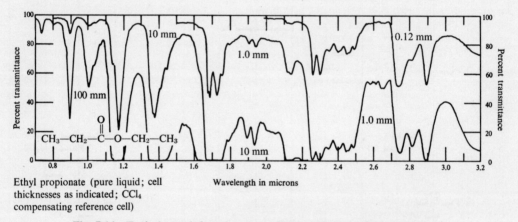

Ethyl propionate (pure liquid; cell
thicknesses as indicated; CCl₄
compensating reference cell)

Fig. 7.14 Typical near-infrared spectra of esters. Note the first overtone of
the carbonyl stretching vibration in the 2.7 to 2.9μ region. (Courtesy Beckman Instruments, Inc.)

ester carbonyl overtones absorb at shorter wavelengths than do the aliphatic
ketones, which are still shorter in wavelength than the conjugated and aromatic ketone carbonyl overtone bands. These relationships parallel the 5.5
to 6.1μ region of the spectrum; however, they offer no additional information.

7.3.5 Summary of near-infrared correlations. Other groups also exhibit
weak absorptions in the near-infrared region. However, much remains to be
investigated concerning the utility of this area in the analysis of a number of
functional group entities. Figure 7.13 summarizes the functional group correlations available within this region and also indicates, where possible, the
relative intensities of these characteristic group absorptions.

SUGGESTED READING

1. W. KAYE, *Spectrochim. Acta,* **6** (1954), 257.
2. W. KAYE, *Spectrochim. Acta,* **7** (1955), 181.
3. O. H. WHEELER, *Chem. Revs.,* **59** (1959), 629.
4. L. J. BELLAMY, *The Infrared Spectra of Complex Molecules.* Wiley, New York, 1958.
5. R. N. JONES AND C. SANDORFY in *Techniques of Organic Chemistry,* Vol. IX, ed. W. West. Interscience, New York, 1956.

ADDITIONAL READING

W. J. ALLAN AND A. R. GAHLER, *Anal. Chem.,* **31** (1959), 1778.

J. C. AMBELANG AND J. L. BINDER, *J. Am. Chem. Soc.,* **75** (1953), 977.

F. A. L. ANET AND P. M. G. BAVIN, *Can. J. Chem.,* **34** (1956), 1756.

A. M. BUSWELL, W. H. RODEBUSH, AND R. M. WHITNEY, *J. Am. Chem. Soc.,* **69** (1947), 770.

A. R. H. COLE AND P. R. JEFFRIES, *J. Chem. Soc.* (1956), 4391.

A. R. H. COLE AND M. T. MITCHELL, *J. Chem. Soc.* (1959), 2005.

M. ST. C. FLETT, *Spectrochim. Acta,* **10** (1957), 21.

R. F. GODDU, *Anal. Chem.,* **29** (1957), 1790.

R. F. GODDU AND D. A. DELKER, *Anal. Chem.,* **30** (1958), 2013.

R. F. GODDU AND D. A. DELKER, *Anal. Chem.,* **32** (1960), 140.

K. T. HECHT AND D. L. WOOD, *Proc. Royal Soc. (London),* **A235** (1956), 174.

R. T. HOLMAN AND P. R. EDMONDSON, *Anal. Chem.,* **28** (1956), 1533.

R. T. HOLMAN, S. ENER, AND P. R. EDMONDSON, *Arch. Biochem. Biophys.,* **80** (1959), 72.

L. P. KUHN, *J. Am. Chem. Soc.,* **74** (1952), 2492.

J. LAUER AND E. J. ROSENBAUM, *Appl. Spectroscopy,* **6** (1952), 529.

R. MOCCIA AND H. W. THOMPSON, *Spectrochim. Acta,* **10** (1957), 240.

R. A. RUSSELL AND H. W. THOMPSON, *J. Chem. Soc.* (1955), 483.

P. VON R. SCHLEYER, D. S. TRIFAN, AND R. BACSKAI, *J. Am. Chem. Soc.,* **80** (1958), 6691.

J. SICHER, M. HORAK, AND M. SVOBODA, *Collection Czechoslov. Chem. Communs.,* **24** (1959), 950.

W. H. WASHBURN AND M. J. MAHONEY, *J. Am. Chem. Soc.,* **80** (1958), 504.

K. B. WHETSEL, W. C. ROBERSON, AND M. W. KRELL, *Anal. Chem.,* **30** (1958), 1598.

8

Infrared Spectra of
Polymers and Resins

The advances in a particular area of chemical endeavor as a result of the application of a single instrumental method has rarely equaled the impact of the infrared method on the area of polymer chemistry. The previous chapters have introduced the utilization of infrared spectroscopy in the evaluation of structural features of molecules that are relatively small and usually well defined. It is not inconsistent that the chemist in his never-ending search for improved methods of characterization has extended the application of the infrared method to polymeric materials of high molecular weight. In many cases these substances are extremely complex and often ill defined. The use of frequencies calculated from theoretical considerations is quite a difficult task for molecules larger than a few atoms. Therefore, such calculations are not readily adaptable for high polymer spectral investigations. On the other hand, the correlations between characteristic group frequencies and functional groups, such as O—H, N—H, C—H, C=O, C=C, C≡N, as well as many other gross features relating to the polymer repeating unit, are extrapolatable to polymeric materials.

The interpretation of infrared data obtained from the examination of polymer spectra must be approached with care. The characteristic group frequencies established for simple organic structures (Chap. 5) are not absolute values. Rather, these values fall into definite, narrow regions found to be characteristic by the examination of a large number of organic molecules of known structure. In high molecular-weight systems, shifts due to solvent interactions, hydrogen bonding, crystallization, or ordering of the polymer structure to varying degrees can markedly affect the infrared spectrum recorded for substances presumed to be chemically identical.

Experimentally the preparation of a polymer sample for spectral examination presents the most formidable problem in the utilization of the infrared method. The reader should review the common procedures outlined in Chap. 4 prior to extending those most applicable to polymers in the subsequent sections.

8.1 POLYMER SAMPLING TECHNIQUES

8.1.1 Films. The method most generally adaptable to polymer studies is the film technique. The most direct procedure is the spreading of a thick, solvent-polymer paste on a sodium chloride plate and then evaporating the solvent. Usually the evaporation is carried out "in vacuo" or at low temperatures in an inert atmosphere, to prevent degradation. For reproducible films, fairly good results can be obtained by carefully spreading the paste with a "doctor blade." Alternately, a film can be deposited from solution directly on the salt window by using a retaining ring to control the surface area covered. "Free" or nonsupported films of polymers may be cast from solvent on any nonadhering surface. Such films can be mounted in appropriate holders and examined directly. Some polymers, such as polyethylene, can be formed from a melt of the polymer or by heating and pressing. In these cases, care must be exercised to prevent thermal or oxidative degradation of the sample. For resinous materials such as phenyl-formaldehyde and furfuryl alcohol resins, which can be thermoset at reasonably low temperatures in inert atmospheres, the film technique is the method of choice for preparing samples to be examined by infrared.

The major advantage of using films are that the sample can be easily stored, subjected to further treatment after its spectrum has been recorded, and no corrections need be made for solvent absorptions. With proper care, the pure polymer is examined directly in its own environment and is not subject to the problems encountered in other solid sampling procedures. The problems encountered in working with film samples are also worthy of note. In very thin film samples, the spectral changes due to crystallinity and sample contamination, such as residual solvent, oftentimes make interpretation of the resulting spectrum difficult. In many cases interference fringes are obtained from the thin film, which make the spectrum difficult to interpret. Such a situation is shown in Fig. 8.1. The reader will note the rather intense fringe pattern, particularly throughout the functional group region (2 to 7μ).

8.1.2 Solutions. The solution technique (Sec. 4.2.1) is limited in its application to polymeric materials, mainly because of the poor solubility characteristics of most polymers in nonpolar solvents or the complete insolubility of most cured resins in any organic solvent. Solvent-polymer interaction in polar solvent severely limits the interpretation of spectral data obtained from

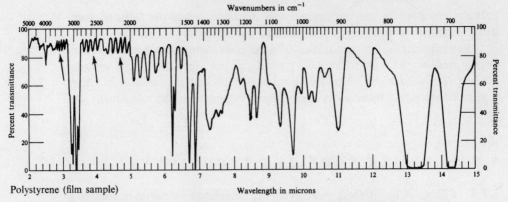

Polystyrene (film sample)

Fig. 8.1. Spectrum of polystyrene showing typical fringe patterns (arrows) obtained from thin film samples.

such samples. The major advantages of the solution technique are the precise control of concentration, the ability to eliminate spectral changes due to crystallinity, and the ability to protect the system from oxidation. As mentioned previously, the disadvantages may be more subtle. Among these, the effect of solvent-polymer interactions, such as hydrogen bonding, and the possibility of reactions between the polymer and solvent (or solvent impurities such as peroxides and hydroperoxides) can cause the distortion of the infrared spectrum to the point that correlation to spectra obtained by other techniques is impossible.

8.1.3   Mulls and pellets.   As discussed in Secs. 4.1.1 and 4.1.2, the most commonly used methods for the preparation of a solid sample for infrared examination are the mulling or pelletizing methods. Although useful in polymer systems, each technique must be carefully evaluated before conclusions derived from the spectral data are drawn. Consideration must be given to the possibility that degradation of the polymer has occurred during sample preparation. In the case of resinous thermosetting materials, advancing the degree of polymerization oftentimes occurs. When such difficulties are experienced, the chemist must realize that the recorded spectrum is not that of the original polymer or resin sample.

The advantages for routine analyses of polymers, however, far outweigh most of the disadvantages. In a large number of cases, the mull and pellet techniques are the only satisfactory methods for preparing samples for infrared examination.

8.1.4   Pyrolysis.   The controlled pyrolysis of samples to give characteristic degradation products has been rather extensively studied. Since many materials are not adaptable to infrared analysis by conventional techniques because of their physical intractability, pyrolysis of such materials is frequently the only recourse to gain information concerning their structure. Generally the dry distillation products of these complex materials permit the recording of a reproducible spectrum that will be characteristic of the original material. Two such cases are exemplified in Fig. 8.2 for Nylon 66 and Saran polymers.

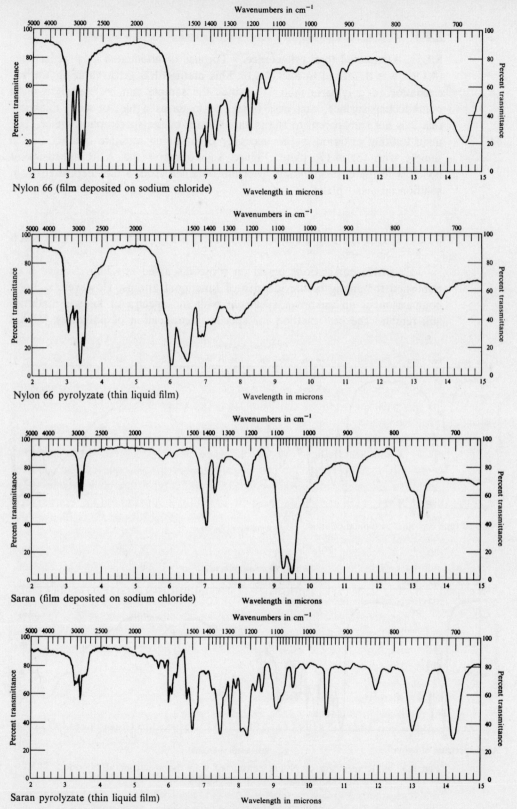

Fig. 8.2 Typical spectra of Nylon and Saran pyrolyzates contrasted with their respective polymer spectra.

8.1.5 Attenuated total reflectance. The use of attenuated total reflectance (ATR) was discussed in Sec. 4.1.6. This method has great value in the examination of polymeric materials, since the sample can be deposited on a nonreflecting surface, cast in a block, or made as a film of such thickness that it is not transparent to the infrared beam of the spectrophotometer. The main limiting criterion is the necessity of attaining intimate contact of the sample with the ATR plate. Figure 8.3 compares the ATR spectrum of Nylon with the corresponding spectrum obtained from a film deposited from solution on a salt plate.

8.2 QUALITATIVE ANALYSIS OF POLYMERS

Extensive correlations based on those discussed in Chap. 5 have been published for aiding in the identity of functional groups. However, a direct comparison of an unknown spectrum with the spectra of known materials still remains the best method for specific identification of polymers. Within

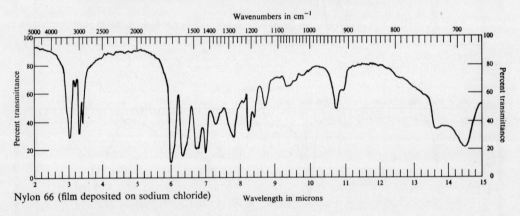

Nylon 66 (film deposited on sodium chloride)

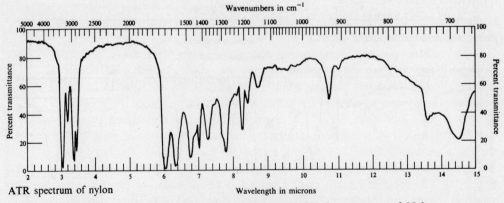

ATR spectrum of nylon

Fig. 8.3 ATR spectrum of Nylon contrasted with the spectrum of Nylon obtained from a film sample.

a particular category of polymeric materials, such as polyesters or polyamides, correlations based on "skeletal" vibrations characteristic of the repeating chain unit have been most generally applied in the identification of specific substances. However, a systematic scheme as shown in Fig. 8.4 has gained considerable use in analyzing unknown polymer spectra. Such a chart allows the chemist either to identify the polymer or to classify the polymer as to type for comparison with the spectra of known materials.

Extensive variations exist in the recorded spectra of polymers, which should be carefully examined by the reader. Some polymers produce very clearly defined spectra; others, only broad diffuse bands indicative of a relatively impure substance. Figure 8.5 illustrates several typical examples of such spectra. Table 8.1 summarizes literature references to the infrared spectra of polymers.

As exemplary of the comparison technique, Fig. 8.6 shows the spectrum of a copolymer contrasted with the spectra of the pure homopolymers. The reader should note the ready evaluation of the functional groups in each case.

8.3 QUANTITATIVE ANALYSIS OF POLYMERS

Based upon the relationships discussed in Chap. 6, it is possible to examine quantitatively certain functional groups in polymers. For example, in silicone polymers containing both methyl and phenyl substituents on the chain, the ratio of methyl to phenyl groups is characteristic of the relative numbers of such groups. Figure 8.7 indicates the spectrum of a typical silicone polymer as a cast film, containing both methyl and phenyl groups, contrasted with a methyl silicone and a phenyl silicone polymer. To determine the relative amounts of phenyl to methyl, the ratio of the 7.4 to 6.94μ bands can be determined, since these are noticeably characteristic of the methyl (7.4μ) and the phenyl groups (6.94μ). The typical calibration curve obtained from a determination of the ratios from known samples is shown in Fig. 8.8. The utilization of this technique for the determination of methyl-to-phenyl content in silicone polymers is far more accurate than that attainable by other methods of analysis.

In certain polymers containing specific residual functional groups (formed during polymerization), analyses can be set up by using the Beer's law relationship to determine the amounts of such functional species in the polymer. In resinous materials of relatively low molecular weight (compared to typical vinyl polymers) in which characteristic bands of the end groups can be assigned, it is possible to determine the average molecular weight of the resin from the absorbance of the end-group band. Figure 8.9 indicates the spectrum of a typical epoxy resin having the repeating unit shown in Fig. 8.10. The band at 12.05μ can be shown to be indicative of the epoxide group at the ends of the chain. Using the absorption band at 6.21μ as a reference band, the ratio of the absorbance at 12.05μ to the absorbance at 6.21μ

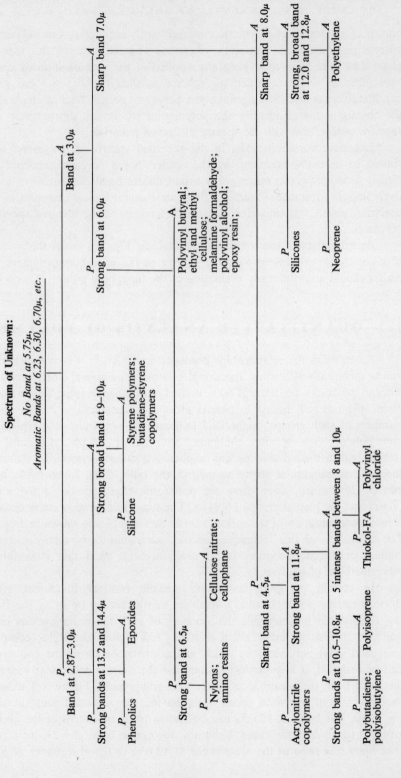

Spectrum of Unknown:

No Band at 5.75μ,
Aromatic Bands at 6.23, 6.30, 6.70μ, etc.

246

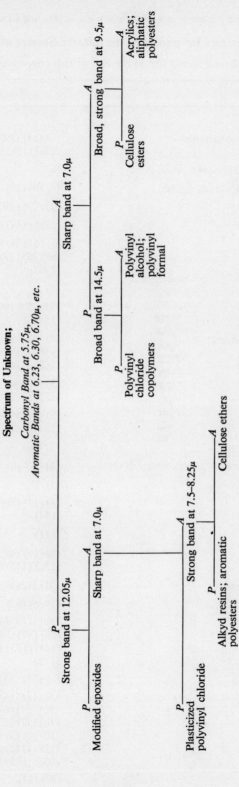

Figure 8.4. A systematic scheme for the identification of polymers from their infrared spectra. *A* = band absent; *P* = band present.

Table 8.1. Literature References to the Infrared Spectra of Polymers

(See the numbered list at the end of this chapter.)

Polymer	Lit. Reference
Acrylonitrile	(6)
Acrylonitrile-butadiene copolymer	(6) (13) (19) (117) (119) (126) (136) (137) (170)
Acrylonitrile-butadiene-phenolic resin	(6)
Acrylonitrile-vinyl chloride copolymer	(3) (6) (20)
Aldehydes	(95) (96) (100)
Alkyd resins	(135) (149) (152) (160) (163)
Amides	(3) (5) (6) (14) (35) (41) (48) (68) (85) (99) (104) (129) (190)
Benzylcellulose	(3)
Butadiene	(43) (50) (60) (130) (138) (151)
Butadiene-styrene copolymer	(4) (6) (19) (129) (136) (138) (139) (151) (159) (161) (168) (176)
Cellulose	(3) (30) (45) (58) (98) (110) (111) (112) (125) (154)
Cellulose acetate	(3) (5) (30) (56) (131) (154) (162)
Cellulose acetate-butyrate	(3) (30)
Cellulose butyrate-stearate	(3)
Cellulose caprate	(3)
Cellulose nitrate	(3) (17) (18) (104) (111) (154)
Cellulose triacetate	(111)
Chloroprene	(6) (19) (44) (89) (118) (136) (145) (149) (158)
Chlorosulfonate ethylene	(91) (121)
Epoxy resins	(3) (6) (82)
Esters	(2) (3) (6) (39) (40) (66) (86) (87) (88) (122) (123) (124) (153) (173) (174) (179)
Ethylcellulose	(3) (19) (131)
Ethylene	(3) (12) (14) (42) (46) (48) (56) (61) (62) (63) (64) (65) (78) (97) (101) (105) (108) (109) (113) (114) (115) (128) (141) (146) (148) (156) (165) (172)
Ethylene glycol	(80) (81)

Table 8.1—Cont.

Polymer	Lit. Reference
p-Fluorostyrene	(71)
Ethylene terephthalate	(5) (6) (36) (39) (51)
Glyceryl phthalate	(125) (126)
Hydroxylethylcellulose	(30)
Isobutylene	(19) (72) (128) (129)
Isobutene-isoprene copolymer	(6) (13) (19) (44) (136)
Melamine-formaldehyde resin	(6)
Methylacrylate	(129)
Methacrylonitrile	(22)
Methylmethacrylate	(3) (22) (104) (129) (131) (161)
m-Methylstyrene	(31)
Peptides	(8) (11) (15) (26) (27) (28) (29) (57)
Phenol-formaldehyde resin	(2) (3) (6) (9) (10) (104) (106) (137) (171)
Phenylbutadiene	(103)
Propylene	(5) (84) (102)
Propylene glycols	(143)
Rubber (natural)	(6) (13) (19) (37) (41) (67) (83) (107) (116) (117) (118) (119) (125) (126) (129) (131) (132) (149)
Rubber (synthetic)	(19) (107) (139) (170)
Silicones	(3) (6) (7) (74) (75) (120) (133) (140) (150) (155)
Styrene	(3) (56) (69) (104) (125) (129) (167) (189)
Sulfides	(19) (136)
Tetrafluoroethylene	(3) (5) (90)
Tetrafluorethylene-trifluorochloroethylene copolymer	(59)
Trifluorochlorethylene	(3) (6) (70)
Urea-formaldehyde resin	(3) (6) (23)
Urethanes	(5) (147)
Vinyl acetate	(3) (14) (21) (41) (56) (125) (129)
Vinyl acetate-vinyl chloride copolymer	(5) (111) (129) (131) (178)

Table 8.1—Cont.

Polymer	Lit. Reference
Vinyl alcohol	(3) (14) (21) (29) (41) (48) (52) (79) (129)
Vinyl chloride	(3) (14) (38) (41) (48) (54) (55) (56) (92) (93) (94) (118) (129) (142) (157)
Vinyl chloride-vinylidene chloride copolymer	(6) (33) (76) (92) (129) (164)
Vinyl ethers	(34)
Vinyl formal	(6) (21)
Vinyl fluoride	(16)
Vinyl nitrate	(77)

can be determined. From these data a plot of the ratio value versus molecular weight can be used for average molecular weight determinations. This method has been found to compare very favorably with chemical methods based on epoxide group titration for molecular weight determination.

8.3.1   Polymerization.   In general the application of quantitative measurements in polymer systems can be extremely valuable. For example, the loss of epoxide end groups can be followed spectrophotometrically to determine the rate of polymerization. Other polymerizations should, in a like fashion, lend themselves favorably to kinetic study by the infrared method (see Sec. 6.8). A summary of quantitative applications using infrared spectroscopy is given in Table 8.2.

8.3.2   Polymer reaction studies: qualitative and quantitative applications.
The application of the infrared method, both qualitatively and quantitatively, to the study of polymer reactions can best be exemplified by the study of chemical changes in a particular polymer system. In the "Suggested Reading" section at the end of the chapter, the reader will find several examples suggestive of the power of the infrared technique in polymer reaction studies. These articles will be found valuable additional reading from an applications point of view. The basic principles in applying the infrared method to polymeric materials lie in the fact that, under reaction conditions (as in polymerization, Sec. 8.3.1), changes in the number or type of functional groups are usually detectable by the examination at successive time intervals of the infrared spectrum of the polymer. In effect, it provides a means of monitoring the decay or generation of functional groups under reaction conditions in the bulk phase of the polymer. The coupling of information gained in this way with analysis of the gaseous products (if any) from the reaction offers the chemist a powerful tool for elucidating the nature of the chemical transformations taking place.

Table 8.2.   Literature References to Quantitative Infrared Methods for Polymers

(See the numbered list at the end of this chapter.)

Polymer	Lit. Reference
Acrylonitrile-butadiene copolymer	(170)
Acrylonitrile-butadiene-methylisopropenyl ketone terpolymer	(175)
Acrylonitrile-styrene copolymer	(167)
Alkyd resins	(135) (149) (152) (160) (163)
Butadiene-methylmethacrylate copolymer	(169)
Butadiene-styrene copolymer	(139) (151) (159) (161) (168) (176)
Butadiene	(138)
Cellulose	(154)
Cellulose acetate	(162)
Cellulose plastics	(166)
Chloroprene	(145) (158)
Esters	(153) (173) (174) (179)
Ethylene	(141) (146) (148) (156) (165) (172)
Ethylene-propylene copolymer	(180)
Isoprene	(139) (170)
Methylmethacrylate	(161)
Methylmethacrylate-vinyl acetate copolymer	(144)
Phenolic resin	(137) (171)
Propylene glycols	(143)
Rubber (natural and synthetic)	(136) (145) (149) (177)
Silicone	(140) (150) (155)
Urethane	(147)
Vinyl acetate-vinyl chloride copolymer	(178)
Vinyl chloride	(142) (157)
Vinyl chloride-vinylidene chloride	(164)

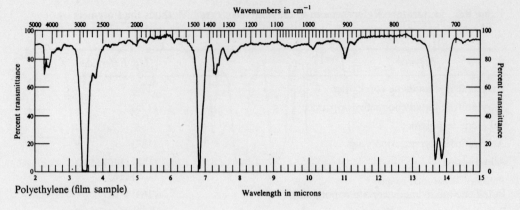

Polyethylene (film sample)

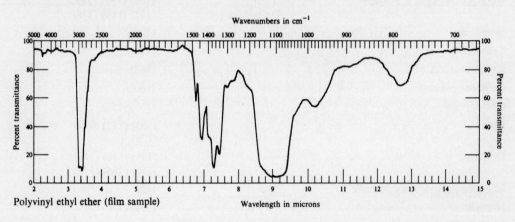

Polyvinyl ethyl ether (film sample)

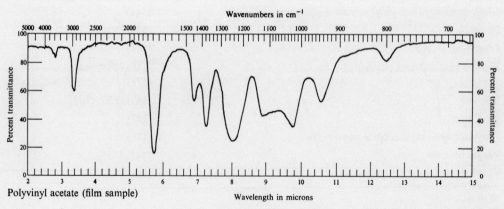

Polyvinyl acetate (film sample)

Fig. 8.5 Representative spectra of polymers and resins.

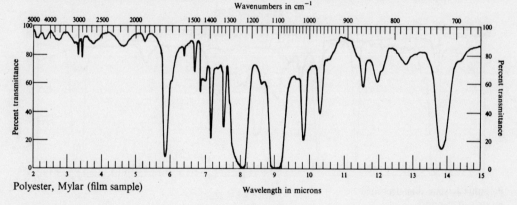

Polyester, Mylar (film sample)

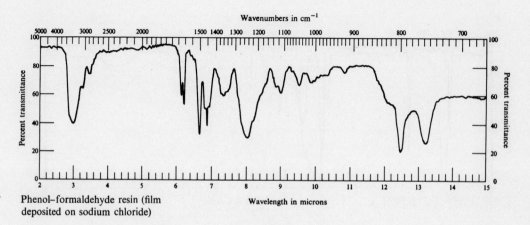

Phenol–formaldehyde resin (film
deposited on sodium chloride)

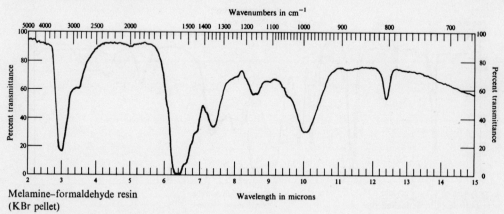

Melamine–formaldehyde resin
(KBr pellet)

For other examples see Figs. 8.1, 8.2, 8.6, 8.7, and 8.9.

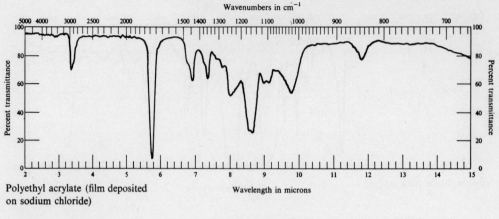

Polyethyl acrylate (film deposited
on sodium chloride)

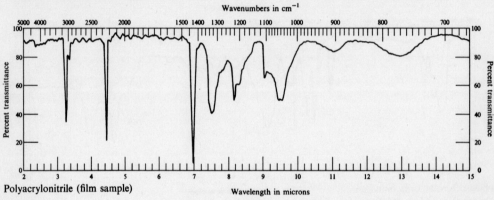

Polyacrylonitrile (film sample)

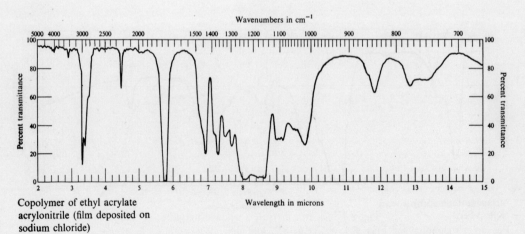

Copolymer of ethyl acrylate
acrylonitrile (film deposited on
sodium chloride)

Fig. 8.6   Typical copolymer contrasted with the corresponding homopolymers.

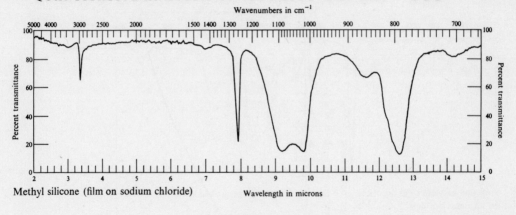

Methyl silicone (film on sodium chloride)

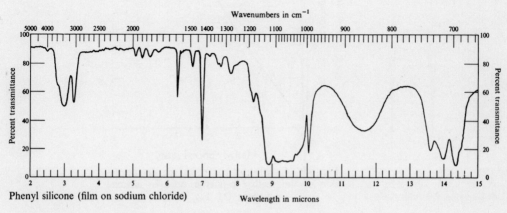

Phenyl silicone (film on sodium chloride)

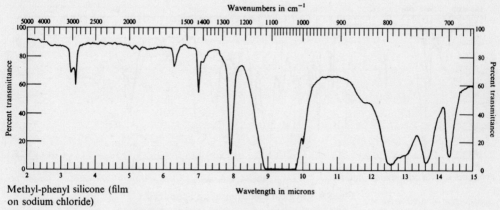

Methyl-phenyl silicone (film
on sodium chloride)

Fig. 8.7   Spectra of typical silicone polymers.

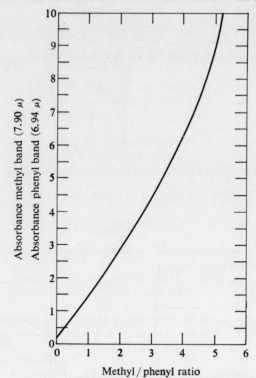

Fig. 8.8 Calibration curve for the determination of the methyl-to-phenyl ratio in silicone polymers (cf. Fig. 8.7).

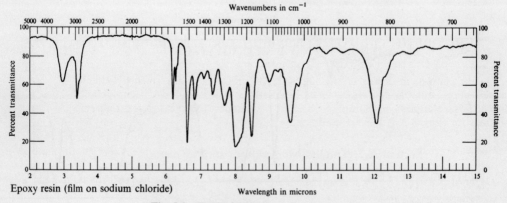

Fig. 8.9 Typical spectrum of an epoxy resin.

n = repeat unit

Fig. 8.10 Structural repeat unit for the epoxy resin in Fig. 8.9.

SUGGESTED READING

1. W. J. POTTS, "The Use of Infrared Spectroscopy in the Characterization of Polymer Structure," *ASTM Special Tech. Publ. 247* (1958), 225–241.

2. O. D. SHREVE, "Infrared, Ultraviolet and Raman Spectroscopy," *Anal. Chem.,* **24** (1952), 1692.

3. R. E. KAGARISE AND L. A. WEINBERGER, "Infrared Spectra of Plastics and Resins," *Naval Research Laboratory Report 4369, Naval Research Laboratory,* Washington 25, D.C., May 26, 1964.

4. R. B. BARNES, R. C. GORE, R. W. STAFFORD AND V. Z. WILLIAMS, "Qualitative Organic Analysis and Infrared Spectrometry," *Anal. Chem.,* **20** (1948), 402.

5. American Society for Testing Materials (ASTM) 1961 Preprint Rept. of Committee D-13, pp. 72–78.

6. D. L. HARMS, "Identification of Complex Organic Materials," *Anal. Chem.,* **25** (1953), 1140.

7. J. H. LADY, G. M. BOWER, R. E. ADAMS, AND F. R. BYRNE, "Determination of the Ratio of Methyl to Phenyl Groups in Silicone Polymers," *Anal. Chem.,* **31** (1959), 1100.

8. M. IDELSON AND E. R. BLOUT, "Polypeptides. XV. Infrared Spectroscopy and the Kinetics of the Synthesis of Polypeptides: Primary Amine Initiated Reactions," *J. Am. Chem. Soc.,* **79** (1957), 3948.

9. R. T. CONLEY AND J. F. BIERON, "A Study of the Oxidative Degradation of Phenol-Formaldehyde Polycondensates Using Infrared Spectroscopy," *J. Appl. Polymer Sci.,* **7** (1963), 103.

10. R. T. CONLEY AND J. F. BIERON, "A Kinetic Study of the Oxidative Degradation of Phenol-Formaldehyde Polycondensates Using Infrared Spectroscopy," *J. Appl. Polymer Sci.,* **7** (1963), 171.

ADDITIONAL READING

For convenient access to the literature, the references are given by chapter and section, number and title. Only representative articles have been included here. For references pertaining to specific techniques (Sec. 8.1), see reference listings for Secs. 8.2, 8.3, 8.3.1, and 8.3.2.

Section 8.2: Qualitative Analyses of Polymers

11. N. B. ABBOTT AND E. J. AMBROSE, *Proc. Roy. Soc. (London),* **A219** (1953), 17.

12. S. L. AGGARIVAL, G. P. TILLEY, AND O. J. SWEETING, *J. Appl. Polymer Sci.,* **1** (1959), 91.

13. A. R. ALLISON AND I. J. STANLEY, *Anal. Chem.,* **24** (1952), 630.

14. E. J. AMBROSE, A. ELLIOTT, AND R. B. TEMPLE, *Proc. Roy. Soc. (London),* **A199** (1949), 183.

15. M. ASAI, M. TSUBOI, T. SHIMANOUCHI, AND S. MIZUSHIMA, *J. Phys. Chem.,* **59** (1955), 322.

16. B. BAK AND D. CHRISTENSEN, *Spectrochim. Acta,* **12** (1958), 355.

17. R. B. BARNES, *Phys. Rev.,* **39** (1932), 562.

18. R. B. BARNES AND L. G. BONNER, *J. Opt. Soc. Amer.,* **26** (1936), 428.

19. R. B. BARNES, U. LIDDEL, AND V. Z. WILLIAMS, *Anal. Chem.,* **15** (1944), 83.
20. H. BAYZER AND J. SCHURZ, *Z. Phy. Chem.,* **13** (1957), 223.
21. H. C. BEACHELL, P. FOTIS, AND J. HUCKS, *J. Polymer Sci.,* **7** (1951), 353.
22. R. G. BEAMAN, *J. Am. Chem. Soc.,* **70** (1948), 3115.
23. H. J. BECKER, *Chem. Ber.,* **89** (1956), 1951.
24. M. BEER, *Proc. Roy. Soc. (London),* **236** (1956), 136.
25. W. A. BISHOP, *Anal. Chem.,* **33** (1961), 456.
26. E. R. BLOUT, *Ann. N.Y. Acad. Sci.,* **69** (1957), 84.
27. E. R. BLOUT AND A. ASADOURIAN, *J. Am. Chem. Soc.,* **78** (1956), 955.
28. E. R. BLOUT AND M. IDELSON, *J. Am. Chem. Soc.,* **80** (1958), 4909.
29. E. R. BLOUT AND R. KARPLUS, *J. Am. Chem. Soc.,* **70** (1948), 862.
30. L. BROWN, P. HOLLIDAY, AND I. F. TROTTER, *J. Chem. Soc.* (1951), 1532.
31. K. C. BRYANT, G. T. KENNEDY, AND E. M. TANNER, *J. Chem. Soc.* (1949), 2389.
32. S. BURGESS AND H. SPEDDING, *Chem. & Ind. (London),* (1961), 1166.
33. R. L. BURTON, W. H. COBBS, JR., AND V. C. HASKELL, *J. Polymer Sci.,* **7** (1951), 569.
34. G. B. BUTLER, *J. Am. Chem. Soc.,* **77** (1955), 482.
35. C. G. CANNON, *Mikrochim. Acta* (1955), 555.
36. W. H. COBBS, JR., AND R. L. BURTON, *J. Polymer Sci.,* **10** (1953), 275.
37. P. J. CORISH, *J. Appl. Polymer Sci.,* **4** (1960), 86.
38. J. D. COTMAN, JR., *Ann. N.Y. Acad. Sci.,* **57** (1953), 417.
39. W. W. DANIELS AND R. E. KITSON, *J. Polymer Sci.,* **33** (1958), 161.
40. W. H. T. DAVISON AND P. J. CORISH, *J. Chem. Soc.* (1955), 2428.
41. A. ELLIOTT, E. J. AMBROSE, AND R. B. TEMPLE, *J. Chem. Phys.,* **16** (1948), 877.
42. E. E. FERGUSON, *J. Chem. Phys.,* **24** (1956), 1115.
43. J. E. FIELD, D. E. WOODFORD, AND S. D. GEHMAN, *J. Appl. Phys.,* **17** (1946), 386.
44. J. E. FIELD, D. E. WOODFORD, AND S. D. GEHMAN, *J. Polymer Sci.,* **15** (1955), 51.
45. F. H. FORZIATI, J. W. ROWEN, AND E. K. PLYLER, *J. Research NBS,* **46** (1951), 288.
46. J. J. FOX AND A. E. MARTIN, *Proc. Roy. Soc. (London),* **A175** (1940), 208.
47. J. A. GARLEY, *Anal. Chem.,* **33** (1961), 1831.
48. L. GLATT AND J. W. ELLIS, *J. Chem. Phys.,* **19** (1951), 449.
49. R. F. GODDU AND D. A. DELKER, *Anal. Chem.,* **30** (1958), 2013.
50. M. A. GOLUB AND J. J. SHIPMAN, *Spectrochim. Acta,* **16** (1960), 1165.
51. D. GRIME AND I. M. WARD, *Trans. Faraday Soc.,* **54** (1958), 959.
52. H. C. HAAS, *J. Polymer Sci.,* **26** (1957), 391.
53. M. C. HARVEY AND A. D. KETLEY, *J. Appl. Polymer Sci.,* **5** (1961), 247.
54. M. R. HARVEY, J. E. STEWART, AND B. G. ACHHAMMER, *J. Research NBS,* **56** (1956), 225.
55. J. HASLAM, W. SOPPET, AND H. A. WILLIS, *J. Appl. Chem.,* **1** (1951), 112.
56. H. H. HAUSDORFF, *Appl. Spectroscopy,* **5** (1950), 8.
57. C. D. HURD, L. BAUER, AND I. M. KLOTZ, *J. Am. Chem. Soc.,* **75** (1953), 624.
58. F. G. HURTUBISE AND H. KRASSIG, *Anal. Chem.,* **32** (1960), 177.
59. M. IWASAKI, M. AOKI, AND K. OKUHARA, *J. Polymer Sci.,* **26** (1957), 116.
60. R. V. JONES, C. W. MOBERLY, AND W. B. REYNOLDS, *Ind. Eng. Chem.,* **45** (1953), 1117.
61. R. KAISER, *Naturwissenschaften,* **42** (1955), 483.
62. R. KAISER, *Kolloidzschr.,* **148** (1956), 168.
63. R. KAISER, *Kolloidzschr.,* **149** (1956), 84.

64. R. KAISER, *Kolloidzschr.*, **158** (1958), 108.

65. A. KELLER AND I. SANDEMAN, *J. Polymer Sci.*, **15** (1955), 133.

66. D. N. KENDALL, R. R. HAMPTON, H. HAUSDORFF, AND F. PRISTERA, *Appl. Spectroscopy*, **7** (1953), 179.

67. W. KIMMER AND E. O. SCHMALZ, *Z. Anal. Chem.*, **170** (1959), 132.

68. G. KING AND F. WOOD, *Nature*, **195** (1962), 1093.

69. G. W. KING, R. M. HAINER, AND H. O. MCMAHON, *J. Appl. Phys.*, **20** (1949), 559.

70. J. S. KIRBY-SMITH AND E. A. JONES, *J. Opt. Soc. Am.*, **39** (1949), 780.

71. M. KOBAYASHI, K. NAGAI, AND E. NAGAI, *Bull. Chem. Soc. (Japan)*, **33** (1960), 1421.

72. M. S. KOSYREVA, *Optika i Spektroskopiya*, **6** (1959), 478.

73. A. P. KRESKOV, J. J. MICHAJLENKO, AND E. A. KIRICENKO, *J. Anal. Chem. (Moscow)*, **13** (1958), 127.

74. H. KRIEGSMANN, *Z. Elekrochem.*, **64** (1960), 541.

75. H. KRIEGSMANN, *Z. Elekrochem.*, **64** (1960), 848.

76. S. KRIMM AND C. Y. LIANG, *J. Polymer Sci.*, **22** (1956), 95.

77. S. KRIMM AND C. Y. LIANG, *J. Appl. Phys.*, **29** (1958), 1407.

78. S. KRIMM, C. Y. LIANG, AND G. B. B. M. SUTHERLAND, *J. Chem. Phys.*, **25** (1956), 549.

79. S. KRIMM, C. Y. LIANG, AND G. B. B. M. SUTHERLAND, *J. Polymer Sci.*, **22** (1956), 227.

80. Y. KURODA AND M. KUBO, *J. Polymer Sci.*, **26** (1957), 323.

81. Y. KURODA AND M. KUBO, *J. Polymer Sci.*, **36** (1959), 453.

82. H. L. LEE, *Plastics Tech.* (Feb. 1961), 47.

83. F. J. LINNIG AND J. E. STEWART, *J. Research NBS*, **60** (1958), 9.

84. J. P. Luongo, *J. Appl. Polymer Sci.*, **3** (1960), 302.

85. E. E. MAGAT, L. B. CHANDLER, B. F. FARIS, J. E. REITH, AND E. F. SALISBURY, *J. Am. Chem. Soc.*, **73** (1951), 1031.

86. J. MANN AND H. W. THOMPSON, *Proc. Roy. Soc. (London)*, **A211** (1952), 168.

87. R. G. J. MILLER AND H. A. WILLIS, *Trans. Faraday Soc.*, **49** (1953), 433.

88. A. MIYAKE, *J. Polymer Sci.*, **38** (1959), 479.

89. W. E. MOCHEL AND M. B. HALL, *J. Am. Chem. Soc.*, **71** (1949), 4082.

90. R. E. MOYNIHAN, *J. Am. Chem. Soc.*, **81** (1959), 1045.

91. K. NAMBU, *J. Appl. Polymer Sci.*, **4** (1960), 69.

92. S. NARITA, S. ICHINOHE, AND S. ENOMOTO, *J. Polymer Sci.*, **36** (1959), 389.

93. S. NARITA, S. ICHINOHE, AND S. ENOMOTO, *J. Polymer Sci.*, **37** (1959), 251.

94. S. NARITA, S. ICHINOHE, AND S. ENOMOTO, *J. Polymer Sci.*, **37** (1959), 273.

95. A. NOVAK AND E. WHALLEY, *Trans. Faraday Soc.*, **55** (1959), 1484.

96. A. NOVAK AND E. WHALLEY, *Trans. Faraday Soc.*, **55** (1959), 1490.

97. W. G. OAKES AND R. B. RICHARDS, *J. Chem. Soc.* (1949), 2929.

98. R. T. O'CONNER, E. F. DUPRE, AND E. R. MCCALL, *Anal. Chem.*, **29** (1957), 998.

99. D. E. PEERMAN, W. TOLBERG, AND H. WITTCOFF, *J. Am. Chem. Soc.*, **76** (1954), 6085.

100. A. R. PHILPOTTS, D. O. EVANS, AND N. SHEPPARD, *Trans. Faraday Soc.*, **51** (1955), 1051.

101. F. PRISTERA, *Appl. Spectroscopy*, **6** (1952), 29.

102. R. G. QUYNN, J. L. RILEY, D. A. YOUNG, AND H. D. NOETHER, *J. Appl. Polymer Sci.*, **2** (1959), 166.

103. P. DE RADZITSKI, M. C. DE WILDE, AND G. SMET, *J. Polymer Sci.*, **13** (1954), 477.

104. H. M. RANDALL, *Rev. Sci. Instr.*, **11** (1940), 365.

105. F. P. RESING AND A. BROWN, *J. Appl. Phys.*, **25** (1954), 848.

106. R. E. RICHARDS AND H. W. THOMPSON, *J. Chem. Soc.* (1947), 1260.

107. W. S. RICHARDSON AND A. SACHER, *J. Polymer Sci.,* **10** (1953), 353.

108. K. ROSSMAN, *J. Polymer Sci.,* **19** (1955), 141.

109. K. ROSSMAN, *J. Chem. Phys.,* **23** (1955), 1355.

110. J. W. ROWAN, F. H. FORZIATI, AND R. E. REEVES, *J. Am. Chem. Soc.,* **73** (1951), 4484.

111. J. W. ROWEN AND E. F. PLYLER, *J. Research NBS,* **44** (1950), 313.

112. J. W. ROWEN, C. M. HUNT, AND E. K. PLYLER, *J. Research NBS.,* **39** (1947), 133.

113. F. M. RUGG, J. J. SMITH, AND J. V. ATKINSON, *J. Polymer Sci.,* **9** (1952), 579.

114. F. M. RUGG, J. J. SMITH, AND L. H. WARTMAN, *Ann. N.Y. Acad., Sci.,* **57** (1953), 398.

115. G. SALOMON, A. CHR. VAN DER SCHEE, J. A. A. KETELAAR, AND B. J. VAN EYK, *Discussions Faraday Soc.,* **9** (1950), 291.

116. G. SALOMON AND A. CHR. VAN DER SCHEE, *J. Polymer Sci.,* **14** (1954), 181.

117. R. A. SAUNDERS AND D. C. SMITH, *J. Appl. Phys.,* **20** (1949), 953.

118. W. C. SEARS, *J. Appl. Phys.,* **12** (1941), 35.

119. N. SHEPPARD AND G. B. B. M. SUTHERLAND, *Trans. Faraday Soc.,* **41** (1945), 261.

120. A. L. SMITH AND J. A. McHARD, *Anal. Chem.,* **31** (1959), 1174.

121. M. A. SMOOK, E. T. PIESKI, AND C. F. HAMMER, *Ind. Eng. Chem.,* **45** (1953), 2731.

122. R. W. STAFFORD, R. S. FRANCEL, AND J. F. SHAY, *Anal. Chem.,* **21** (1949), 1454.

123. R. W. STAFFORD, J. F. SHAY, *Ind. Eng. Chem.,* **46** (1954), 1625.

124. R. W. STAFFORD, J. F. SHAY, AND R. J. FRANCEL, *Anal. Chem.,* **26** (1954), 656.

125. R. STAIR AND W. W. COBLENTZ, *J. Research NBS,* **15** (1935), 295.

126. G. B. B. M. SUTHERLAND AND A. V. JONES, *Discussions Faraday Soc.,* **9** (1950), 281.

127. H. W. THOMPSON AND P. TARKINGTON, *J. Chem. Soc.* (1944), 597.

128. H. W. THOMPSON AND P. TARKINGTON, *Proc. Roy. Soc. (London),* **A184** (1945), 3.

129. H. W. THOMPSON AND P. TARKINGTON, *Trans. Faraday Soc.,* **41** (1945), 246.

130. W. B. TREUMANN AND F. T. WALL, *Anal. Chem.,* **21** (1949), 1161.

131. A. J. WELLS, *J. Appl. Phys.,* **11** (1940), 137.

132. D. WILLIAMS, *Physics,* **7** (1936), 399.

133. N. WRIGHT AND M. J. HUNTER, *J. Am. Chem. Soc.,* **69** (1947), 803.

134. C. W. YOUNG, P. C. SERVAIS, C. C. CURIE, AND M. J. HUNTER, *J. Am. Chem. Soc.,* **70** (1948), 3758.

Section 8.3: Quantitative Analyses of Polymers

135. M. L. ADAMS AND M. H. SWANN, *Anal. Chem.,* **30** (1958), 1322.

136. R. B. BARNES, V. Z. WILLIAMS, A. R. DAVIS, AND P. GIESCKE, *Anal. Chem.,* **16** (1944), 9.

137. F. F. BENTLEY AND G. RAPPAPORT, *Anal. Chem.,* **26** (1954), 1980.

138. J. L. BINDER, *Anal. Chem.,* **26** (1954), 1877.

139. J. L. BINDER AND H. C. RAWSON, *Anal. Chem.,* **29** (1957), 503.

140. P. BROWN AND A. L. SMITH, *Anal. Chem.,* **30** (1958), 549.

141. W. M. D. BRYANT AND R. C. VOTER, *J. Am. Chem. Soc.,* **75** (1953), 6113.

142. R. A. BURLEY AND W. J. BENNETT, *Appl. Spectroscopy,* **14** (1960), 32.

143. E. A. BURNS AND R. F. MURACA, *Anal. Chem.,* **31** (1959), 397.

144. S. N. CHINAI AND R. H. CAMPBELL, *Anal. Chem.,* **33** (1961), 577.
145. V. A. CIRILLO, *Anal. Chem.,* **32** (1960), 299.
146. G. L. COLLIER AND A. C. M. PANTING, *Spectrochim. Acta,* **14** (1959), 104.
147. P. J. CORISH, *Anal. Chem.,* **31** (1959), 1298.
148. L. H. CROSS, R. B. RICHARDS, AND H. A. WILLIS, *Discussions Faraday Soc.,* **9** (1950), 235.
149. H. L. DINSMORE AND D. C. SMITH, *Anal. Chem.,* **20** (1948), 11.
150. C. D. GRANT AND A. L. SMITH, *Anal. Chem.,* **30** (1958), 1017.
151. R. R. HAMPTON, *Anal. Chem.,* **21** (1949), 923.
152. R. L. HARRIS AND G. R. SVOBODA, *Anal. Chem.,* **34** (1962), 1655.
153. C. L. HILTON, *Anal. Chem.,* **31** (1959), 1610.
154. L. P. KUHN, *Anal. Chem.,* **22** (1950), 276.
155. J. H. LADY, G. M. BOWER, R. E. ADAMS, AND F. P. BYRNE, *Anal. Chem.,* **31** (1959), 1100.
156. J. N. LEMONTE, *Anal. Chem.,* **34** (1962), 129.
157. H. LUTHER, H. MEYER, AND H. LOEW, *Z. Anal. Chem.,* **170** (1959), 155.
158. J. T. MAYNARD AND W. E. MOCHEL, *J. Polymer Sci.,* **13** (1954), 235.
159. A. I. MEDALIA AND H. H. FREEDMAN, *J. Am. Chem. Soc.,* **75** (1953), 4790.
160. C. D. MILLER AND O. D. SHREVE, *Anal. Chem.,* **28** (1956), 200.
161. R. G. J. MILLER AND H. A. WILLIS, *J. Appl. Chem.,* **6** (1956), 385.
162. J. A. MITCHELL, C. D. BOCKMANN, JR., AND A. V. LEE, *Anal. Chem.,* **29** (1957), 499.
163. J. F. MURPHY, *Appl. Spectroscopy,* **16** (1962), 139.
164. S. NARITA, S. ICHINOHE, AND S. ENOMOTO, *J. Polymer Sci.,* **36** (1959), 389.
165. M. ROHMER, *Z. Anal. Chem ,* **170** (1959), 147.
166. H. M. ROSENBERGER AND C. J. SHOEMAKER, *Anal. Chem.,* **31** (1959), 1315.
167. R. T. SCHEDDEL, *Anal. Chem.,* **30** (1958), 1303.
168. R. S. SILAS, J. YATES, AND V. THORNTON, *Anal. Chem.,* **31** (1959), 529.
169. R. M. B. SMALL, *Anal. Chem.,* **31** (1959), 478.
170. R. M. B. SMALL, *Anal. Chem.,* **31** (1959), 1742.
171. J. J. SMITH, F. M. RUGG, AND H. M. BOWMAN, *Anal. Chem.,* **24** (1952), 497.
172. H. L. SPELL AND R. D. EDDY, *Anal. Chem.,* **32** (1960), 1811.
173. R. W. STAFFORD AND J. F. SHAY, *Ind. Eng. Chem.,* **46** (1954), 1625.
174. R. W. STAFFORD, J. F. SHAY, AND R. J. FRANCEL, *Anal. Chem.,* **26** (1954), 656.
175. G. B. STERLING, J. G. COBLER, D. S. ERLEY, AND F. A. BLANCHARD, *Anal. Chem.,* **31** (1959), 1612.
176. W. B. TREUMANN AND F. T. WELL, *Anal. Chem.,* **21** (1949), 1161.
177. M. TRYRON, E. HOROWITZ, AND J. MANDEL, *J. Research NBS,* **55** (1955), 219.
178. S. E. WIBERLEY, J. W. SPRAGUE, AND J. E. CAMPBELL, *Anal. Chem.,* **29** (1957), 210.
179. I. M. WARD, *Trans. Faraday Soc.,* **53** (1957), 1406.
180. P. E. WEI, *Anal. Chem.,* **33** (1961), 215.

Section 8.3.1: Polymerization

181. J. R. BEATTY AND B. M. G. ZWICKER, *Ind. Eng. Chem.,* **44** (1944), 742.
182. G. B. BUTLER, *J. Am. Chem. Soc.,* **77** (1955), 482.
183. R. T. CONLEY AND I. METIL, *J. Appl. Polymer Sci.,* **7** (1963), 37.
184. M. ST.C. FLETT AND P. H. PLESCH, *J. Chem. Soc.* (1952), 3355.
185. C. GENTILHOMME, A. PIGUET, J. ROSSET, AND C. EYRAUD, *Bull. Soc. Chim. France* (1960), 901.

186. E. J. HART AND A. W. MEYER, *J. Am. Chem. Soc.,* **71** (1949), 1980.
187. A. R. JONES, *J. Chem. Phys.,* **32** (1960), 953.
188. H. SOBUE AND S. FUKUHARA, *J. Chem. Soc. (Japan),* **61** (1958), 377.

Section 8.3.2: Polymer Reaction Studies; Qualitative and Quantitative Applications

189. B. G. ACHHAMMER, M. J. REINEY, AND F. W. REINHART, *J. Research NBS,* **47** (1951), 116.
190. B. G. ACHHAMMER, F. W. REINHART, AND G. M. KLINE, *J. Research NBS,* **46** (1951), 391.
191. B. G. ACHHAMMER, *Anal. Chem.,* **24** (1952), 1925.
192. A. R. ALLISON AND I. J. STANLEY, *Anal. Chem.,* **24** (1952), 630.
193. F. F. BENTLEY AND G. RAPPAPORT, *Anal. Chem.,* **26** (1954), 1980.
194. C. F. BERSCH, M. R. HARVEY, AND B. G. ACHHAMMER, *J. Research NBS,* **60** (1958), 481.
195. W. A. BISHOP, *Anal. Chem.,* **33** (1961), 456.
196. J. K. BUXBAUM, *Anal. Chem.,* **29** (1957), 492.
197. J. O. COLE AND J. E. FIELD, *Ind. Eng. Chem.,* **39** (1947), 174.
198. R. T. CONLEY AND J. F. BIERON, *Appl. Spectroscopy,* **15** (1961), 81.
199. R. T. CONLEY AND I. METIL, *J. Appl. Polymer Sci.,* **7** (1963), 1083.
200. H. A. HILLIARD AND R. E. SRAIL, *Offic. Dig. Federation Soc. Paint Technol.,* **33** (1961), 1132.
201. J. H. LADY, I. KESSE, AND R. E. ADAMS, *J. Appl. Polymer Sci.,* **3** (1960), 71.
202. J. H. LADY, R. E. ADAMS, AND I. KESSE, *J. Appl. Polymer Sci.,* **3** (1960), 65.
203. J. P. LUONGO, *J. Polymer Sci.,* **42** (1960), 139.
204. C. D. MILLER, *Ind. Eng. Chem.,* **50** (1958), 125.
205. G. R. MITCHELL AND J. R. SHELTON, *Ind. Eng. Chem.,* **45** (1953), 386.
206. G. S. POPOVA AND E. V. SUVALOVA, *Bull. Acad. Sci. (USSR), Phys. Ser.,* **23** (1959), 1205.
207. F. M. RUGG, J. J. SMITH, AND C. R. BACON, *J. Polymer Sci.,* **13** (1954), 535.
208. A. L. SMITH, L. H. BROWN, L. J. TYLER, AND M. J. HUNTER, *Ind. Eng. Chem.,* **49** (1957), 1903.
209. R. R. STROMBERG, S. STRAUS, AND B. G. ACHHAMMER, *J. Research NBS,* **60** (1959), 147.

9

Problems in the Interpretation of Infrared Spectra

The problems in this chapter are presented as exercises for the reader in the use of functional group analyses and as examples of the application of infrared spectra interpretation to practical laboratory problems.

PROBLEM 9.1

A thin liquid-film sample of compound A on spectral examination gave rise to the spectrum in Fig. 9.1. Elemental analyses of the compound indicated only carbon (89.94%) and hydrogen (10.06%) were present. From these data, suggest a structure for compound A.

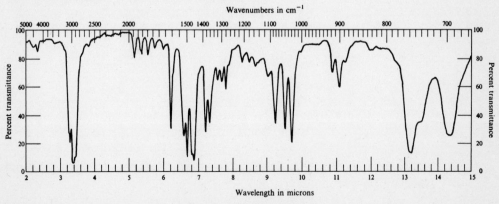

Fig. 9.1   Thin liquid film.

PROBLEM 9.2

Compound *B*, as a pure liquid, exhibited the spectral data shown in Fig. 9.2. Mass spectral examination of compound *B* indicated that the molecular weight was 108. The elemental analysis of *B* suggested an empirical formula of C_7H_8O. On the basis of this information, what is the structure of compound *B*?

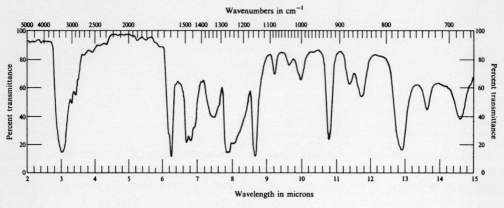

Fig. 9.2   Thin liquid film.

PROBLEM 9.3

The following compounds are potentially the products of a reaction performed in your laboratory:

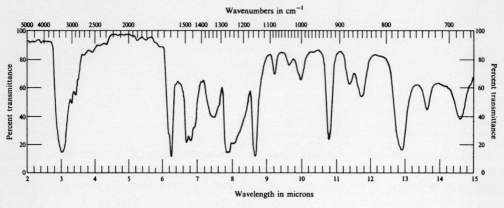

On the basis of Fig. 9.3, which of the compounds was most probably the reaction product?

Wavenumbers in cm⁻¹

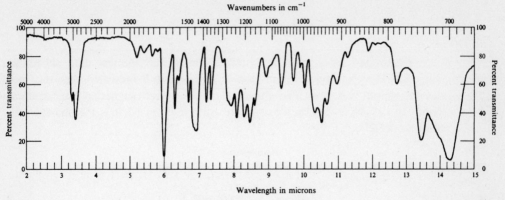

Fig. 9.3   Thin liquid film.

PROBLEM 9.4

The spectrum in Fig. 9.4 was obtained from a small sample of material smeared on a polished sodium chloride plate. This material was found as a substance insoluble in both reaction mixture and extracting solvent during one of your attempted synthetic processes. On the basis of its infrared spectrum, can you suggest the possible nature of this unknown substance?

Wavenumbers in cm⁻¹

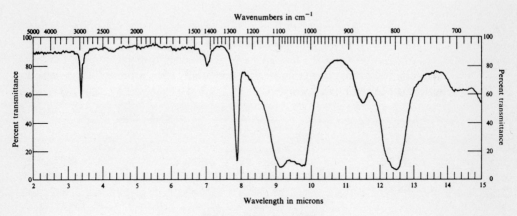

Fig. 9.4   Thin liquid film.

PROBLEM 9.5

Figure 9.5 indicates the spectral characteristics of a compound C isolated as the end product of a two-step reaction sequence starting from 6-nitrocamphene as follows:

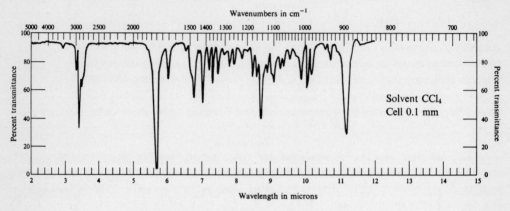

Can you suggest a reasonable structure for compound *C*, based upon its past history and its spectrum?

Fig. 9.5   CCl₄ solution (0.1-mm cell).

PROBLEM 9.6

A pure liquid sample of compound *D* was shown to have an empirical formula of C_7H_8O, isomeric with compound *B* (Prob. 9.2). Can you suggest a possible structure for compound *D*, based upon its spectrum as shown in Fig. 9.6?

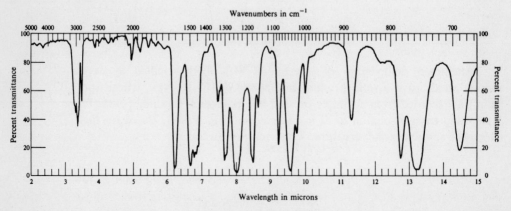

Fig. 9.6   Thin liquid film.

PROBLEM 9.7

The spectrum in Fig. 9.7 is that of the crude reaction product mixture obtained from the following reaction:

$$CH_3-\underset{\underset{CH_2}{\|}}{C}-CH_2-\underset{\underset{CH_3}{\|}}{\overset{CH_3}{C}}-COOH \xrightarrow[\text{120°C, 10 minutes}]{\text{polyphosphoric acid}} \text{compound } E \text{ and compound } F$$

$$1:1$$

Analysis of the product mixture by gas chromatography indicates the presence of two components in approximately equal amounts. Trapping of the components indicates that compound E, $C_8H_{12}O$, possesses the strong absorption at 5.87μ, whereas compound F, $C_8H_{14}O_2$, possesses the strong absorption at 5.69μ. Suggest structures for compounds E and F based upon these data.

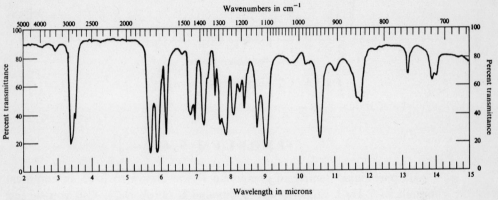

Fig. 9.7   Thin liquid film.

PROBLEM 9.8

Attempted dialkylation of α-tetralone with methyl iodide in excess sodium amide gave a solid product, compound G ($C_{12}H_{17}NO$), whose spectrum was recorded from a sample pressed in a potassium bromide pellet (Fig. 9.8A) and from a solution of G in chloroform (Fig. 9.8B). Based on these two spectra, what is the structure of the reaction product?

$$\xrightarrow[\text{NaNH}_2 \text{ (excess)}]{\text{CH}_3\text{I}} \text{compound } G$$

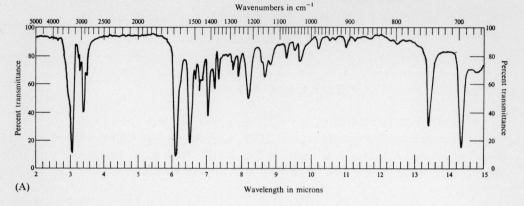

(A)

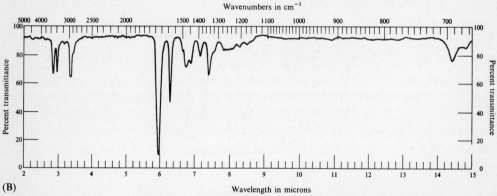

(B)

Fig. 9.8 (A) KBr pellet. (B) CHCl₃ solution (0.1-mm cell).

PROBLEM 9.9

Compound *H* was found to have an empirical formula of $C_{11}H_{13}Cl$. On spectral examination a thin liquid film between polished sodium chloride

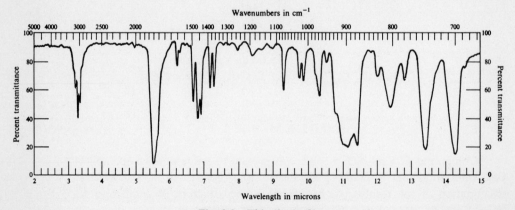

Fig. 9.9   Thin liquid film.

plates gave the infrared spectrum in Fig. 9.9. What can be said about the structure and functionality of compound *H*?

PROBLEM 9.10

Figures 9.10A and 9.10B show typical spectra of two very similar substances. The spectrum of compound *I*, $C_4H_6O_2$, is shown in Fig. 9.10A, and that of compound *J*, $C_6H_{10}O_2$, is shown in Fig. 9.10B. What is the functionality of both substances and how do they differ in skeletal structure?

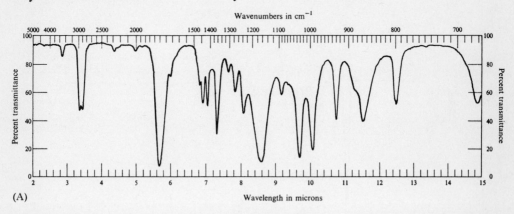

(A)

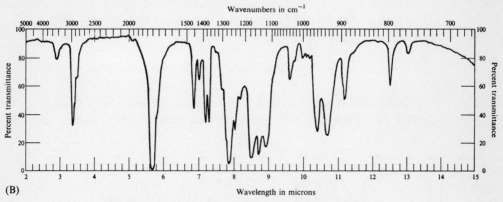

(B)

Fig. 9.10   (A) Thin liquid film. (B) Thin liquid film.

PROBLEM 9.11

Compound *K*, C_8H_5NO, a solid, was ground to a fine powder and pelletized with potassium bromide. Figure 9.11 was recorded from the spectral examination of the resulting pellet. What is the structure of compound *K*, based upon the data clearly discernible from its spectrum?

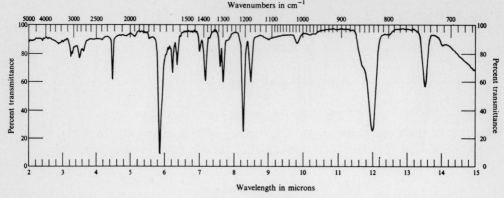

Fig. 9.11   KBr pellet.

PROBLEM 9.12

Compound *L*, C_9H_8O, was isolated from natural sources as a by-product of rather simple structure. Its synthesis was carried out in a single step from readily available materials. The compound has been sent to you for infrared evaluation. Can you suggest a plausible structure for compound *L*, based on Fig. 9.12?

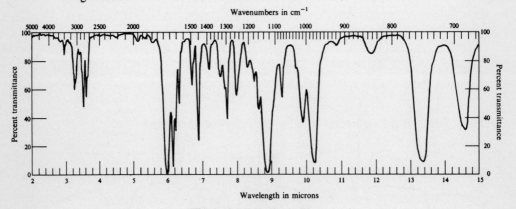

Fig. 9.12   Thin liquid film

PROBLEM 9.13

A polymeric material was cast as a film on a silver chloride plate. Figure 9.13 was recorded, using the cast film sample. Can you suggest the types of functionalities present in the sample? From your interpretation, propose the monomer (or monomers) used to prepare the polymer.

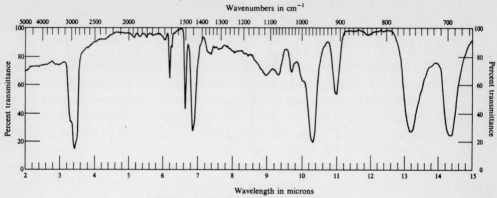

Fig. 9.13   Film deposited from solution.

PROBLEM 9.14

Figure 9.14 was recorded on an unknown sample submitted for infrared evaluation. The chemist suspected the sample to be one of the following materials, based upon its past history:

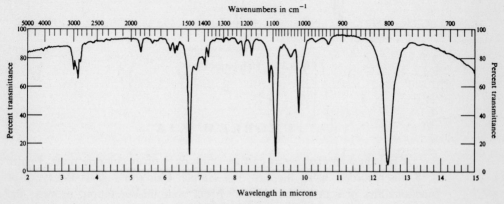

Which, if any, of the structures best fits the recorded spectrum?

Fig. 9.14   Thin liquid film.

PROBLEM 9.15

Treatment of 2,2,4-trimethyl-3-pentenal (compound *M*) with silver nitrate in base, followed by acidification of the reaction mixture, gave a compound *N*, which analyzed for $C_8H_{14}O_2$. Figure 9.15A was obtained by the examination of a thin liquid film of compound *N*. Compound *N* was characterized by reacting the oxidation product first with oxalyl chloride, followed by treatment of the reaction mixture with ammonia. The product compound *O* ($C_8H_{15}NO$) was examined in chloroform solution (Fig. 9.15B).

On treatment of compound *O* with *p*-toluenesulfonyl chloride in pyridine, compound *P*, $C_8H_{13}N$, was obtained. A thin-film sample was obtained and its spectrum recorded (Fig. 9.15C). Compound *P* could also be prepared from the treatment of the oxime of *M* with *p*-toluenesulfonyl chloride in pyridine. However, a second species was found present in the crude reaction product mixture by infrared examination (Fig. 9.15D).

1. What are the most likely structures of compounds *N, O,* and *P*?
2. What is the structure of the impurity in the spectrum of Fig. 9.15D?

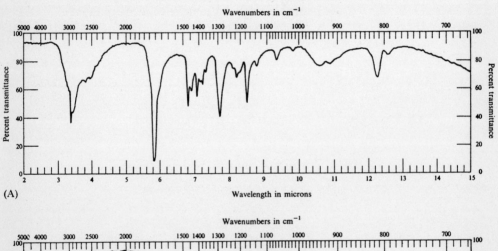

(A)

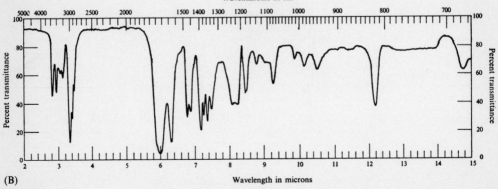

(B)

Fig. 9.15   (A) Thin liquid film. (B) CHCl₃ solution.

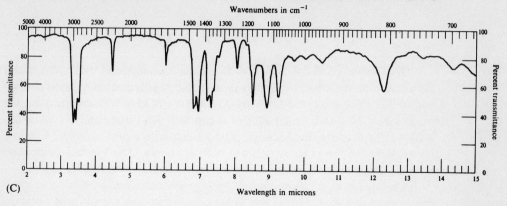

(C)

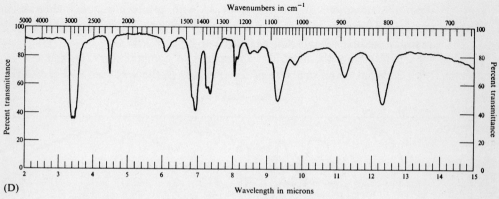

(D)

Fig. 9.15—cont.   (C) Thin liquid film. (D) Thin liquid film.

Appendix I

WAVELENGTH-WAVENUMBER
CONVERSION TABLES

For the relationship

$$\text{Wavelength } (\mu) = \frac{1}{\text{wavenumber (cm}^{-1})}$$

the following table of reciprocals is constructed for easy reference from 2 to 19.9μ. Below 2μ and above 19.9μ, values can be obtained by simply moving the decimal point in the appropriate direction:

$$1.0\mu = 10,000 \text{ cm}^{-1}$$
$$20.0\mu = 500 \text{ cm}^{-1}$$

are values taken from the tabular material at 10.0 and 2.00μ respectively.

Wavenumber (cm^{-1})

Wavelength (μ)	0	1	2	3	4	5	6	7	8	9
2.0	5000	4975	4950	4926	4902	4878	4854	4831	4808	4785
2.1	4762	4739	4717	4695	4673	4651	4630	4608	4587	4566
2.2	4545	4525	4505	4484	4464	4444	4425	4405	4386	4367
2.3	4348	4329	4310	4292	4274	4255	4237	4219	4202	4184
2.4	4167	4149	4132	4115	4098	4082	4065	4049	4032	4016
2.5	4000	3984	3968	3953	3937	3922	3906	3891	3876	3861
2.6	3846	3831	3817	3802	3788	3774	3759	3745	3731	3717
2.7	3704	3690	3676	3663	3650	3636	3623	3610	3597	3584
2.8	3571	3559	3546	3534	3521	3509	3497	3484	3472	3460
2.9	3448	3436	3425	3413	3401	3390	3378	3367	3356	3344
3.0	3333	3322	3311	3300	3289	3279	3268	3257	3247	3236
3.1	3226	3215	3205	3195	3185	3175	3165	3155	3145	3135
3.2	3125	3115	3106	3096	3086	3077	3067	3058	3049	3040
3.3	3030	3021	3012	3003	2994	2985	2976	2967	2959	2950
3.4	2941	2933	2924	2915	2907	2899	2890	2882	2874	2865
3.5	2857	2849	2841	2833	2825	2817	2809	2801	2793	2786
3.6	2778	2770	2762	2755	2747	2740	2732	2725	2717	2710
3.7	2703	2695	2688	2681	2674	2667	2660	2653	2646	2639
3.8	2632	2625	2618	2611	2604	2597	2591	2584	2577	2571
3.9	2564	2558	2551	2545	2538	2532	2525	2519	2513	2506
4.0	2500	2494	2488	2481	2475	2469	2463	2457	2451	2445
4.1	2439	2433	2427	2421	2415	2410	2404	2398	2392	2387
4.2	2381	2375	2370	2364	2358	2353	2347	2342	2336	2331
4.3	2326	2320	2315	2309	2304	2299	2294	2288	2283	2278
4.4	2273	2268	2262	2257	2252	2247	2242	2237	2232	2227

| | 0 | 1 | 2 | 3 | 4 | 5 | 6 | 7 | 8 | 9 |

Wavenumber (cm^{-1})

	0	1	2	3	4	5	6	7	8	9
4.5	2222	2217	2212	2208	2203	2198	2193	2188	2183	2179
4.6	2174	2169	2165	2160	2155	2151	2146	2141	2137	2132
4.7	2128	2123	2119	2114	2110	2105	2101	2096	2092	2088
4.8	2083	2079	2075	2070	2066	2062	2058	2053	2049	2045
4.9	2041	2037	2033	2028	2024	2020	2016	2012	2008	2004
5.0	2000	1996	1992	1988	1984	1980	1976	1972	1969	1965
5.1	1961	1957	1953	1949	1946	1942	1938	1934	1931	1927
5.2	1923	1919	1916	1912	1908	1905	1901	1898	1894	1890
5.3	1887	1883	1880	1876	1873	1869	1866	1862	1859	1855
5.4	1852	1848	1845	1842	1838	1835	1832	1828	1825	1821
5.5	1818	1815	1812	1808	1805	1802	1799	1795	1792	1789
5.6	1786	1783	1779	1776	1773	1770	1767	1764	1761	1757
5.7	1754	1751	1748	1745	1742	1739	1736	1733	1730	1727
5.8	1724	1721	1718	1715	1712	1709	1706	1704	1701	1698
5.9	1695	1692	1689	1686	1684	1681	1678	1675	1672	1669
6.0	1667	1664	1661	1658	1656	1653	1650	1647	1645	1642
6.1	1639	1637	1634	1631	1629	1626	1623	1621	1618	1616
6.2	1613	1610	1608	1605	1603	1600	1597	1595	1592	1590
6.3	1587	1585	1582	1580	1577	1575	1572	1570	1567	1565
6.4	1563	1560	1558	1555	1553	1550	1548	1546	1543	1541
6.5	1538	1536	1534	1531	1529	1527	1524	1522	1520	1517
6.6	1515	1513	1511	1508	1506	1504	1502	1499	1497	1495
6.7	1493	1490	1488	1486	1484	1481	1479	1477	1475	1473
6.8	1471	1468	1466	1464	1462	1460	1458	1456	1453	1451
6.9	1449	1447	1445	1443	1441	1439	1437	1435	1433	1431
7.0	1429	1427	1425	1422	1420	1418	1416	1414	1412	1410
7.1	1408	1406	1404	1403	1401	1399	1397	1395	1393	1391
7.2	1389	1387	1385	1383	1381	1379	1377	1376	1374	1372
7.3	1370	1368	1366	1364	1362	1361	1359	1357	1355	1353
7.4	1351	1350	1348	1346	1344	1342	1340	1339	1337	1335
7.5	1333	1332	1330	1328	1326	1325	1323	1321	1319	1318
7.6	1316	1314	1312	1311	1309	1307	1305	1304	1302	1300
7.7	1299	1297	1295	1294	1292	1290	1289	1287	1285	1284
7.8	1282	1280	1279	1277	1276	1274	1272	1271	1269	1267
7.9	1266	1264	1263	1261	1259	1258	1256	1255	1253	1252
8.0	1250	1248	1247	1245	1244	1242	1241	1239	1238	1236
8.1	1235	1233	1232	1230	1229	1227	1225	1224	1222	1221
8.2	1220	1218	1217	1215	1214	1212	1211	1209	1208	1206
8.3	1205	1203	1202	1200	1199	1198	1196	1195	1193	1192
8.4	1190	1189	1188	1186	1185	1183	1182	1181	1179	1178
8.5	1176	1175	1174	1172	1171	1170	1168	1167	1166	1164
8.6	1163	1161	1160	1159	1157	1156	1155	1153	1152	1151
8.7	1149	1148	1147	1145	1144	1143	1142	1140	1139	1138
8.8	1136	1135	1134	1133	1131	1130	1129	1127	1126	1125
8.9	1124	1122	1121	1120	1119	1117	1116	1115	1114	1112
9.0	1111	1110	1109	1107	1106	1105	1104	1103	1101	1100
9.1	1099	1098	1096	1095	1094	1093	1092	1091	1089	1088
9.2	1087	1086	1085	1083	1082	1081	1080	1079	1078	1076
9.3	1075	1074	1073	1072	1071	1070	1068	1067	1066	1065
9.4	1064	1063	1062	1060	1059	1058	1057	1056	1055	1054

Wavelength (μ)

| | 0 | 1 | 2 | 3 | 4 | 5 | 6 | 7 | 8 | 9 |

Wavenumber (cm⁻¹)

	0	1	2	3	4	5	6	7	8	9
9.5	1053	1052	1050	1049	1048	1047	1046	1045	1044	1043
9.6	1042	1041	1040	1038	1037	1036	1035	1034	1033	1032
9.7	1031	1030	1029	1028	1027	1026	1025	1024	1022	1021
9.8	1020	1019	1018	1017	1016	1015	1014	1013	1012	1011
9.9	1010	1009	1008	1007	1006	1005	1004	1003	1002	1001
10.0	1000.0	999.0	998.0	997.0	996.0	995.0	994.0	993.0	992.1	991.1
10.1	990.1	989.1	988.1	987.2	986.2	985.2	984.3	983.3	982.3	981.4
10.2	980.4	979.4	978.5	977.5	976.6	975.6	974.7	973.7	972.8	971.8
10.3	970.9	969.9	969.0	968.1	967.1	966.2	965.3	964.3	963.4	962.5
10.4	961.5	960.6	959.7	958.8	957.9	956.9	956.0	955.1	954.2	953.3
10.5	952.4	951.5	950.6	949.7	948.8	947.9	947.0	946.1	945.2	944.3
10.6	943.4	942.5	941.6	940.7	939.8	939.0	938.1	937.2	936.3	935.5
10.7	934.6	933.7	932.8	932.0	931.1	930.2	929.4	928.5	927.6	926.8
10.8	925.9	925.1	924.2	923.4	922.5	921.7	920.8	920.0	919.1	918.3
10.9	917.4	916.6	915.8	914.9	914.1	913.2	912.4	911.6	910.7	909.9
11.0	909.1	908.3	907.4	906.6	905.8	905.0	904.2	903.3	902.5	901.7
11.1	900.9	900.1	899.3	898.5	897.7	896.9	896.1	895.3	894.5	893.7
11.2	892.9	892.1	891.3	890.5	889.7	888.9	888.1	887.3	886.5	885.7
11.3	885.0	884.2	883.4	882.6	881.8	881.1	880.3	879.5	878.7	878.0
11.4	877.2	876.4	875.7	874.9	874.1	873.4	872.6	871.8	871.1	870.3
11.5	869.6	868.8	868.1	867.3	866.6	865.8	865.1	864.3	863.6	862.8
11.6	862.1	861.3	860.6	859.8	859.1	858.4	857.6	856.9	856.2	855.4
11.7	854.7	854.0	853.2	852.5	851.8	851.1	850.3	849.6	848.9	848.2
11.8	847.5	846.7	846.0	845.3	844.6	843.9	843.2	842.5	841.8	841.0
11.9	840.3	839.6	838.9	838.2	837.5	836.8	836.1	835.4	834.7	834.0
12.0	833.3	832.6	831.9	831.3	830.6	829.9	829.2	828.5	827.8	827.1
12.1	826.4	825.8	825.1	824.4	823.7	823.0	822.4	821.7	821.0	820.3
12.2	819.7	819.0	818.3	817.7	817.0	816.3	815.7	815.0	814.3	813.7
12.3	813.0	812.3	811.7	811.0	810.4	809.7	809.1	808.4	807.8	807.1
12.4	806.5	805.8	805.2	804.5	803.9	803.2	802.6	801.9	801.3	800.6
12.5	800.0	799.4	798.7	798.1	797.4	796.8	796.2	795.5	794.9	794.3
12.6	793.7	793.0	792.4	791.8	791.1	790.5	789.9	789.3	788.6	788.0
12.7	787.4	786.8	786.2	785.5	784.9	784.3	783.7	783.1	782.5	781.9
12.8	781.3	780.6	780.0	779.4	778.8	778.2	777.6	777.0	776.4	775.8
12.9	775.2	774.6	774.0	773.4	772.8	772.2	771.6	771.0	770.4	769.8
13.0	769.2	768.6	768.0	767.5	766.9	766.3	765.7	765.1	764.5	763.9
13.1	763.4	762.8	762.2	761.6	761.0	760.5	759.9	759.3	758.7	758.2
13.2	757.6	757.0	756.4	755.9	755.3	754.7	754.1	753.6	753.0	752.4
13.3	751.9	751.3	750.8	750.2	749.6	749.1	748.5	747.9	747.4	746.8
13.4	746.3	745.7	745.2	744.6	744.0	743.5	742.9	742.4	741.8	741.3

Wavelength (μ)

| | 0 | 1 | 2 | 3 | 4 | 5 | 6 | 7 | 8 | 9 |

Wavenumber (cm^{-1})

Wavelength (μ)	0	1	2	3	4	5	6	7	8	9
13.5	740.7	740.2	739.6	739.1	738.6	738.0	737.5	736.9	736.4	735.8
13.6	735.3	734.8	734.2	733.7	733.1	732.6	732.1	731.5	731.0	730.5
13.7	729.9	729.4	728.9	728.3	727.8	727.3	726.7	726.2	725.7	725.2
13.8	724.6	724.1	723.6	723.1	722.5	722.0	721.5	721.0	720.5	719.9
13.9	719.4	718.9	718.4	717.9	717.4	716.8	716.3	715.8	715.3	714.8
14.0	714.3	713.8	713.3	712.8	712.3	711.7	711.2	710.7	710.2	709.7
14.1	709.2	708.7	708.2	707.7	707.2	706.7	706.2	705.7	705.2	704.7
14.2	704.2	703.7	703.2	702.7	702.2	701.8	701.3	700.8	700.3	699.8
14.3	699.3	698.8	698.3	697.8	697.4	696.9	696.4	695.9	695.4	694.9
14.4	694.4	694.0	693.5	693.0	692.5	692.0	691.6	691.1	690.6	690.1
14.5	689.7	689.2	688.7	688.2	687.8	687.3	686.8	686.3	685.9	685.4
14.6	684.9	684.5	684.0	683.5	683.1	682.6	682.1	681.7	681.2	680.7
14.7	680.3	679.8	679.3	678.9	678.4	678.0	677.5	677.0	676.6	676.1
14.8	675.7	675.2	674.8	674.3	673.9	673.4	672.9	672.5	672.0	671.6
14.9	671.1	670.7	670.2	669.8	669.3	668.9	668.4	668.0	667.6	667.1
15.0	666.7	666.2	665.8	665.3	664.9	664.5	664.0	663.6	663.1	662.7
15.1	662.3	661.8	661.4	660.9	660.5	660.1	659.6	659.2	658.8	658.3
15.2	657.9	657.5	657.0	656.6	656.2	655.7	655.3	654.9	654.5	654.0
15.3	653.6	653.2	652.7	652.3	651.9	651.5	651.0	650.6	650.2	649.8
15.4	649.4	648.9	648.5	648.1	647.7	647.2	646.8	646.4	646.0	645.6
15.5	645.2	644.7	644.3	643.9	643.5	643.1	642.7	642.3	641.8	641.4
15.6	641.0	640.6	640.2	639.8	639.4	639.0	638.6	638.2	637.8	637.3
15.7	639.9	636.5	636.1	635.7	635.3	634.9	634.5	634.1	633.7	633.3
15.8	632.9	632.5	632.1	631.7	631.3	630.9	630.5	630.1	629.7	629.3
15.9	628.9	628.5	628.1	627.7	627.4	627.0	626.6	626.2	625.8	625.4
16.0	625.0	624.6	624.2	623.8	623.4	623.1	622.7	622.3	621.9	621.5
16.1	621.1	620.7	620.3	620.0	619.6	619.2	618.8	618.4	618.0	617.7
16.2	617.3	616.9	616.5	616.1	615.8	615.4	615.0	614.6	614.3	613.9
16.3	613.5	613.1	612.7	612.4	612.0	611.6	611.2	610.9	610.5	610.1
16.4	609.8	609.4	609.0	608.6	608.3	607.9	607.5	607.2	606.8	606.4
16.5	606.1	605.7	605.3	605.0	604.6	604.2	603.9	603.5	603.1	602.8
16.6	602.4	602.0	601.7	601.3	601.0	600.6	600.2	599.9	599.5	599.2
16.7	598.8	598.4	598.1	597.7	597.4	597.0	596.7	596.3	595.9	595.6
16.8	595.2	594.9	594.5	594.2	593.8	593.5	593.1	592.8	592.4	592.1
16.9	591.7	591.4	591.0	590.7	590.3	590.0	589.6	589.3	588.9	588.6
17.0	588.2	587.9	587.5	587.2	586.9	586.5	586.2	585.8	585.5	585.1
17.1	584.8	584.5	584.1	583.8	583.4	583.1	582.8	582.4	582.1	581.7
17.2	581.4	581.1	580.7	580.4	580.0	579.7	579.4	579.0	578.7	578.4
17.3	578.0	577.7	577.4	577.0	576.7	576.4	576.0	575.7	575.4	575.0
17.4	574.7	574.4	574.1	573.7	573.4	573.1	572.7	572.4	572.1	571.8
	0	1	2	3	4	5	6	7	8	9

Wavenumber (cm^{-1})

	0	1	2	3	4	5	6	7	8	9
17.5	571.4	571.1	570.8	570.5	570.1	569.8	569.5	569.2	568.8	568.5
17.6	568.2	567.9	567.5	567.2	566.9	566.6	566.3	565.9	565.6	565.3
17.7	565.0	564.7	564.3	564.0	563.7	563.4	563.1	562.7	562.4	562.1
17.8	561.8	561.5	561.2	560.9	560.5	560.2	559.9	559.6	559.3	559.0
17.9	558.7	558.3	558.0	557.7	557.4	557.1	556.8	556.5	556.2	555.9
18.0	555.6	555.2	554.9	554.6	554.3	554.0	553.7	553.4	553.1	552.8
18.1	552.5	552.2	551.9	551.6	551.3	551.0	550.7	550.4	550.1	549.8
18.2	549.5	549.1	548.8	548.5	548.2	547.9	547.6	547.3	547.0	546.7
18.3	546.4	546.1	545.9	545.6	545.3	545.0	544.7	544.4	544.1	543.8
18.4	543.5	543.2	542.9	542.6	542.3	542.0	541.7	541.4	541.1	540.8
18.5	540.5	540.2	540.0	539.7	539.4	539.1	538.8	538.5	538.2	537.9
18.6	537.6	537.3	537.1	536.8	536.5	536.2	535.9	535.6	535.3	535.0
18.7	534.8	534.5	534.2	533.9	533.6	533.3	533.0	532.8	532.5	532.2
18.8	531.9	531.6	531.3	531.1	530.8	530.5	530.2	529.9	529.7	529.4
18.9	529.1	528.8	528.5	528.3	528.0	527.7	527.4	527.1	526.9	526.6
19.0	526.3	526.0	525.8	525.5	525.2	524.9	524.7	524.4	524.1	523.8
19.1	523.6	523.3	523.0	522.7	522.5	522.2	521.9	521.6	521.4	521.1
19.2	520.8	520.6	520.3	520.0	519.8	519.5	519.2	518.9	518.7	518.4
19.3	518.1	517.9	517.6	517.3	517.1	516.8	516.5	516.3	516.0	515.7
19.4	515.5	515.2	514.9	514.7	514.4	514.1	513.9	513.6	513.3	513.1
19.5	512.8	512.6	512.3	512.0	511.8	511.5	511.2	511.0	510.7	510.5
19.6	510.2	509.9	509.7	509.4	509.2	508.9	508.6	508.4	508.1	507.9
19.7	507.6	507.4	507.1	506.8	506.6	506.3	506.1	505.8	505.6	505.3
19.8	505.1	504.8	504.5	504.3	504.0	503.8	503.5	503.3	503.0	502.8
19.9	502.5	502.3	502.0	501.8	501.5	501.3	501.0	500.8	500.5	500.3

Wavelength (μ)

	0	1	2	3	4	5	6	7	8	9

Appendix II

SIMPLIFIED METHOD OF CALCULATING
BAND POSITIONS FOR STRETCHING
FREQUENCIES, BASED ON HOOKE'S LAW

It is often advantageous to estimate the spectral region in which absorption is anticipated for a particular pair of atoms. To accomplish such an approximation, a knowledge of the masses of the atoms involved and the force constant of the bond to be estimated is required. With this information, Hooke's law for the simple harmonic oscillator can be used to calculate an approximate vibrational frequency. Such calculations, it must be emphasized, are oversimplifications and result only in a reasonable first approximation for the positions of vibrating atom pairs. With such information and a knowledge of spectral shifts caused by substituent groups on analogous functional moieties (Chap. 5), a qualitative prediction of the region of absorption of a particular group can be applied in the interpretation of an infrared spectrum.

If Eq. 2.9 is modified to express v as the frequency in wavenumbers (cm^{-1}), μ as the reduced mass of the atom pairs (calculated from gram-atomic weights), and k as the force constant in units of 10^5 dynes/cm, the equation can be rewritten as

$$v_{cm^{-1}} = 1307 \sqrt{\frac{k}{\mu}} \qquad \text{(A-1)}$$

By using Eq. A-1, we can calculate the expected position of absorption for several exemplary function groups. From these calculations the reader should note that the masses of the system are well established, but that the force constant used is empirically derived and, at best, accurate to $\pm 5\%$.[1-3]

EXAMPLE 1

Calculation of the expected positions of absorption of the C—H and C—D stretching frequencies in $CHCl_3$ and $CDCl_3$. The reduced mass of the C—H atom pair is calculated from Eq. 2.5:

$$\mu = \frac{m_C m_H}{m_C + m_H} = \frac{12.00(1.00)}{12.00 + 1.00} = 0.923$$

In similar fashion the reduced mass of the C—D pair is calculated as

$$\mu = \frac{m_C m_D}{m_C + m_D} = \frac{12.00(2.00)}{12.00 + 2.00} = 1.71$$

From the literature the value of the force constant for the methane C—H stretching vibrations is approximately 5×10^5 dynes/cm. Substituting for the values of K and μ, the frequencies for the C—H and C—D vibrations can be determined from Eq. A-1 as follows: For the C—H stretching vibration

$$\nu_{(C-H)} = 1307\sqrt{\frac{5}{0.923}} = 3000 \text{ cm}^{-1}$$

For the C—D stretching vibration, assuming the force constants for C—H and C—D bonds to be approximately the same:

$$\nu_{(C-D)} = 1307\sqrt{\frac{5}{1.71}} = 2335 \text{ cm}^{-1}$$

The reader should note that the factor relating the position of the two bands is therefore approximately $\sqrt{2}$.

The observed positions of absorption for the C—H stretching frequency in chloroform and for the C—D stretching frequency in deuterochloroform are 2915 and 2256 cm^{-1}, respectively.

EXAMPLE 2

Calculation of the positions of absorption of the C=O and P=S stretching frequencies. The reduced masses for the C=O and P=S groups are 6.86 and 15.75. From the literature the value of the force constant for the multiple-bond stretching frequencies, such as C=O, is approximately 12×10^5 dynes/cm and the P=S force constant[2] is approximately 5×10^5 dynes/cm.

Substituting in Eq. A-1 gives

$$\nu_{C=O} = 1307\sqrt{\frac{12}{6.86}} = 1725 \text{ cm}^{-1}$$

and

$$\nu_{P=S} = 1307\sqrt{\frac{5.0}{15.75}} = 730 \text{ cm}^{-1}$$

respectively.

For the C=O group the absorption is usually found in the 1750- to 1680-cm^{-1} region for a wide variety of compounds, whereas the P=S stretching frequency is presumed to be in the 750- to 600-cm^{-1} region.

EXAMPLE 3

Calculation of the position of absorption of the H—Cl stretching vibration. Using the rule of Badger[1], the force constant for H—Cl is calculated as 5.1. The reduced mass is equal to 0.973; therefore Eq. A-1 becomes

$$\nu_{H-Cl} = 1307\sqrt{\frac{5.1}{0.973}} = 2993 \text{ cm}^{-1}$$

The observed band position is 2886 cm^{-1}. It can be seen that reasonably good agreement as to the correct order of magnitude for the absorption-band position is obtained in a fairly wide variety of cases.

SUGGESTED READING

1. R. M. BADGER, *J. Chem. Phys.,* **2** (1934), 128.

2. W. GORDY, *J. Chem. Phys.,* **14** (1946), 305.

3. G. HERZBERG, *Spectra of Diatomic Molecules.* D. van Nostrand Company, Inc., Princeton, N.J., 1950, pp. 455–459.

Index

Index of Infrared Spectra

291